Publication Number 2

of the MATHEMATICS RESEARCH CENTER
United States Army
The University of Wisconsin

Boundary Problems In Differential Equations

Proceedings of a Symposium Conducted by the Mathematics Research Center at the University of Wisconsin, Madison, April 20–22, 1959

edited by

Rudolph E. Langer

Madison

The University of Wisconsin Press

1960

Published by
THE UNIVERSITY OF WISCONSIN PRESS
430 Sterling Court, Madison 6, Wisconsin

Prepared for the camera by Phyllis J. Kern
Printed in the United States of America by the
George Banta Company, Inc., Menasha, Wisconsin

Library of Congress Catalog Card Number 60-60003

Foreword

This symposium, the second one to be conducted by this Mathematics Research Center, United States Army, at the University of Wisconsin, was held on 20-22 April, 1959. The inspiration for it sprung initially from a realization that much significant research in the field of Partial Differential Equations is currently being done. A forum for the discussion of some of this work therefore seemed timely, and to hold promise of being highly worth while. It became evident soon enough, however, that the whole field of Partial Differential Equations is of such breadth that a mere three-day conference to survey it would be either fragmentary or superficial. It was therefore decided, in due course, to restrict the subject to Boundary Problems, compensating this limitation somewhat by the inclusion of such problems for Ordinary as well as for Partial Differential Equations. Initial Value Problems were therefore not included. Some future symposium may possibly be given over to them.

The symposium was opened by a message of welcome from Professor John E. Willard, Dean of the Graduate School of the University of Wisconsin. The lectures, of which there were nineteen, were all held in the auditorium of the Wisconsin Center Building. They were each of about thirty minutes length, and were followed by discussion periods. The attendance was such as to fill the auditorium to its capacity of about two hundred and ten places.

The chairmen of the respective morning and afternoon sessions were

Dr. A. H. Taub, University of Illinois,
Dr. P. D. Lax, Institute of Mathematical Sciences, New York University,
Dr. E. H. Bareiss, Argonne National Laboratory,
Dr. G. Horvay, General Electric Research Laboratory,
Dr. J. W. Cell, North Carolina State College,
Dr. K. G. Guderley, Aeronautical Research Laboratory, Wright Air Development Center.

The first session of the third day was adjourned in mid morning to permit attendance at the dedication exercises of the quarters in which this Mathematics Research Center now finds itself. These quarters are in a newly constructed building on the University campus. The principal dedication speaker was Lieutenant General Arthur G. Trudeau, Chief of Research and Development of the United States Army.

A general reception for symposium attendants, and for members of this Research Center and of the Mathematics Department of the University, was held in the lounge of the Wisconsin Center Building on Monday evening. A tea was presented by the wives of Mathematics Research Center in the informal room of the Center on Tuesday afternoon.

Of the lecturers six were from overseas, five of them having crossed the ocean specifically to participate in this conference. We extend our sincere thanks to them, and indeed to all the lecturers, the chairmen and to the members of the program committee. The latter were

Dr. H. F. Bueckner, chairman,
Dr. Preston Hammer,
Dr. L. M. Milne-Thomson,
Dr. W. Wasow.

Preface

The function of mathematics, in its role as "handmaiden of the sciences", is to render firm and precise formulations of the laws that are taken to govern natural phenomena. That is a large assignment. Even a single phenomenon can run its course in an infinite variety of actual manifestations. For, its aspect is in each particular instance answerable to matters of configuration and of the prevailing environment, and is, aside from that, under the sway of the conditions of its inception. The flight of a projectile is a simple phenomenon. However, each trajectory comports, on the one hand, qualitatively, with the features of the projectile's design, with the gravitational field, and with the characteristics of the ambient medium, and on the other hand, quantitatively, with the initially imparted direction and velocity.

The mathematical means for the formulation of natural laws must have a corresponding flexibility. They are, therefore, in the main the differential equations. For the differential equation which formulates a phenomenon is qualitatively adjustable to a specific manifestation through value assignments to parameters which it can be taken to depend upon. And it permits the isolation of a particular solution from the infinite family of such by the application of boundary conditions. A differential equation conjoined with boundary conditions defines a boundary problem.

A mathematical formulation is, in the ultimate sense, a conceptual model of a reality. It is an idealization and simplification of what it represents, and as such is more accessible to analysis. The results of analyses upon it are, to the extent that the formulation is valid, interpretable into relevant natural terms. That is the way in which scientific prediction is achieved. The study of a "boundary problem in differential equations" is thus in actual fact the pursuit, in simplified but precise terms, of an understanding of the orderly inner nature of a phenomenon, and how, in given circumstances, it may be expected to manifest itself.

Rudolph E. Langer

Contents

Page

Boundary Problems in Differential Equations

K. O. FRIEDRICHS

Boundary Problems of Linear Differential Equations Independent of Type

It is a basic fact in the theory of elliptic, hyperbolic and parabolic equations that the solutions of these equations have completely different properties. In particular, completely different boundary or initial data are to be imposed on these solutions. It may therefore seem absurd to attempt a unified treatment of boundary and initial problems for such equations. Nevertheless, up to a certain point such a unified approach is possible.

Among the various methods that so far have been developed for the equations mentioned, there are some that use closely related tools: inequalities between quadratic forms; and it is possible -- up to a point --to give a unified description of these methods.

If this is done one will observe that it is not the elliptic, hyperbolic or parabolic character of the equation that makes a boundary or initial value problem well posed. What matters are different, though related, algebraic properties of the coefficients.

As a consequence, this unified approach also covers certain equations of mixed type, i. e. equations which are of different type in different parts of the domain. In particular, certain problems of the Tricomi equation are covered.

Also, the unified approach enables one to formulate unified finite difference substitutes of the differential equation problems. As a matter of fact, the attempt at finding such a finite difference substitute for problems of the Tricomi equation was the starting point for the present investigation.

It is convenient to describe the unified approach not in terms of equations of the second order, but in terms of systems of linear equations of the first order. We will consider k functions $u_1, u_2, \ldots, u_k$ of n variables $x_1, \ldots, x_n$ which are combined into a point $x = x_1, \ldots, x_n$. The linear differential equation may be written in the form

$$\sum_{\rho=1}^{n} \sum_{\nu=1}^{k} \left(a^{\rho}_{\lambda\nu} \frac{\partial}{\partial x_\rho} u_\nu + \frac{\partial}{\partial x_\rho} a^{\rho}_{\lambda\nu} u_\nu + \kappa_{\lambda\nu} u_\nu \right) = f_\lambda \ ,$$

$$\lambda = 1, \ldots, k \ ,$$

where the $a^\rho_{\lambda\mu}$, $\kappa_{\lambda\mu}$ and f_λ are given functions of x. Combining the functions u_ν and f_λ as $\{u_\nu\} = u$, $\{f_\lambda\} = f$ and combining the coefficients into matrices $a^\rho = \{a^\rho_{\lambda\nu}\}$, $\kappa = \{\kappa_{\lambda\nu}\}$, we may write the equation in the form

$$Ku = f$$

where K stands for the differential operator

$$K \equiv \sum_\rho \left(a^\rho \frac{\partial}{\partial x_\rho} + \frac{\partial}{\partial x_\rho} a^\rho \right) + K .$$

The differential equations that we shall study are characterized by two requirements imposed on the coefficients.

I. The matrices a_ρ are symmetric.

II. The matrix $\kappa + \kappa'$ is positive definite. Here κ' is the transpose of κ. If these requirements are met the operator K will be called "symmetric positive".

It is easy to write the linear elliptic, hyperbolic and parabolic equations of the second order in the above form. The same is true of the Tricomi equation and many others; no uniformity of type is required.

The first important problem is to impose appropriate boundary conditions. Assume the functions u and f, and the coefficients a^ρ, κ to be defined in a region $\mathscr{R}$ and on its boundary $\mathscr{B}$. Then the boundary condition, for convenience assumed homogeneous, will be written in the form

$$Mu = 0 \text{ on } \mathscr{B} ,$$

where M is an appropriate k by k matrix defined on the boundary $\mathscr{B}$.

We shall select a special class of such matrices, depending on the nature of the matrices a^ρ on the boundary $\mathscr{B}$. We shall make this selection by imposing the requirements of "maximality" introduced by P. Lax in a related context; we employ a version of this requirement which is specifically adapted to our approach.

Denote the interior unit normal vector of the boundary $\mathscr{B}$ by $n = \{n_1, \ldots, n_m\}$ and introduce the matrix

$$\beta = \Sigma_\rho n_\rho a^\rho .$$

Furthermore, introduce a matrix μ on $\mathscr{B}$ by writing M in the form

$$M = \beta + \mu .$$

Our requirements on M will then be formulated as two requirements, III_0 and III_1 on the matrix μ. The first one is III_0 : $\mu + \mu'$ is non-negative, while III_1 will not be described here. We shall speak of an "adapted" boundary condition $Mu = 0$ if it can be written in the form $(\beta + \mu)u = 0$ with μ satisfying requirement III $= III_0 + III_1$. Requirement III_0 is sufficiently strong to guarantee the uniqueness of the solutions; requirement III_1 insures that the boundary condition is weak enough to make existence of the solution possible.

By virtue of the symmetry requirement I the identity

$$\int_{\mathscr{R}} \cdots \int u \cdot Ku \, dx_1 \ldots dx_m + \int_{\mathscr{B}} u \cdot Mu \, dx_1 \ldots dx_m \Big/ \sum_\rho n_\rho dx_\rho$$

$$= \int_{\mathscr{R}} \cdots \int u \cdot \kappa u \, dx_1 \ldots dx_m + \int_{\mathscr{B}} u \cdot \mu u \, dx_1 \ldots dx_m \Big/ \sum_\rho n_\rho dx_\rho$$

holds as easily verified. Here $u \cdot v = \Sigma_{\lambda=1}^{k} u_\lambda v_\lambda$. By virtue of II and III_0 the right hand side is positive definite. Consequently, the solution of the problem

$$Ku = f \text{ in } \mathscr{R} \quad , \quad Mu = 0 \text{ on } \mathscr{B}$$

is unique.

The existence of a weak solution of this problem--in the case of the Tricomi problem--was proved by C. Morawetz [4]. The existence of a solution, sufficiently strong to imply uniqueness, was proved by the author [5] under severe additional conditions, which at the same time allowed him to prove a differentiability theorem.* A direct proof of the equivalence of the weak and the strong solution was subsequently given by P. Lax [10] and extended by R. Phillips [11] so as to include the case of corners at the boundary.

It should be mentioned that Phillips [3, 6] has independently developed a theory of symmetric positive§ equations and established the unique existence of a solution under a "global" maximality requirement on the boundary condition. Using our results he has shown that the local maximality here adopted is a special case of his global maximality.

In our description of the symmetric positive differential equation no reference to its type was made; in fact, the equation may be elliptic, hyperbolic, parabolic, or in the case of more than three variables, it may be of a more general type; its type may even be different in different parts of the domain. Which boundary conditions are adapted to the differential equation depends only on the nature of the coefficients of the equation at the boundary. Such conditions remain therefore adapted if the differential equation is changed in the interior of the domain provided it remains symmetric positive there. The restriction imposed by requirement III is very severe, however.

Let me explain how this restriction operates in three cases concerning a hyperbolic, an elliptic, and a mixed equation. Instead of considering equations of the second order we shall consider systems of two equations of the first order for two functions $u = \{u_1, u_2\}$ defined in the rectangle $|x_1| \leq a$, $|x_2| \leq b$. Specifically, these systems will be of the form

$$2\begin{pmatrix} 1 & 0 \\ 0 & p \end{pmatrix} \frac{\partial u}{\partial x_2} - 2\begin{pmatrix} 0 & 1 \\ 1 & 0 \end{pmatrix} \frac{\partial u}{\partial x_1} + \kappa \begin{pmatrix} 1 & 0 \\ 0 & 1 \end{pmatrix} u = f$$

in which the function $p = p(x_2)$ is to be chosen.

A hyperbolic equation results if we take $p(x_2) = 1$. Then on $x_2 = -b$ the matrix $\beta = \alpha^2$ is positive definite while $\beta = -\alpha^2$ is negative on $x_2 = b$. Requirement III now allows us to set $\mu = \alpha^2$; we find that on $x_2 = -b$ the boundary condition $2\alpha^2 u = 2u = 0$ is adapted, which simply means $u_1 = 0$, $u_2 = 0$ may be imposed there. On $x_2 = b$, where $\beta + \mu = 0$, no condition is to be imposed. On $x_1 = \pm a$ one has $\beta = \pm\alpha^1$; requirement III then implies that condition $(\mu \pm \alpha^1)u = 0$ is equivalent to prescribing just one quantity.

An elliptic equation results by taking $p(x_2) = -1$. It then turns out that the matrix β is semi-definite everywhere at the boundary and that just one quantity can be prescribed there.

Suppose we take $p(x_2) = x_2$; then the type of the equation changes: it is elliptic for $x_2 < 0$, hyperbolic for $x_2 > 0$. Consequently, β will be semi-definite on $x_2 = -b$, as for an elliptic equation, while β is negative definite on $x_2 = b$, as for the hyperbolic equation considered above. Consequently, only one condition is to be imposed on $x_2 = -b$, and no condition on $x_2 = b$.

While for the elliptic, as well as for the hyperbolic equation, the total number of conditions imposed on the segments $x_2 = b$ and $x_2 = -b$ is "two", this total number is "one" for the mixed equation considered. Therefore, we may speak of a loss of a boundary condition. Loss of boundary condition of a similar kind was discovered by Tricomi in 1924.

This loss of a boundary condition poses a peculiar problem if one wants to replace the differential equation by a finite difference equation for the purpose of numerical computation. Let us consider an equation of the second order for one function. Suppose we place a net into the rectangular domain $|x_1| \leq a$, $|x_2| \leq b$. Then for the finite difference equation usually taken as a substitute, the molecule involves one center point in the interior of the domain and four neighbors. If now the equation is elliptic and the values of the function are prescribed along the boundary, the number of equations agrees with the number of unknowns. The same is true if the equation is hyperbolic and the values of the function are prescribed on two rows near $x_2 = -b$ and not on $x_2 = b$. If, however, values are prescribed on $x_2 = -b$ and not on $x_2 = b$, as may happen for an equation of mixed type, the number of equations is less than the number of unknowns. Thus the boundary problem for the mixed difference equation cannot be handled in the indicated manner.

To be sure, effective finite difference methods of handling boundary problems of mixed equations have been developed, but in these methods the regions where the equation is of different type are treated differently. I asked myself whether it should not be possible to set up a finite difference procedure which works even if one does not pay any attention to the type of the equation. Such a procedure can indeed be set up if the problem can be formulated as a symmetric positive equation with an adapted boundary condition.

In order to describe this set-up, it is convenient to consider first a differential equation for one function u of one variable x ,

$$\alpha \frac{du}{dx} + \frac{d}{dx} \alpha u + \kappa u = f \ , \quad |x| \leq a \ .$$

Here the numbers α and $\kappa > 0$ are functions of x . Evidently $\beta = \mp\alpha$ at $x = \pm a$. We set $\mu = |\alpha|$ and write down the boundary conditions

$$(|\alpha| - \alpha)u = 0 \quad \text{at} \quad x = a \ ,$$

$$(|\alpha| + \alpha)u = 0 \quad \text{at} \quad x = -a \ .$$

If the function $\alpha(x)$ does not change sign, one of the two quantities $|\alpha| \mp \alpha$ is zero; thus actually one boundary condition is imposed. If, however, $\alpha(x)$ does change sign, either two or no boundary conditions are imposed, i.e., there is either a loss or a gain of a condition.

Suppose we introduce a net of points $x = \sigma h$, $\sigma = 0, \pm 1, \ldots, \pm s$, $sh = a$. For a set of values u_σ , $|\sigma| < s$, we then take as difference equations

$$\alpha_{\sigma + \frac{1}{2}} u_{\sigma + 1} - \alpha_{\sigma - \frac{1}{2}} u_{\sigma - 1} + h\kappa \, u_\sigma = hf_\sigma \ ,$$

which is easily recognized as a proper substitute. As boundary conditions we take

$$|\alpha_{\pm s}| \, u_{\pm s} \mp \alpha_{\pm s - \frac{1}{2}} u_{\pm(s-1)} + \tfrac{1}{2} hK_{\pm s} \, u_{\pm s} = \tfrac{1}{2} hf_{\pm s} \ .$$

As $h \to 0$ these conditions go over into $(|\alpha| \mp \alpha)u = 0$ as required. On the other hand, it can be shown that the set of equations thus described has exactly one solution as desired. Note that no attention was paid to the question of whether or not, and if so, where the coefficient α changes its sign.

The set-up here described can be carried over immediately to the case of two or more independent variables provided the domain is rectangular. An extension to non-rectangular domains was described by C. K. Chu [8]. Various other modifications of this set-up, proposed by P. Lax and C. K. Chu, are sometimes of advantage. C. K. Chu has also established the convergence of the solution of the finite difference equation to that of the differential equation under appropriate circumstances.

Naturally one asks whether the claims made here about the finite difference scheme are borne out by numerical computation. Such computations were carried out by S. Schechter [9]. As earlier attempts have shown, it is important to use a very effective scheme for solving the linear equations. S. Schechter writes the equation as triple diagonal block equations, each block matrix acting on the unknowns in a row. The associated recursion formulas turn out to be well manageable. Schechter has applied such a procedure to a problem for the Tricomi equation with a known solution. The result is quite satisfactory. It is interesting to note that no peculiarities occur near the line of type transition.

In conclusion I should like to emphasize that I do not at all claim that every partial differential equation problem can be brought under the scheme here presented; in fact, it actually is not always possible to do so as could be demonstrated with explicit counter-examples. On the other hand, it would seem that a large fraction of the manifold of the linear differential equation problems which arise naturally in mathematical physics are of such a character that they can be cast in the form of a symmetric positive differential equation with an adapted boundary condition.

To be sure, it would be inappropriate to insist that every problem that can be treated in this manner should be so treated; but still, such a treatment may yield valuable information whenever this can be done.

NOTES

*In doing this the solution of an equation was used which is elliptic in the interior of the domain but degenerates at the boundary. Reference should be made to the work of Višik, Fichera and others on partly elliptic, partly parabolic equations. See [1, 7]. The other main ingredient in proving the differentiability theorem is an adaptation of a basic inequality of P. Lax involving a norm of negative order [2].

§Phillips calls the operator - K "dissipative" if it satisfies I and II; perhaps our operator K should then be called "accretive".

REFERENCES

1. Višik, M. I., Boundary problems for elliptic equations degenerating on the boundary of the domain, Mat. Sbornik N. S., vol. 35, 1954, pp. 513-573, and references given there.

2. Lax, P. D., On Cauchy's problem for hyperbolic equations and the differentiability of solutions of elliptic equations, Comm. Pure Appl. Math., vol. 8, 1955, pp. 615-633.

3. Phillips, R.S., (A) Dissipative hyperbolic systems, Trans. Amer. Math. Soc., vol. 86, 1957, pp. 109-173.

4. Morawetz, C.S., A weak solution for a system of equations of elliptic-hyperbolic type, Comm. Pure Appl. Math., vol. 11, 1958, pp. 315-331.

5. Friedrichs, K.O., Symmetric Positive Linear Differential Equations, Comm. Pure Appl. Math., vol. 11, 1958, pp. 333-418.

6. Phillips, R.S., Dissipative operators and parabolic partial differential equations, Comm. Pure Appl. Math., vol. 12, 1959, pp.

7. Fichera, G., On a unified theory of boundary value problems for elliptic-parabolic equations of second order, This symposium volume.

8. Chu, C.K., Type insensitive finite difference schemes, Ph. D. thesis, New York University, 1959.

9. Schechter, S., Quasi-tridiagonal matrices and type-insensitive difference equations, to appear as NYO report.

10, 11. Papers by P. Lax and R. Phillips, to appear.

PAUL R. GARABEDIAN

Numerical Estimates of Contraction and Drag Coefficients

It will be our aim in this paper to describe a method that has been used to calculate axially symmetric flows with free streamlines. We shall consider primarily the classical example of the vena contracta. Thus we are concerned with the steady, irrotational flow of an incompressible, inviscid fluid through a circular orifice in a plane wall. This axially symmetric motion can be described by means of a stream function ψ in a meridian (x, y)-plane. Here the x-axis plays the role of the axis of symmetry and y represents the radius of a cylindrical coordinate system. As a function of x and y, the stream function ψ satisfies the partial differential equation

$$(1) \qquad \psi_{xx} + \psi_{yy} = \frac{1}{y}\psi_y$$

in the region occupied by the fluid, which is supposed to consist of the left half-plane $x < 0$ plus a jet issuing from the orifice $|y| < Y$, $x = 0$. The jet is bounded in the upper half-plane by a free streamline Γ which descends vertically from the point of separation $(0, Y)$, bends gradually through a right angle, and becomes asymptotic to the line $y = X$ as $x \to +\infty$. Along the free streamline Γ and along the wall $x = 0$, $y \geq Y$ the stream function ψ vanishes,

$$(2) \qquad \psi = 0 ,$$

whereas along the x-axis it is assumed to have the constant value

$$(3) \qquad \psi = X^2/2 .$$

Furthermore, the pressure in the fluid along the free streamline Γ is supposed to be constant, and this yields the additional free boundary condition

$$(4) \qquad \frac{1}{y}\frac{\partial\psi}{\partial n} = 1$$

there, where n denotes the normal pointed into the region of flow. This extra condition should serve, roughly speaking, to determine the shape of Γ, which is not given in advance.

We are interested in the problem of calculating the contraction coefficient

$$C = X^2/Y^2 , \tag{5}$$

which represents the ratio between the area πX^2 of the cross section of the jet at infinity and the area πY^2 of the orifice. For plane flow, the corresponding contraction coefficient X/Y is known to have the value

$$\frac{X}{Y} = \frac{\pi}{\pi + 2} = .6110 . \tag{6}$$

The plane model corresponds to flow in space through an infinite slot in a flat wall. Trefftz [3] has conjectured that the contraction coefficient might be independent of the shape of the orifice and has attempted to back this up with numerical evidence that in the axially symmetric case also $C = .61$. This is the value accepted by many of the handbooks of hydraulics. However, we shall present here a numerical calculation of C which indicates that it lies much closer to the value

$$C = .58 , \tag{7}$$

and we shall corroborate this result with experimental evidence to the same effect.

Our method is to generalize the problem of the vena contracta to flows satisfying the partial differential equation

$$\psi_{xx} + \psi_{yy} = \frac{\lambda}{y} \psi_y \tag{8}$$

and to consider the dependence of the solution on the parameter λ. We retain the boundary condition (2) along the free streamline Γ and along the wall $x = 0$, $y \geq Y_\lambda$, but we replace (3) along the x-axis by

$$\psi = X_\lambda^{1+\lambda}/(1 + \lambda) \tag{9}$$

for the generalized problem and we use the new free boundary condition

$$\frac{1}{y^\lambda} \frac{\partial \psi}{\partial n} = 1 \tag{10}$$

along Γ. Our notation here takes into account the fact that the radii X_λ and Y_λ may vary with λ in this formulation of the question. The reader will recognize that when λ is a non-negative integer the equations (2), (8), (9) and (10) characterize the axially symmetric vena contracta in space of $\lambda + 2$ dimensions. However, the problem we have posed makes sense for any complex value of λ in the half-plane

$$\text{Re}\,\{\lambda\} > -1 \quad . \tag{11}$$

We are interested in studying the behavior of the contraction coefficient defined by

$$C_\lambda = \frac{X_\lambda^{1+\lambda}}{Y_\lambda^{1+\lambda}} \tag{12}$$

in its dependence on the parameter λ .

The case $\lambda = 0$ is that of the plane vena contracta and can be solved in closed form by the hodograph method to yield the result (6), which takes the form

$$C_0 = \frac{X_0}{Y_0} = \frac{\pi}{\pi + 2} = .6110 \tag{13}$$

in our new notation. On the other hand, the case $\lambda = 1$ corresponds to our original problem of the three-dimensional vena contracta, and it is C_1 that we really wish to compute. In line with the Trefftz conjecture that the contraction coefficient does not depend on the shape of the orifice, we might guess that C_λ does not vary with λ , so that $C_1 = C_0$. We shall begin our discussion by establishing that this is false.

Our proof is based on Euler's momentum theorem, which can be interpreted for the generalized flow (8) as the statement that

$$\oint \left[\psi_x \frac{\partial \psi}{\partial n} - \psi \frac{\partial \psi_x}{\partial n} \right] \frac{ds}{y^\lambda} = 0 \tag{14}$$

for any closed path of integration bounding a region in which ψ is regular. This result is easily deduced from (8) by an application of Green's theorem. We choose for the contour of integration a locus composed of the arc cut out of a large circle about the origin by the second quadrant, plus a segment of the x-axis extending from this arc far to the right, plus a vertical segment rising to the free streamline Γ , plus the arc of Γ returning to the point of separation $(0, Y_\lambda)$, plus, finally, a portion of the y-axis to complete the circuit. If we allow the large circle to expand to infinity and at the same time let the vertical segment joining the x-axis to Γ move off to the right without limit, we derive from (14) the identity

$$C_\lambda = \tfrac{1}{2} + \frac{1 + \lambda}{2 Y_\lambda^{1+\lambda}} \int_{Y_\lambda}^{\infty} \psi_x^2 \frac{dy}{y^\lambda} \, , \tag{15}$$

where the integral on the right is to be evaluated along the y-axis. An immediate consequence of (15) is the classical estimate

$$C_\lambda \geq \tfrac{1}{2} \tag{16}$$

of the contraction coefficient. We shall improve on this result by deriving an explicit positive lower bound on ψ_x^2 along the segment $y \geq Y_\lambda$ of the y-axis.

To this end, we introduce the special solution

$$\Psi = \frac{X_\lambda^{1+\lambda} \int_{\pi/2}^{\theta} \sin^\lambda \theta_1 \, d\theta_1}{(1+\lambda) \int_{\pi/2}^{\pi} \sin^\lambda \theta_1 \, d\theta_1} \tag{17}$$

of (8), which depends on the angle

$$\theta = \tan^{-1}(y/x) \tag{18}$$

only and represents the flow from a source at infinity to a sink at the origin. We notice that $\psi - \Psi$ is a solution of (8) in the second quadrant which vanishes along the negative x-axis and along the segment $y \geq Y_\lambda$ of the y-axis, but which is positive along the segment $0 < y < Y_\lambda$ of the y-axis, since $\Psi = 0$ there and since by the maximum principle $\psi > 0$ there. Thus, again by the maximum principle for (8), the function $\psi - \Psi$ must be positive in the second quadrant. Hence at points of the segment $y \geq Y_\lambda$ of the y-axis, where it vanishes, $\psi - \Psi$ must have a non-negative derivative in the direction of decreasing x, so that

$$-\psi_x \geq -\Psi_x \tag{19}$$

there. We evaluate Ψ_x explicitly and substitute the lower bound (19) into the integral on the right in (15) to derive the new estimate

$$C_\lambda \geq \tfrac{1}{2} + C_\lambda^2 \frac{\left(\int_{\pi/2}^{\pi} \sin^\lambda \theta_1 \cos \theta_1 \, d\theta_1\right)^2}{2\left(\int_{\pi/2}^{\pi} \sin^\lambda \theta_1 \, d\theta_1\right)^2} \tag{20}$$

of the contraction coefficient. We have made use here of the fact that

$$\frac{1}{1+\lambda} = -\int_{\pi/2}^{\pi} \sin^\lambda \theta_1 \cos \theta_1 \, d\theta_1 \ . \tag{21}$$

In order to show that C_λ varies with λ, we study the inequality (20) in the limit as $\lambda \to -1$. The two integrals on the right approach infinity at the same rate, and we obtain

$$C_{-1} \geq \tfrac{1}{2} + \tfrac{1}{2} C_{-1}^2 \ . \tag{22}$$

It follows immediately that

$$C_{-1} = 1 \ , \tag{23}$$

and a comparison with the explicit result (13) shows that C_λ cannot remain constant as λ varies. However, the statement (23) does not provide any information about the value of the ratio X_{-1}/Y_{-1}, since the exponent in the definition (12) vanishes at $\lambda = -1$.

In order to calculate X_{-1}/Y_{-1}, we solve the free boundary problem (2), (8), (9), (10) explicitly in the degenerate case $\lambda = -1$. We notice that the limiting form

(24) $$\Psi = \int_{\pi/2}^{\theta} \frac{d\theta_1}{\sin\theta_1}$$

of (17) is a function which satisfies (8) for $\lambda = -1$, which satisfies the requirements that the x-axis and the y-axis should be streamlines, and which furthermore satisfies the limiting form

(25) $$y\frac{\partial\Psi}{\partial n} = 1$$

of the free boundary condition (10) along the y-axis, as can be verified by direct calculation. Hence $\psi = \Psi$ must be the solution of our free boundary problem when $\lambda = -1$, and it follows that as $\lambda \to -1$ the free streamline Γ must collapse toward the segment $0 \le y \le Y_\lambda$ of the y-axis and the segment $x \ge 0$ of the x-axis. Therefore we have

(26) $$X_{-1}/Y_{-1} = 0 \ .$$

We have now obtained the two specific values (13) and (26) of the ratio X_λ/Y_λ at $\lambda = 0$ and $\lambda = -1$. From (12) and (16) we can derive the inequality

(27) $$\frac{X_\lambda}{Y_\lambda} \ge \left(\tfrac{1}{2}\right)^{1/(1+\lambda)} ,$$

and since evidently $X_\lambda \le Y_\lambda$ for positive choices of λ, we conclude that

(28) $$X_\infty/Y_\infty = \lim_{\lambda\to+\infty} X_\lambda/Y_\lambda = 1 \ .$$

These results suggest interpolating to calculate the value of X_1/Y_1.

We cannot use a polynomial in λ as an interpolating expression for X_λ/X_λ because of the finite value (28) which occurs at infinity. It is suggestive, however, that the conformal mapping

(29) $$\delta = \frac{\lambda}{\lambda + 2}$$

transforms the half-plane (11) of choices of the parameter λ for which the free boundary problem defined by (2), (8), (9) and (10) makes sense onto the unit circle

$$|\delta| < 1 , \tag{30}$$

so that we can expect X_λ/Y_λ to be a regular analytic function of δ in this circle and to have a convergent power series representation

$$\frac{X_\lambda}{Y_\lambda} = a_0 + a_1\delta + a_2\delta^2 + \dots \tag{31}$$

there. Our procedure will therefore be to express X_λ/Y_λ as a quadratic in δ, to determine the three coefficients a_0, a_1 and a_2 of this quadratic so that X_λ/Y_λ assumes the three known values given by (13), (26) and (28) at the points $\delta = 0$, $\delta = -1$ and $\delta = 1$ corresponding to $\lambda = 0$, $\lambda = -1$ and $\lambda = \infty$, and to compute X_1/Y_1 by substituting into this quadratic the value $\delta = 1/3$ corresponding to $\lambda = 1$. The approximation that we obtain in this manner for the ratio X_λ/Y_λ is

$$\frac{X_\lambda}{Y_\lambda} = .6110 + .5000\delta - .1110\delta^2 , \tag{32}$$

and the consequent numerical estimate for X_1/Y_1 is

$$X_1/Y_1 = .7653 , \tag{33}$$

whence by (5)

$$C_1 = .5857 . \tag{34}$$

It is possible to improve on this result and to appraise its accuracy by calculating the exact value of the coefficient a_1 in the expansion (31) from a perturbation scheme based on the assumption that δ is small. Because the vena contracta is known explicitly in the plane case corresponding to $\delta = 0$, its first order variation with respect to perturbations in δ can be found in closed form, and this turns out to provide an expression for a_1 as a double integral. For the details here we refer to a previous publication [1], and we merely state the final result

$$a_1 = .4857 \tag{35}$$

obtained by numerical evaluation of the integral.

It is natural to use the four items of data (13), (26), (28) and (35) to determine the coefficients a_0, a_1, a_2 and a_3 in a cubic interpolation formula for the ratio X_λ/Y_λ. This yields

$$\frac{X_\lambda}{Y_\lambda} = .6110 + .4857\delta - .1110\delta^2 + .0143\delta^3 , \tag{36}$$

and we can set $\delta = 1/3$ here to derive the final results

(37) $$X_1/Y_1 = .7611$$

and

(38) $$C_1 = .58 \ .$$

The rapid decline in the magnitude of the successive terms on the right in (36) provides us with numerical confirmation of the excellent convergence of the series representation (31). Also, the smallness of the change in the coefficients a_1 and a_3 as we proceed from the first approximation (32) to the second approximation (36) and the smallness of the difference between the results (38) and (34) justify some confidence in the convergence of our interpolation scheme as more and more data are brought to bear on the answer. We presume from a careful analysis of this kind that the error in the estimate (38) of the contraction coefficient could not exceed two per cent, and it is probably much less than that.

A very careful series of experimental measurements of contraction coefficients for circular orifices of various sizes has been made by Medaugh and Johnson [2]. They have studied in detail the dependence of their data on pressure head and on Reynolds number, and they concluded that for our idealized model the contraction coefficient would be about

(39) $$C = .588 \ .$$

Within the margin of accuracy of our work and theirs, the results (38) and (39) can be viewed as evidence of a very satisfactory agreement between theory and experiment.

It is of interest that our preliminary estimate (34) involved no elaborate numerical analysis. In this connection, it would be amusing to attempt an improvement in the accuracy by means of an exact calculation of the contraction coefficient C_2 for four-dimensional flow. Since the function

(40) $$u = y \int \frac{\psi_y \, dx - \psi_x \, dy}{y^2}$$

is harmonic when ψ is a solution of (8) with $\lambda = 2$, this is not quite hopeless and poses an intriguing unsolved free boundary problem.

Finally, we note that the method we have described here is quite general and applies to a variety of models of free streamline flow. In particular, the drag coefficient C_D for a circular disc in fully cavitating flow at cavitation number zero has been computed [1] to be

(41) $$C_D = .827 \ ,$$

and it can also be estimated for higher cavitation numbers.

BIBLIOGRAPHY

1. P. R. Garabedian, "Calculation of axially symmetric cavities and jets," Pac. J. Math., vol. 6, 1956, pp. 611-684.

2. F. W. Medaugh and G. D. Johnson, "Investigation of the discharge and coefficients of small circular orifices," Civil Engineering, vol. 10, 1940, pp. 422-424.

3. E. Trefftz, "Ueber die Kontraktion kreisfoermiger Fluessigkeitsstrahlen," Zeit. Math. Phys., vol. 64, 1916, pp. 34-61.

PETER HENRICI

Complete Systems of Solutions for a Class of Singular Elliptic Partial Differential Equations

1. INTRODUCTION

One of the oldest methods for solving boundary value problems involving a linear and homogeneous partial differential equation consists in representing or approximating the unknown solution by linear combinations of particular solutions of the differential equation. These particular solutions do not depend on the imposed boundary conditions, and it is desirable that they should also be independent of the domain of the problem. The following two problems arise naturally in this connection: (i) Given a partial differential equation, how does one construct a system of solutions which, in some sense, is "complete"? (ii) If a system of solutions of a partial differential equation is known, how does one decide whether it is "complete" or not?

For the differential equation

$$(1) \qquad \ell(u) = \frac{\partial^2 u}{\partial x^2} + \frac{\partial^2 u}{\partial y^2} + a\frac{\partial u}{\partial x} + b\frac{\partial u}{\partial y} + cu = 0 \ ,$$

where a, b, and c are analytic functions of x and y in the domain under consideration, I. N. Vekua in [8] has provided the tools which the problems mentioned above (as well as many others) can be solved. In the paper [6], whose terminology will be followed here, the present author has summarized Vekua's theory and has added a number of illustrative examples. This theory admittedly rests on rather strong assumptions; however, the results are of a constructive nature, and their validity is not restricted to the neighborhood of a point.

Little is known about extensions of Vekua's theory to equations whose coefficients have singularities within the domain under consideration. In this paper we shall state some results of Vekua's type for the equation

$$(2) \qquad \ell_\nu(u) \equiv \frac{\partial^2 u}{\partial x^2} + \frac{\partial^2 u}{\partial y^2} + \frac{2\nu}{y}\frac{\partial u}{\partial y} + a\frac{\partial u}{\partial x} + cu = 0 \ ,$$

where $\nu > 0$, and where a and c are analytic functions of x alone. Equations of this type frequently occur in problems involving axial symmetry. The case $a = c = 0$ has been studied extensively [9, 7, 1, 5].

2. REVIEW OF SOME RESULTS FOR THE REGULAR CASE

In what follows it is convenient to think of x and y as of two independent complex variables. The mainspring of the Vekua theory then becomes obvious if the new variables

$$z = x + iy \;, \quad z^* = x - iy \tag{3}$$

are introduced. (For complex x and y, z and z^* are in general not conjugate complex numbers.) Equations (1) then transforms into the following formally hyperbolic equation for the function $U(z, z^*) = u(x, y)$:

$$L[U] \equiv \frac{\partial^2 U}{\partial z \partial z^*} + A\frac{\partial U}{\partial z} + B\frac{\partial u}{\partial z^*} + CU = 0 \;. \tag{4}$$

Here

$$A = A(z, z^*) = \tfrac{1}{4}[a(x, y) + i\, b(x, y)]$$

$$B = B(z, z^*) = \tfrac{1}{4}[a(x, y) - i\, b(x, y)]$$

$$C = C(z, z^*) = \tfrac{1}{4}c(x, y) \;.$$

It is assumed--and this assumption is basic to the whole theory--that the functions A, B, C, which are originally defined only for $z^* = \overline{z}$, can be continued analytically as functions of two independent complex variables into the domain $(z, z^*) \in (D, \overline{D})$, where D is some fixed simply connected domain, called the fundamental domain of the operator $L[U]$. It then is proved in [8] (see also [6], section 2.2) that for $(z, z^*, t, t^*) \in (D, \overline{D}, D, \overline{D})$ the integral equation

$$V(z, z^*) - \int_t^z B(s, z^*)\, V(s, z^*)ds - \int_{t^*}^{z^*} A(z, s^*)\, V(z, s^*)ds^* + \int_t^z ds \int_{t^*}^{z^*} C(s, s^*)\, V(s, s^*)ds^* = 1$$

has a solution $V(z, z^*) = R(z, z^*, t, t^*)$ which depends analytically on its four complex arguments in the domain $(D, \overline{D}, D, \overline{D})$. For obvious formal reasons, R is called the complex Riemann function of the differential operator (1). It can, in principle, be calculated to any desired degree of precision by a process of successive approximations and is known explicitly for a number of special differential equations. Vekua's theory is essentially built upon properties of this function.

We shall require a representation of the following special Cauchy problems involving (1). Let the fundamental domain D be symmetric with respect to the x-axis, and let $f(z)$ be holomorphic* in a simply connected domain $G \subset D$. The problem is to find a solution of (1) satisfying

(5) $$u(x, 0) = f(x) \quad , \quad \frac{\partial u}{\partial y}(x, 0) = 0 \quad , \quad x \in G \cap \{y = 0\} \quad .$$

It is shown in [6] that this problem has a solution $u(x, y)$ which is analytic for $x \pm iy \in G$. The function $U(z, z^*) = u(x, y)$ is given by the formula

(6) $$\begin{cases} 2U(z, z^*) = f(z)\, R(z, z, z, z^*) + f(z^*)\, R(z^*, z^*, z, z^*) \\ \qquad - \int_z^{z^*} f(t)\, \{2R(t, t, z, z^*)[B(t, t) - A(t, t)] \\ \qquad + R_2(t, t, z, z^*) - R_1(t, t, z, z^*)\}dt \quad , \end{cases}$$

R_i denoting the derivative of R with respect to the i-th variable.§

3. SOLUTION OF A SINGULAR CAUCHY PROBLEM

The aim of this section is a representation of the solution of the Cauchy problem (5) for the singular equation (2) (with the data given on the singular line $y = 0$) in a form similar to (6). An elementary power series argument (similar to one carried out, e.g., in [2], section 12.11) shows that for $\nu > 0$ any solution $u(x, y)$ of $\ell_\nu(u) = 0$ which is analytic on $y = 0$ automatically satisfies $\frac{\partial u}{\partial y}(x, 0) = 0$ and is uniquely determined by its values on $y = 0$.

Our construction is based on the following simple observation.

Lemma 1. Let $u_0(x, y)$ be a solution of $\ell_0(u_0) = 0$ defined in a domain G which together with every point (x, y) also contains# all points (x, ty), $-1 \leq t \leq 1$. Then for $\nu > 0$ the function

(7) $$u(x, y) = c_\nu \int_0^\pi u_0(x, y \cos \vartheta) \sin^{2\nu-1} \vartheta \, d\vartheta \quad ,$$

where

$$c_\nu^{-1} = \int_0^\pi \sin^{2\nu-1} \vartheta \, d\vartheta$$

is a solution of $\ell_\nu(u) = 0$ defined in G and satisfying

(8) $$u(x, -y) = u(x, y) \quad ,$$

(9) $$u(x, 0) = u_0(x, y) \quad .$$

Proof. The relations (8) and (9) are obvious. The proof that $u(x, y)$ satisfies the desired differential equation can be carried out by calculus. Instead of repeating this argument here, we shall give a proof which, although valid only for integral values of 2ν , is more intuitive. If Δ denotes the Laplacian operator in the Euclidean space E_p of $p = 2\nu + 2$ dimensions, then the equation $\ell_\nu(u) = 0$ can be interpreted as the condition that a function u defined in E_p, but depending only on the variables $x = x_1$ and $y = (x_2^2 + \ldots + x_p^2)^{\frac{1}{2}}$, satisfies

$$\Delta u + a(x_1)\frac{\partial u}{\partial x_1} + c(x_1)u = 0 \quad . \tag{10}$$

Obviously the function $u_0(x_1, x_2)$ is a solution of (10). More generally, if $\underline{\xi} = (0, \xi_1, \ldots, \xi_p)$, $\xi_2^2 + \ldots + \xi_p^2 = 1$, is a vector of length one whose first component is zero, and if $\underline{y} = (0, x_2, \ldots, x_p)$, then the function $u_0(x_1, \underline{\xi}\ \underline{y})$ satisfies (10) in view of the invariance of Δ under orthogonal transformations. Thus the same is true for the function

$$\int u_0(x_1, \underline{\xi}\ \underline{y})dw \tag{11}$$

where the integration is over the sphere $|\xi| = 1$ whose surface element we call dw. It is clear that the integral (11) depends only on $x = x_1$ and $y = |\underline{y}|$. If evaluated, it is seen to be identical with (7), up to a constant factor.

In view of Lemma 1, our problem is reduced to the solution of a regular Cauchy problem of a type considered in the preceding section. We shall from now on denote by R the complex Riemann function of the special equation $\ell_0(u) = 0$. It is assumed that the functions $a(z)$ and $c(z)$ are holomorphic in a simply connected domain D symmetric about $y = 0$, which we choose as the fundamental domain. We shall also assume momentarily that both the domain D and the domain G in which the function $f(z)$ is assumed to be holomorphic are <u>convex</u>. Since now $A = B$, the function $U_0(z, z^*)$ solving the Cauchy problem (5) for $\ell_0(u) = 0$ is given by

$$U_0(z, z^*) = \tfrac{1}{2}f(z)\, M(z, z^*) + \tfrac{1}{2}f(z^*)\, N(z, z^*) + \int_z^{z^*} f(t)\, K_0(z, z^*; t)dt \quad , \tag{12}$$

where

$$M(z, z^*) = R(z, z, z, z^*) , \quad N(z, z^*) = R(z^*, z^*, z, z^*)$$

$$K_0(z, z^*, t) = \tfrac{1}{2}(R_1(t, t, z, z^*) - R_2(t, t, z, z^*)) \quad .$$

As a consequence of the general functional relations satisfied by the Riemann function (see [6], Theorem 2.14) and of the special properties of the operator $\ell_0(u)$ it can be verified that

$$M(z, z^*) = N(z^*, z) \quad , \tag{13}$$

$$K_0(z, z^*, t) = -K_0(z^*, z, t) \quad . \tag{14}$$

Replacing y by $y \cos \vartheta$ amounts to replacing z by $z\theta + z^*\theta'$ and z^* by $z\theta' + z^*\theta$, where

$$\theta = \tfrac{1}{2}(1 + \cos \vartheta) , \quad \theta' = \tfrac{1}{2}(1 - \cos \vartheta) .$$

The function $U(z, z^*) = u(x, y)$ defined by (7) is in terms of $f(t)$ expressed as follows:

$$U(z, z^*) = c_\nu \int_0^\pi U_0(z\theta + z^*\theta', z\theta' + z^*\theta) \sin^{2\nu-1} \vartheta \, d\vartheta$$

$$= c_\nu \int_0^\pi \{ \tfrac{1}{2} f(z\theta + z^*\theta') M(z\theta + z^*\theta', z\theta' + z^*\theta)$$

$$+ \tfrac{1}{2} f(z\theta' + z^*\theta) N(z\theta + z^*\theta', z\theta' + z^*\theta)$$

$$+ \int_{z\theta + z^*\theta'}^{z\theta' + z^*\theta} f(t) K_0(z\theta + z^*\theta', z\theta' + z^*\theta; t) dt \} \sin^{2\nu-1} \vartheta \, d\vartheta .$$

Introducing a new variable φ by setting

$$t = z\phi + z^*\phi' ,$$

where

$$\phi = \tfrac{1}{2}(1 + \cos \varphi) , \quad \phi' = \tfrac{1}{2}(1 - \cos \varphi) ,$$

and using (13), we find

$$U(z, z^*) = c_\nu \int_0^\pi \{ f(z\theta + z^*\theta') M(z\theta + z^*\theta', z\theta' + z^*\theta)$$

$$- \frac{z - z^*}{2} \int_\vartheta^{\pi - \vartheta} f(z\phi + z^*\phi') K_0(z\theta + z^*\theta' + z^*\theta; z\phi + z^*\phi') \sin \varphi \, d\varphi \} \times$$

$$\times \sin^{2\nu-1} \vartheta \, d\vartheta .$$

Interchanging the two integrations and making use of (14), we finally find

$$(15) \qquad U(z, z^*) = c_\nu \int_0^\pi f(z\theta + z^*\theta') K_\nu(z, z^*; \vartheta) d\vartheta ,$$

where

$$(16) \qquad K_\nu(z, z^*, \vartheta) = M(z\theta + z^*\theta', z\theta' + z^*\theta) \sin^{2\nu-1} \vartheta$$

$$- (z - z^*) \sin \vartheta \int_0^\vartheta K_0(z\phi + z^*\phi', z\phi' + z^*\phi; z\theta + z^*\theta') \sin^{\nu-1} \varphi \, d\varphi .$$

This is the desired result, established under the hypothesis that G and D are convex. It shows that the resulting function $U(z, z^*)$ is analytic for $(z, z^*) \in (G, \overline{G})$ and hence, in particular, that the solution $u(x, y)$ is analytic for real x and y satisfying $x \pm iy \in G$. In order that $u(x, y)$ is defined for real values of x and y it is obviously necessary that the domain G intersects the real axis.

As ϑ increases from 0 to π through real values, the point $z\theta + z^*\theta'$ moves from z to z^* along a straight line. If G is not convex, it may thus be necessary to deform the path of integration in (15) into the complex ϑ-plane in such a way that $z\theta + z^*\theta' \in G$ along the path. This makes it necessary to continue the function $K_\nu(z, z^*, \vartheta)$ to certain complex values of ϑ. This continuation can be effected in the following manner. With every pair of point $(z, z^*) \in (B, G)$ we associate a simple rectifiable arc c_{zz^*} joining the points $\vartheta = 0$ and $\vartheta = \pi$ and having the following properties:

(a) The transformation $\zeta = z\theta + z^*\theta'$ maps c_{zz^*} on a simple arc entirely contained in G ;

(b) c_{zz^*} depends continuously on z and z^* ;

(c) For $z = z^*$, c_{zz^*} reduces to the straight line segment joining $\vartheta = 0$ and $\vartheta = \pi$.

For each $(z, z^*) \in (G, G)$, the function $K_\nu(z, z^*, \vartheta)$ is first defined only for $\vartheta \in c_{zz^*}$ by integrating in (16) along a piece of c_{zz^*} and giving $\sin^{2\nu-1}\varphi$ the definition resulting from deforming c_{zz} into c_{zz^*}. By Cauchy's theorem, and by the conditions (a) and (b) above, the variable path of integration can be replaced by a fixed path in the neighborhood of every $(z, z^*) \in (G, G)$ and every $\vartheta \in c_{zz^*}$, $\vartheta \neq 0$, $\vartheta \neq \pi$. Since the functions M and K_0 are analytic, it follows that the function $K(z, z^*, \vartheta)$ depends analytically on its three arguments for $(z, z^*) \in (G, G)$ and for the above-mentioned values of ϑ. In (15) we integrate along the full path c_{zz^*}, and a repetition of the above argument shows that the function $U(z, z^*)$ thus defined is an analytic function of z and z^* in (G, G). Since (G, G) is simply connected, it is clear that the values of $U(z, z^*)$ do not depend on the choice of the path c_{zz^*}.

For points z and z^* which are close together we may integrate along a straight line, as before, and the old reasoning holds. It follows that the function $u(x, y)$ satisfies the relations (5) and the differential equation $\ell_\nu(u) = 0$ near $y = 0$ and thus, by the principle of permanence of functional equations, for all $(z, z^*) \in (G, G)$.

We sum up these results as follows:

Theorem 1. Let G be simply connected and symmetric about $y = 0$, and let $f(z)$ be holomorphic in G. Then the function $u(x, y)$ defined for $\nu > 0$ by (15), where $u(x, y) = U(x + iy, x - iy)$, has the following properties:

(i) $u(x, y)$ is analytic for $x + iy \in G$, $x - iy \in G$

(ii) $u(x, 0) = f(x)$, $x \in G$

(iii) $\frac{\partial u}{\partial x}(x, 0) = 0$, $x \in G$

(iv) $\ell_\nu(u) = 0$, $x + iy \in G$, $x - iy \in G$.

Complex values of x and y are admitted in these statements.

4. EXAMPLES

The most general equation of the form $\ell_0(u) = 0$ for which the Riemann function is known is

$$\frac{\partial^2 u}{\partial x^2} + \frac{\partial^2 u}{\partial y^2} + \frac{2\mu}{x}\frac{\partial u}{\partial x} + k^2 u = 0 ,$$

where μ and k are arbitrary constants. We have (see [6], Table 2)

$$R(t, t^*, z, z^*) = \left(\frac{t + t^*}{z + z^*}\right)^{\mu} \Xi\left(\mu, 1-\mu, 1, X, -\frac{k^2R^2}{4}\right) ,$$

where Ξ denotes a confluent hypergeometric function of two variables defined by

$$\Xi(\alpha, \beta, \gamma, x, y) = \sum_{m, n = 0}^{\infty} \frac{(\alpha)_m (\beta)_m}{(\gamma)_{m+n} m!\, n!} x^m y^n$$

and where

$$X = -\frac{(z - t)(z^* - t^*)}{(z + z^*)(t + t^*)} , \quad R^2 = (z - t)(z^* - t^*) .$$

Calculating the functions $M(z, z^*)$ and $K_0(z, z^*, t)$ and carrying out the required integration, one finds

$$K_\nu(z, z^*, \vartheta) = \left(1 + \frac{z-z^*}{z+z^*}\cos\vartheta\right)^{\mu} \sin^{2\nu-1}\vartheta \cdot \Xi(\mu, 1-\mu, \nu; \xi, \eta) , \tag{17}$$

where

$$\xi = \frac{(z - z^*)^2 \sin^2\vartheta}{8(z + z^*)(z\theta + z^*\theta')} = -\frac{y^2 \sin^2\vartheta}{4x(x + iy\cos\vartheta)} ,$$

$$\eta = \frac{k^2}{4}\left(\frac{z-z^*}{2}\right)^2 \sin^2\vartheta = -\frac{k^2y^2}{4}\sin^2\vartheta .$$

By using known series expansions for the function Ξ, we can express K_ν in either of the following two forms:

(17a) $$K_\nu(z, z^*, t) = (1 + \frac{iy}{x} \cos \vartheta)^\mu \left(\frac{2 \sin \vartheta}{ky}\right)^\nu \Gamma(\nu) \times \sum_{m=0}^{\infty} \frac{(\mu)_m (1-\mu)_m}{m!} \left(\frac{-y \sin \vartheta}{2kx(x + iy \cos \quad)}\right)^m J_{\nu+m-1}(ky \sin \vartheta);$$

(17b) $$K_\nu(z, z^*; \vartheta) = (1 + \frac{iy}{x} \cos \vartheta)^\mu \sin^{2\nu-1} \vartheta \cdot \sum_{n=0}^{\infty} \frac{\eta^n}{(\nu)_n n!} F(\mu, 1-\mu; v + m; \xi) .$$

The first makes evident that for $\mu = 0$, K_ν reduces to

(17c) $$K_\nu(z, z^*, \vartheta) = \left(\frac{2 \sin \vartheta}{ky}\right)^\nu \Gamma(\nu) J_{\nu-1}(ky \sin \vartheta) .$$

Letting $k = 0$, we obtain from the second expansion**

(17d) $$K_\nu(z, z^*, \vartheta) = (1 + \frac{iy}{x} \cos \vartheta)^\mu \sin^{2\nu-1} \vartheta \quad F(\mu, 1-\mu, \nu; \xi) .$$

From either (17c) or (17d) we get for $\mu = k = 0$ the well-known result

(17e) $$K_\nu(z, z^*, \vartheta) = \sin^{2\nu-1} \vartheta .$$

5. THE CLASS OF SOLUTIONS REPRESENTED BY (15)

We return to the general equation $\ell_\nu(u) = 0$. The representation (15) enables us to find many solutions of this equation, namely one corresponding to each function $f(z)$ holomorphic in G. The question arises whether the class of solutions which are representable in this form can be characterized in some independent way. The answer will be given in Theorem 3, which is a simple consequence of the following Theorem 2.

As before, G denotes a simply connected domain symmetric about $y = 0$ and contained in the fundamental domain D. We shall write

$$G^+ = G \cap \{x + iy \mid y > 0\} ,$$

$$I = G \cap \{x + iy \mid y = 0\} .$$

Theorem 2. Let the function $u(x, y)$ satisfy $\ell_\nu(u) = 0$ for $x + iy \in G^+$ (x, y real) and let u, $\frac{\partial u}{\partial x}$, and $\frac{\partial u}{\partial y}$ be continuous in $G^+ \cup I$. Assume, moreover, that

(18) $$\frac{\partial u}{\partial y}(x, 0) = 0 , \quad (x, 0) \in I .$$

Then there exists a function $f(z)$, holomorphic in G, such that $f(x) = u(x, 0)$, $x \in I$.

In other words, the function $u(x, 0)$ is analytic on I and can, as a function of the single complex variable x, be continued analytically into G.

It suffices to prove the statement of the theorem for every simply connected symmetric subdomain E of G whose closure is contained in G. We may even assume that E is bounded by a differentiable Jordan curve C. We shall denote by E^+ and C^+ the parts of E and C which lie in $y > 0$.

The proof of Theorem 2 makes use of a fundamental singularity of $\ell_\nu(u)$ on the singular line. By this we mean a function $v(x, y, \xi)$ defined in G^+ and having the following properties:

(α) As a function of x and y, v satisfies in G^+ the adjoint equation of $\ell_\nu(u) = 0$ defined by

$$(19)\qquad (\ell_\nu)^*(v) = \frac{\partial^2 v}{\partial x^2} + \frac{\partial^2 v}{\partial y^2} - \frac{\partial}{\partial x}(z(x)v) - \frac{\partial}{\partial y}\left(\frac{2\nu}{y} v\right) + c(x)v = 0 .$$

(β) Near the line segment I, but excluding a (small) disk c_ρ of radius ρ about the point ξ,

$$v(x, y, \xi) = 0(y^{2\nu}) .$$

(γ) In c_ρ, $v(x, y, \xi) = y^{2\nu} r^{-2\nu}\{1 + 0(r)\}$, where

$$r^2 = (x - \xi)^2 + y^2 .$$

Lemma 2. There exists a fundamental singularity $v(x, y, \xi)$ which, in addition to satisfying conditions (α), (β), (γ) above, has the following property: For every point $x + iy \in C^+$, v as a function of ξ can be continued analytically into E.

We shall represent v in the form

$$v = y^{2\nu} w(x, y; \xi) .$$

It is easily verified that (19) then yields the following condition for w:

$$(20)\qquad (\ell_0^*)_\nu(w) \equiv \frac{\partial^2 w}{\partial x^2} + \frac{\partial^2 w}{\partial y^2} + \frac{2\nu}{y}\frac{\partial w}{\partial y} - \frac{\partial}{\partial x}(a(x)w) + c(x)w = 0 .$$

If the Riemann function for $\ell_0(u)$ is known, the Riemann function R^* for the adjoint operator $\ell_0{}^*(u)$ can be obtained from it by a simple interchange of variables and is analytic in the same domain. If a kernel K^* is defined by means of (16) (with R replaced by R^*), then for every $f(z)$ which is holomorphic in some simply connected, symmetric domain G_1 the function

(21) $$w(x, y) = c_\nu \int_0^\pi f(z\theta + z^*\theta')\, K^*_\nu(z, z^*; \vartheta)\, d\vartheta$$

is by Theorem 1 a solution of (20) satisfying

$$w(x, 0) = f(x) \quad , \quad x \in G_1 \ .$$

We now define $w(x, y, \xi)$ by choosing for f the function

(22) $$f(z) = f(z, \xi) = (z - \xi)^{-2\nu} \quad ,$$

which is holomorphic in the domain G_1 obtained from G by deleting the points $(x, 0)$, $x \leq \xi$. It follows that $w(x, y, \xi)$ solves (20) for $x + iy \in G_1$ (x, y complex) and thus in particular for $x + iy \in G^+$ (x, y real) . Moreover, if $x + iy \in C^+$, we may deform the path of integration in (21) in such a manner that the point $z\theta + z^*\theta'$ travels from $x + iy$ to $x - iy$ in G_1 along C . For every ϑ on this path $f(z\theta + z^*\theta', \xi)$ can be continued analytically into E as a function of ξ . Thus the same is true for the function $w(x, y, \xi)$.

It is clear that for $\xi \in I$, w as a function of x and y is continuous in $G^+ + I - c_\rho$. It follows that (β) is satisfied.

It remains to verify condition (γ) . In the disk c_ρ , $z - z^* = 0(\rho)$. U sing the fact that

$$M^*(z, z^*) = 1 + 0(z - z^*)$$

(see [6], eq. 2.17), it follows from (16) that

$$K^*_\nu(z, z^*; \vartheta) = \sin^{2\nu-1}\vartheta\{1 + 0(r)\} \ .$$

Thus in c_ρ ,

$$w(x, y, \xi) = c_\nu \int_0^\pi \frac{\sin^{2\nu-1}\vartheta}{(z\theta + z^*\theta' - \xi)^{2\nu}} \{1 + 0(r)\}\, d\vartheta \ .$$

The same integral without the $0(r)$-term would result if the kernel (17e) were used with the function (22). It thus would have to yield the solution of

$$\frac{\partial^2 u}{\partial x^2} + \frac{\partial^2 u}{\partial y^2} + \frac{2\nu}{y}\frac{\partial u}{\partial y} = 0$$

which reduces to $(x - \xi)^{-2\nu}$ for $y = 0$. It can be verified directly that this solution is given by $u(x, y) = r^{-2\nu}$. Thus,

$$w(x, y, \xi) = r^{-2\nu}(1 + 0(r)) \ ,$$

and the function $v = y^{2\nu} w$ is shown to satisfy (γ) .

We now turn to the proof of Theorem 2. Applying Green's identity for solutions of (1) to the domain $E^+ - c_\rho$ we find, using (β), that the line integral

$$(23)\qquad \int [u\frac{\partial v}{\partial n} - v\frac{\partial u}{\partial n} - uv(a\cos(n,x) + \frac{2\nu}{y}(\cos n,\ y))]ds$$

(n = exterior normal) has the same value along C^+ as it has along the semicircle

$$x - \xi = \rho\cos\psi\ ,\quad y = \rho\sin\psi\ ,\quad 0 \leq \psi \leq \pi\ .$$

However, making use of (γ) it is easily shown that for $\rho \to 0$ the integral along the semicircle tends to

$$2u(\xi,\ 0)\int_0^{\pi} \sin^{2\nu}\psi\, d\psi\ .$$

Thus $u(\xi,\ 0)$ can be represented by the integral (23) taken along C^+ . This integral depends on ξ only through the function v . By Lemma 2 it is possible to continue the functions $v(x,\ y,\ \xi)$ (and obviously also its derivatives with respect to x and y) analytically as a function of ξ into E for every $x + iy \in C$. Thus $u(\xi,\ 0)$ may be continued likewise, and Theorem 2 is proved.

As a consequence we obtain

Theorem 3. *Every solution* $u(x,\ y)$ *of* $\ell_\nu(u) = 0$ *which, in addition to satisfying the hypotheses of Theorem 2, is analytic at one point* $(x,\ 0) \in I$, *may be represented in the form* (15).

Define f(x) by $u(x,\ 0)$. By Theorem 2, this function is analytic in G . If we apply the operation (15) to it, we obtain a solution which is analytic for $x \pm iy \in G$. There is only one such solution having the values f(x) on I . Because of the analyticity at one point of I this solution must agree with the original $u(x,\ y)$.

In the special case $a(x) = c(x)$, $2\nu \geq 1$ the extra condition of Theorem 3 is automatically satisfied by a result of A. Huber [7]. If equation (2) arises from a spatial problem involving axial symmetry the condition can frequently be shown to be satisfied by a priori considerations.

6. COMPLETE SYSTEMS OF SOLUTIONS

The relationship (15) between the analytic function f(z) and the solution $u(x,\ y)$ may be written in the form

$$u = \Theta f\ .$$

By Theorem 3 the symbol Θ may be thought of as an operator which maps the space of functions f(z) analytic in G onto the space of solutions of $\ell_\nu(u) = 0$ satisfying the conditions of Theorem 3. It is clear that Θ is linear. We now shall show that Θ is continuous, in the following sense:

Theorem 4. Given $\epsilon > 0$ and given a compact, simply connected subdomain $E \subset G$, there exists a $\delta > 0$ such that for every $f(z)$ satisfying

$$|f(z)| < \delta, \qquad z \in E$$

the corresponding solution $u = f$ satisfies

$$|u(x, y)| < \epsilon, \quad x + iy \in E.$$

Proof. We choose the system of paths c_{zz^*} used in carrying out the integration in (15) in such a way that $z\theta + z^*\theta' \in E$ for $\vartheta \in c_{zz^*}$, $(z, z^*) \in (E, E)$. It can be shown from (16) that the kernel $K_\nu(z, z^*, \vartheta)$ is of the form $\sin^{2\nu-1}\vartheta\, F(z, z^*, \vartheta)$ where $|F(z, z^*; \vartheta)| < M$ for $(z, z^*) \in (E, E)$, $\vartheta \in c_{zz^*}$. It thus follows that

$$|u(x, y)| < \delta\, M\, I(z, z^*),$$

where

$$I(z, z^*) = \int_{c_{zz^*}} |\sin^{2\nu-1}\vartheta|\, |d\vartheta|.$$

Since c_{zz^*} depends continuously on (z, z^*), $I(z, z^*)$ is continuous on the compact set (E, E) and hence bounded, $I(z, z^*) \leq B$. The Theorem is thus proved for $\delta < \epsilon \cdot M^{-1} B^{-1}$.

We now have the tools at hand to construct complete systems of solutions, in the following sense:

Definition. A denumerable set of solutions $u_0(x, y), u_1(x, y), \cdots$ of a linear differential equation $\ell(u) = 0$ is called complete with respect to a class C of solutions of $\ell(u) = 0$ in a domain G, if for every choice of $\epsilon > 0$, of $u \in C$, and of a compact subdomain $E \subset G$ there exist an integer $N > 0$ and constants $a_0, \ldots, a_N$ such that

$$\left|\sum_{n=0}^{N} a_n u_n(x, y) - u(x, y)\right| < \epsilon, \quad (x, y) \in E.$$

In view of the fact that every $f(z)$ which is analytic in a simply connected domain G can be approximated by polynomials, uniformly in every compact subregion E of G, the following is an immediate consequence of the Theorems 3 and 4:

Theorem 5. Let G be a simply connected region symmetric about $y = 0$, and let C denote the class of solutions $u(x, y)$ of $\ell_\nu(u) = 0$

which are analytic for $x \pm iy \in G$ (x, y complex). Then the system of functions

$$u_m(x, y) = \Theta z^m \qquad (m = 0, 1, 2, \cdots)$$

is complete with respect to C.

Conversely, let a system of solutions $u_m(x, y)$ of $\ell_\nu(u) = 0$ be known, and assume that every $u_m(x, y)$ is analytic for $x + iy \in G$, where G denotes a simply connected, symmetric region (x, y real). We know already from Theorem 2 that the functions $f_m(x) = u_m(x, 0)$ can be continued analytically into the whole domain G. We then have the following criterion for completeness of the system $\{u_m(x, y)\}$.

Theorem 6. The system of functions $u_0(x, y)$, $u_1(x, y), \cdots$ is complete with respect to the class C if and only if the functions $f_0(z)$, $f_1(z), \cdots$ are complete with respect to the class of holomorphic functions in G.

The sufficiency part is an immediate consequence of the Theorems 3 and 4. In order to prove the necessity part, assume that the functions $f_0, f_1, \cdots$ are not complete. Then there exists a function $f(z)$, holomorphic in G, a number $\epsilon > 0$, and a compact subdomain $E \subset G$ such that, no matter how large the positive integer N and the constants a_n are chosen,

$$\left| f(z) - \sum_{n=0}^{N} a_n f_n(z) \right| > \epsilon \quad , \quad z \in E .$$

This implies that the solution $u = \Theta f$ cannot be approximated on the set $y = 0$, $x \in E$.

7. EXAMPLES OF COMPLETE SYSTEMS §§

The equation

$$\frac{\partial^2 u}{\partial x^2} + \frac{\partial^2 u}{\partial y^2} + \frac{2\nu}{y}\frac{\partial u}{\partial y} = 0 \tag{24}$$

represents a case where the functions Θz^m can be expressed in a simple way. Up to constant factors, they are given by

$$C_m^\nu(\cos\vartheta) r^m \qquad (m = 0, 1, \cdots)$$

where $x = r\cos\vartheta$, $y = r\sin\vartheta$.

However, systems of explicit solutions are known for some other equations of the form (2), and their completeness can be tested by the criterion of Theorem 6. For instance, the equation

$$\frac{\partial^2 u}{\partial x^2} + \frac{\partial^2 u}{\partial y^2} + \frac{2\mu}{x}\frac{\partial u}{\partial x} + \frac{2\nu}{y}\frac{\partial u}{\partial y} + k^2 u = 0 \tag{25}$$

which we shall consider in the half-plane $x > 0$, has the solutions [3]

(26) $$u_m(x, y) = r^{-\mu-\nu} J_{\mu+\nu+m}(kr)\, F(-\frac{m}{2}, \frac{m}{2} + \mu + \nu, \nu + \tfrac{1}{2}, \sin^2 \vartheta),$$

$$m = 0, 1, 2, \cdots .$$

(For m even the hypergeometric function reduces to a Jacobi polynomial.) For $y = 0$ we have $\vartheta = 0$, $r = x$, so that the question of completeness reduces to the question whether the functions

$$f_m(z) = z^{-\mu-\nu} J_{\mu+\nu+m}(kz)$$

are complete. That the answer is in the affirmative is shown by the following consideration. Let it be required to approximate the function $f(z)$, holomorphic in a simply connected region G, in a compact subregion $E \subset G$ with an error not exceeding δ. We first select a polynomial approximation such that

(27) $$|f(z) - \sum_{n=0}^{N} a_n z^n| < \tfrac{1}{2}\delta, \quad z \in E .$$

It can be shown that there exist constants α_{mn} $(m, n = 0, 1, \cdots)$ such that for each m the series $\Sigma_{n=0}^{\infty} \alpha_{mn} f_m(z)$ converges to z^n uniformly in every compact set. Thus it is possible to approximate in E every power z^n occurring in (27) with an error not exceeding $1/2N|a_n|\delta$ by a linear combination of finitely many functions $f_m(z)$. The resulting error in the approximation for $f(z)$ is less than δ, as desired.

For the equation

(28) $$\frac{\partial^2 u}{\partial x^2} + \frac{\partial^2 u}{\partial y^2} + \frac{2\mu}{x}\frac{\partial u}{\partial x} + \frac{2\nu}{y}\frac{\partial u}{\partial y} = 0 ,$$

which we again consider in the half-plane $x > 0$, we obtain by letting $k \to 0$ in (24) the system of solutions

(29) $$u_m(x, y) = r^m F(-\frac{m}{2}, \frac{m}{2} + \mu + \nu, \nu + \tfrac{1}{2}, \sin^2 \vartheta)$$

$$m = 0, 1, 2, \cdots .$$

Since $f_m(z) = z^m$ in this case, the system (29) is seen to be complete by Theorem 5. Another system of solutions of (28) is represented by the functions

(30) $$u_m(x, y) = (\xi - \eta)^{\mu+\nu} (\xi^2 - 1)^{\frac{\mu}{2} - \frac{1}{4}} Q^{\mu - \frac{1}{2}}_{\nu - \frac{1}{2} + m}(\xi)\, C^{\nu}_m(\eta) ,$$

$$m = 0, 1, 2, \cdots ,$$

where

$$\xi = \frac{r^2 + c^2}{\sqrt{(r^2 + c^2)^2 - 4c^2x^2}} , \quad \eta = \frac{r^2 - c^2}{\sqrt{(r^2 + c^2)^2 - 4c^2x^2}}$$

with some constant $c > 0$. It can be shown [4] that, up to constant factors,

$$f_m(z) = u_m(z, 0) = (1 - w)^{2(\mu+\nu)} w^m F(\mu, \mu+\nu+m, \nu+m+1, w^2) ,$$

where

$$w = \frac{z - c}{z + c} .$$

Completeness of the functions $f_m(z)$ for functions $f(z)$ holomorphic in a simply connected region in the right half-plane is equivalent to completeness of the functions $F_m(w) = f_m(z)$ for functions $F(w)$ holomorphic in a simply connected region in $|w| < 1$. The latter follows as in the case of the functions (26) from Runge's theorem and the fact that there exists constants β_{nm} such that the series

$$\sum_{m=0}^{\infty} \beta_{nm} F_m(w) \qquad (n = 0, 1, \cdots)$$

converge to w^n uniformly in every closed subregion of $|w| < 1$. It has thus been shown that the system (30) is complete with respect to the class C of solutions of (28) described in Theorem 5.

NOTES

*Thus we shall call analytic functions of one complex variable, for better distinction.

§A sign error in formula (5.6) of [6] has been corrected.

#Such domains have been called "y-convex" in [1].

**Both (17c) and (17d) have been stated without proof in [6], section 5.4, but unfortunately in slightly erroneous form. The author is indebted to Professor A. Heins for calling his attention to these errors. Relation (17d) has been stated correctly (although in a different notation) in [2].

§§The standard notations of the Bateman manuscript project are used for the special functions occurring in this section.

REFERENCES

1. Erdélyi, A., Singularities of generalized axially symmetric potential, Comm. Pure Appl. Math. 9, 403-414 (1956).

2. Henrici, P., Zur Funktionentheorie der Wellengleichung, Comm. Math. Helv. 27, 235-293, (1953).

3. Henrici, P., On certain series expansions involving Whittaker functions and Jacobi polynomials, Pacific J. Math. 5, 725-744 (1955).

4. Henrici, P., Addition theorems for general Legendre and Gegenbauer functions, J. Rational Mech. Anal. 4, 983-1018 (1955).

5. Henrici, P., On the domain of regularity of generalized axially symmetric potentials, Proc. Amer. Math. Soc. 8, 29-31 (1957).

6. Henrici, P., A survey of I. N. Vekua's theory of elliptic partial differential equations with analytic coefficients, Z. Angew. Math. Physik 8, 169-202 (1957).

7. Huber, A., On the uniqueness of generalized axially symmetric potentials, Annals of Math. 60, 351-358 (1954).

8. Vekua, I. N., Novye metody rešenija elliptičeskikh uravnenij, OGIZ, Moskow and Leningrad, 1948.

9. Weinstein, A., Generalized axially symmetric potential theory, Bull. Amer. Math. Soc. 59, 20Σ38 (1953).

LOTHAR COLLATZ

Application of the Theory of Monotonic Operators to Boundary Value Problems

§ 1. Introduction

Many problems of numerical analysis lead to equations of the form

(1) $$Tu = u \ .$$

Here u is an element of a given space, usually a Banach space R. For instance u may be a vector, a function, a system of functions, etc. T is a given operator, for example, a differential or integral operator, defined upon a domain D which is a subset of R. (For applications of methods of functional analysis, compare for instance [2], [4].) The domain of images TD shall also lie in R. Often such equations are treated by iteration procedures, i.e. from a suitably chosen $u_{(o)}$ one or more additional elements $u_{(1)}, u_{(2)}, \ldots$ are computed according to

(2) $$u_{(n+1)} = Tu_{(n)} \qquad (n = 0, 1, 2, \ldots) \ .$$

In carrying out such iterations the following cases A and B occur quite frequently:

A. The values of $u_{(o)}, u_{(1)}, \ldots, u_{(n)}, \ldots$ show monotonic behavior (either increasing or decreasing) with growing n. If, for example, $u_{(n)}$ is monotonic increasing (in a sense still to be defined exactly), one can often start from a larger element $u_{<o>}$ and compute a second sequence $u_{<n>}$ which is monotonic decreasing according to

(3) $$u_{<n+1>} = Tu_{<n>} \qquad (n = 0, 1, 2, \ldots) \ .$$

In such cases it is the question whether $u_{(n)}$ and $u_{<n>}$ enclose a solution u of (1).

B. Alternating behavior. This also occurs frequently in numerical analysis. In this case every other approximation is smaller (or larger), i.e.

(4) $$u_{(n)} \leqq u_{(n+2)} \leqq u_{(n+3)} \leqq u_{(n+1)} .$$

Here again the question arises whether $u_{(n+2)}$ and $u_{(n+3)}$ enclose a solution u of (1).

C. Of course A and B are not the only possibilities. Since we obtain direct statements about existence and inclusion of solutions when the theorems valid for A and B can be applied, it seems justified to ask for rather general classes of problems which allow such simple inclusion statements.

This report does not contain proofs. It serves only for the exposition of ideas, illustrating them with simple, in some cases nearly trivial, examples. Many more complicated examples have been treated using a computer. There is for a given problem often great latitude in defining the Banach space and the operator, and in determining the meaning of the symbol $\geq$ etc. Thus a complete survey of the methods described is not yet possible.

Monotonic operators have been useful for many purposes. For instance alternating behavior was used by J. Schröder [11] to prove the existence of solutions of certain nonlinear boundary value problems of ordinary differential equations. He also gave an estimation for the error of the approximate values obtained by the method of finite differences.

§2. Applications of SCHAUDER's fixed-point theorem

Let the space R be assumed to be semi-ordered, i.e. for certain pairs of elements $v, w \in R$ a relation $v \leq w$ makes sense. Let the usual rules of computation for inequalities and elementary limit processes hold, in particular $u \geq \theta$ for $u_n \to u$ and $u_n \geqq \theta$ (θ null element of R). Furthermore let $\|v\| \geqq \|w\|$ for $v \geqq w \geq \theta$.

The operator T is called monotonic non-decreasing if

(5) $$Tv \geqq Tw$$

holds for $v \geqq w$ and $v, w \in D$.

The operator T is called monotonic non-increasing if

$$Tv \leqq Tw$$

holds for $v \geqq w$ and $v, w \in D$.

If v and w are two elements for which $v \leq w$ holds, then let $\langle v, w\rangle$ denote the set of all elements $z \in R$ with $v \leq z \leq w$. Such an "interval" $\langle v, w\rangle$ is always convex and closed. The operator T has the property of mapping an interval M always onto a compact set TM . That this is so can often be checked using ASCOLIS's theorem. Here a set M is called compact if each infinite subset of M possesses a limit element which belongs to R but not necessarily to M . If the operator T is continuous, SCHAUDER's fixed-point theorem is applicable. Its statement is [6], [7]: If a continuous operator T maps a convex closed set M of a Banach space into itself and if TM is compact, then at least one solution u of (1) exists in M. Under the stated assumptions the general theorems about monotonic operators can then be proved [8][9][10]. One step of each of the two iteration sequences (2)(3) is needed:

$$u_{(o)} \leqq u_{<o>}, \quad u_{(o)} \leqq u_{(1)}, \quad u_{<1>} \leqq u_{<o>}, \tag{6}$$

the sequences $u_{(n)}$ and $u_{<n>}$ converge toward a solution u of (1) with the inclusion

$$u_{(o)} \leqq u_{(1)} \leqq \dots \leqq u_{(n)} \leqq \dots \leqq u \leqq \dots \leqq u_{<n>} \leqq \dots \leqq u_{<1>} \leqq u_{<o>}. \tag{7}$$

If the operator T is monotonic non-increasing and if

$$u_{(o)} \leqq u_{<o>}, \quad u_{(o)} \leqq u_{<1>}, \quad u_{(1)} \leqq u_{<o>}, \tag{8}$$

a solution u of (1) exists and the inclusion

$$u_{(o)} \leqq u_{<1>} \leqq u_{(2)} \leqq u_{<3>} \leqq \dots \leqq u \leqq \dots \leqq u_{(3)} \leqq u_{<2>} \leqq u_{(1)} \leqq u_{<o>} \tag{9}$$

holds.

§3. Application to Banach spaces the elements of which are functions

The boundary value problem

$$\begin{aligned} Lu &= f(x_j, u) && \text{in } B \\ U_\mu u &= \gamma_\mu(x_j) && \text{on } \Gamma_\mu \quad (\mu = 1, 2, \dots, k) \end{aligned} \tag{10}$$

is considered. L and the U_μ are given linear homogeneous differential operators. $f(x_j, u)$ is a given continuous function possessing a partial derivative with respect to u. The abbreviation x_j (or, even shorter, x) stands for $x_1, \dots, x_m$. B is a given closed domain of the $x_1, x_2, \dots x_m$ - point space. The Γ_μ are (m-1)-dimensional hypersurfaces in this point space on which the functions γ_μ are given.

The boundary value problem $Lu = r(x_j)$ in B, $U_\mu u = 0$ on Γ_μ possess a uniquely determined solution for given continuous $r(x_j)$. This solution is assumed to have the representation

$$u(x_j) = \int_B G(x_j, \xi_j)\, r(\xi_j)\, d\xi_j$$

with a Green's function $G(x_j, \xi_j)$ nonnegative in B.

The problem (10) is equivalent to the integral equation

(11) $$u(x_j) = g(x_j) + \int_B G(x_j, \xi_j) f(\xi_j, u) d\xi_j \, .$$

The Banach space of functions $u(x_j)$ which are continuous in B is taken for R ; as norm $\|u\|$ for example the maximum of $|u|$ in B . $v \geqq w$ shall have the usual meaning.

u lies in a strip $\phi(x) \leqq u \leqq \Psi$ with fixed continuous functions ϕ, Ψ . $\phi = -\infty$ and $\Psi = \infty$ are admitted. For an interval $M = \langle v, w \rangle$ the compactness of TM is easily shown under rather general assumptions about the Green's function $G(x, \xi)$, e.g., under the assumption that for every $\epsilon > 0$ there exists a δ such that

$$\int_B |G(x, \xi) - G(\tilde{x}, \xi)| d\xi < \epsilon \quad \text{for} \quad |x - \tilde{x}| < \delta(\epsilon) \quad x, \tilde{x}, \in B \, .$$

Furthermore let

$$\int_B |K\, r(\xi)| d\xi \leqq \int_B |K| \; |r(\xi)| d\xi \leqq \int_B |K| \; S(\xi) d\xi$$

for $|r| \leqq S$, K signifying either the Green's function G or a difference $G(x, \xi) - G(\tilde{x}, \xi)$.

These assumptions are satisfied, for example, if for the differential equation

$$-\Delta u = -\frac{\partial^2 u}{\partial x^2} - \frac{\partial^2 u}{\partial y^2} = f(x, y, u)$$

the boundary-values u are given on a continuously curved closed boundary curve Γ without double points [12]. Here f and $\frac{\partial f}{\partial u}$ are continuous within and on Γ .

By transformations one can get further types of boundary value problems with monotonic behavior iterations. For instance the problems just considered are changed by transformations of reciprocal radii

(12) $$x_j = \frac{X_j}{R^2} \, , \; X_j = \frac{x_j}{r^2} \, , \; r^2 = \sum_{k=1}^{n} x_k^{\;2} \, , \; rR = 1 \; (j = 1, \ldots, n)$$

into problems with infinite regions, see [3]. The X_j are the new independent variables and a new dependent variable U is introduced by

(13) $$u(x_j) = r^{2-n}\, U(x_j\, r^{-2}) \; ; \; U(X_j) = R^{2-n}\, u(X_j\, R^{-2}) \, .$$

The differential equation

(14) $$-p(x_j)\, \Delta_x u = f(x_j, u)$$

then corresponds to

(15) $$-P(X_j)\, \Delta_X U = F(X_j, U)$$

with

$$P(X_j) = p(X_j R^2) \ , \quad F(X_j , U) = R^{-4} f(X_j R^{-2} , R^{n-2} U) \ ;$$

Δ_x (resp. Δ_X) means the Laplacian operator with respect to the x_j (resp. the X_j) coordinates.

We are considering only solutions U of (15) of the order of magnitude $U = O(R^{3-n})$ for $R \to \infty$. Let a differential equation (15) and boundary values $U = \Phi$ on a surface Γ^* be given. The transformation (12) (13) gives the new problem with the equation (14) and the boundary values $u = \phi$ on Γ . We suppose that one can define $p(x_j) = P(x_j r^{-2})$ at the origin $r = 0$ so that $p(x_j)$ is continuous in $r = 0$, (compare [5]). Thus in two dimensions $(n = 2)$ gives a problem of the type considered above.

Examples:

I. Let the boundary value problem be

$$-\Delta u \equiv -\frac{\partial^2 u}{\partial x^2} - \frac{\partial^2 u}{\partial y^2} = 1 + x^2 + \alpha u \text{ in } B$$

$$u = 0 \text{ on } \Gamma ,$$

where Γ is the boundary of the ellipse B with $x^2 + 2y^2 \leq 1$. We use the simple expression $u_{(o)} = a(1 - x^2 - 2y^2)$ and analogously $u_{<o>}$ with the constant $\hat{a}$ instead of a . We easily obtain

$$u_{(1)} = \frac{1-x^2-2y^2}{612}(\tau + a\alpha\sigma)$$

with $\tau = 113 + 39 x^2 - 6 y^2$

$$\sigma = 77 - 33x^2 - 42 y^2 .$$

Case A: $\alpha = 1$. In this case we have a monotonic nondecreasing operator. It is easy to discuss the best values of a and $\hat{a}$:

$$a = \frac{55}{278} \ , \quad \hat{a} = \frac{19}{71}$$

and the inclusion

$$u_{<1>} \leqq u \leqq u_{(1)} .$$

For instance

$$0.210 \leq u(0,0) \leq 0.218 \text{ holds.}$$

Case B: $\alpha = -1$. In this case the operator is monotonic nonincreasing, and we have alternating behavior. The conditions (8) require

$$0 \leqq a \leqq \hat{a}\ ; \quad 612a + 77\,\hat{a} \leqq 113\ ; \quad 152 \leqq 44\,a + 612\,\hat{a}\ .$$

If in the last two inequalities, we write the sign = instead of the sign $\leqq$, we get

$$a = 0.1548\ , \quad \hat{a} = 0.2375$$

with the inclusion

$$u_{<1>} \leqq u \leqq u_{(1)}$$

and, for instance,

$$0.1548 \leqq u(0,0) \leqq 0.1651\ .$$

II. Given the nonlinear boundary value problem

$$-\Delta u = 1 + (1 + r^2)\,u^2 \quad \text{for } r < 1\ , \text{ where } r^2 = x^2 + y^2$$

$$u = 0 \quad \text{for } r = 1\ .$$

We use the very simple expression

$$u_{(o)} = a(1 - r^2)\ , \quad u_{<o>} = a(1 - r^2)\ .$$

For $a = 0.168\,102$ and $\hat{a} = 169\,742$

we have $u_{(o)} \leqq u_{(1)} \leqq u \leqq u_{<1>} \leqq u_{<o>}$

with $0 \leqq u_{<1>} - u_{(1)} \leqq 0.000\,059$.

The last number $0.000\,059$ gives an upper bound for the error of $u_{(1)}$ and of $u_{<1>}$.

§4. Application to Banach spaces the elements of which are vectors of numbers or functions

The considerations of the previous section are not directly applicable if the right-hand side of the differential equation (10), for example, contains, beside $f(x_j, u)$, terms with partial derivatives of u . The domain of application of the theory can be increased if the significance of the symbol " $\geqq$ " is generalized. Let $u = (u_1, \ldots, u_m)$ be a vector the components u_j of which may be numbers or functions. The subscripts $1, \ldots, m$ are divided into two classes K_1, K_2 . For two vectors v, w with the components v_j, w_j the relation $v \geqq w$ shall mean

$v_j \geqq w_j$ in the usual sense for $j \in K_1$

$v_j \leqq w_j$ in the usual sense for $j \in K_2$.

Let the operator T in $v = Tu$ be defined in one of the two following ways:

A. The components u_j, v_j are numbers and

(16) $$v_j = \phi_j(u_1, \ldots, u_m) \ , \ (j = 1, \ldots, m) \ .$$

The ϕ_j are given functions possessing continuous partial derivatives with respect to the u_k .

B. The components u_j, v_j are functions given in a domain B (as in section 3) and

(17) $$v_j(x) = w_j(x) + \int_B \phi_j(\xi, u_k(\xi))\, G_j(x,\xi)\, d\xi \quad (j = 1, \ldots m) \ .$$

Here $w_j(x)$ and $G_j(x, \xi)$ are given continuous functions of their arguments and, moreover, $G_j \geqq 0$ for x, $\xi \in B$.

In these two cases it follows that

a. for $\dfrac{\partial \phi_k}{\partial u_j} \geqq 0$ for j, $k = 1, \ldots, m$, the operator T is monotonic non-decreasing,

b. for $\dfrac{\partial \phi_k}{\partial u_j} \leqq 0$ for j, $k = 1, \ldots, m$, the operator T is monotonic non-increasing,

c. for $\dfrac{\partial \phi_k}{\partial u_j} \geqq 0$, $\dfrac{\partial \phi_k}{\partial u_j{}'} \leqq 0$, $\dfrac{\partial \phi_k{}'}{\partial u_j} \leqq 0$, $\dfrac{\partial \phi_k{}'}{\partial u_j{}'} \geqq 0$ for $j, k \in K_1$; k', $k' \in K_2$ T is monotonic non-decreasing,

d. for $\dfrac{\partial \phi_k}{\partial u_j} \leqq 0$, $\dfrac{\partial \phi_k}{\partial u_j{}'} \geqq 0$, $\dfrac{\partial \phi_k{}'}{\partial u_j} \geqq 0$, $\dfrac{\partial \phi_k{}'}{\partial u_j{}'} \leqq 0$ for $j, k \in K_1$; $j', k' \in K_2$ T is monotonic non-increasing.

Examples:

In numerical analysis, monotonic or alternating behavior is frequently found, not only in the field of boundary-value problems, but also elsewhere. Here a simple example of an eigenvalue problem of a matrix is stated:

I. Let the eigenvalue problem $Ax = Kx$ where

$$A = (a_{jk}) = \begin{pmatrix} 1 & 1 & 1 \\ 1 & 2 & 2 \\ 1 & 2 & 3 \end{pmatrix} , \quad x = \begin{pmatrix} x_1 \\ x_2 \\ x_3 \end{pmatrix} \ ; \ y = Ax = \begin{pmatrix} y_1 \\ y_2 \\ y_3 \end{pmatrix}$$

be given. K is the wanted characteristic number of A (or $\lambda = \frac{1}{K}$ the eigenvalue of A). To normalize an eigenvector, a component x_r, here for example x_3, is taken to be equal to 1 .

Using $B = A - E$ (E the identity) , $u = \binom{x}{\lambda}$, one obtains

$$v = Tu = \begin{pmatrix} y_1/y_3 \\ y_2/y_3 \\ 1 \\ 1/y_3 \end{pmatrix} .$$

In the domain $0 \leq x_1 \leq 1$, $0 \leq x_2 \leq 1$ the operator T is monotonic nondecreasing if $u \geq \tilde{u}$ is introduced for the case $x \geq \tilde{x}$, $\lambda \leq \tilde{\lambda}$. This yields convenient possibilities of inclusion. From the numbers

u				v			
0.44	0.8	1	λ	0.445	0.802	1	0.199
0.46	0.81	1	λ	0.447	0.804	1	0.197
0.445	0.8019	1	λ	0.445 036	0.801 933	1	0.198 067
0.4451	0.802	1	λ	0.455 050	0.801 945	1	0.198 055

bounds for the eigenvalue and the normalized eigenvector are found to be:

$$0.455 \leq x_1 \leq 0.447 ; \; 0.802 \leq x_2 \leq 0.804 ; \; 0.197 \leq \lambda \leq 0.199$$

or the better bounds from the last two lines, for instance $0.198\,055 \leq \lambda \leq 0.198\,067$.

As an example of an extension in the field of differential equations, let the following problem be taken:

$$-\Delta u = 1 + (u, (\frac{\partial u}{\partial x})^2 + (\frac{\partial u}{\partial y})^2) \text{ in } r^2 = x^2 + y^2 < R^2$$

$$u = \text{const.} \quad \text{for } r = R .$$

$\phi(u, v)$ is to possess continuous first order partial derivatives. For $\frac{\partial \phi}{\partial u} \geqq 0$; $\frac{\partial \phi}{\partial v} \leqq 0$ the problem leads to a monotonic non-decreasing operator, for $\frac{\partial \phi}{\partial v} \leqq 0$; $\frac{\partial \phi}{\partial v} \geqq 0$ to a monotonic non-increasing operator, if we introduce $v = \frac{\partial u}{\partial r}$, and

$$\check{n} = \binom{u}{v} \geqq \check{n}^* = \binom{u^*}{v^*}$$

may hold for $u \geqq u^*$, $v \leqq v^*$.

Consider the equation

$$-\Delta u = 1 + a(u_x^2 + u_y^2) \text{ for } r < 1 , \; r^2 = x^2 + y^2$$

$$u = 0 \text{ for } r = 1 .$$

We start with the elements

$$u_{(o)} = b(1-r^2) \; ; \; u_{<o>} = \hat{b}(1-r^2) \; ;$$

$$v_{(o)} = -2br \; ; \; v_{<o>} = -2\hat{b}r \; .$$

Then we find

$$u_{(1)} = \frac{1}{4}(1-r^2)(1 + ab^2 + ab^2r^2)$$

$$v_{(1)} = -\frac{r}{2} - ab^2r^3$$

and $u_{<1>}$, $v_{<1>}$ similarly.

Case A: Let $a = 1$. Then the operator is monotonic nondecreasing; the conditions (6) hold for

$$0 \leqq b \leqq \frac{1}{4} \; , \quad 1 - \sqrt{\tfrac{1}{2}} \leqq \hat{b} \leqq 1 + \sqrt{\tfrac{1}{2}}$$

and with the best values $b = \frac{1}{4}$, $\hat{b} = 1 - \sqrt{\frac{1}{2}}$ we get the existence of a solution u and the inclusion

$$\frac{1-r^2}{4}(1 + b^2 + b^2r^2) \leqq u \leqq \frac{1-r^2}{4}(1 + \hat{b}^2 + \hat{b}^2r^2) \; ,$$

at the origin $0.2656 \leqq u(0,0) \leqq 0.2715$.

Case B: Let $a = -1$. We have now a nonincreasing operator. The conditions (8) give

$$0 \leqq b \leqq \hat{b} \; ; \; 0.25 \leqq \hat{b} \; ; \; 4b \leqq 1 - 2\hat{b}^2 \; ; \; 1 - b^2 \leqq 4\hat{b} \; ,$$

and the best values $b = \frac{7}{32}$, $\hat{b} = \frac{1}{4}$.

Again we get the existence of a solution u and the bounds

$$\frac{1-r^2}{4}(1-\hat{b}^2 - \hat{b}^2r^2) \leqq u \leqq \frac{1-r^2}{4}(1-b^2 - b^2r^2)$$

$$0.2343 \leqq \frac{15}{64} \leqq u(0,0) \leqq \frac{975}{4096} \leqq 0.2381 \; .$$

§5. Other possibilities for defining monotonic operators

One gets other classes of monotonic operators with the following definition [1]: The operator T, defined in a certain set D as in No. 2 is called monotonic, if from $Tf_1 \leqq Tf_2$ follows $f_1 \leqq f_2$ for every $f_1, f_2 \in D$. In this case one has the possibility for inclusion of a solution u of $Tu = f$ provided the solution exists. Assume we have two approximate solutions v_1, v_2 with

$$Tv_1 \leqq f \leqq Tv_2 \; ;$$

then the inclusion $v_1 \leqq u \leqq v_2$ holds.

Consider for example the nonlinear boundary value problem (10). Then we define the operator

(18) $$Tv = Lv - f(x_j, v) \quad .$$

The domain D of definition of T contains all functions v satisfying the boundary conditions and for which Lv is defined. For two elements $v, w \in D$ we have with $\phi = v-w$:

$$Tv - Tw = L\phi - \phi A(x_j) \quad .$$

Here, according to Taylor's theorem, $A(x_j) = (\frac{\partial f}{\partial u})_{\tilde{w}}$.

A is the partial derivative of f with respect to u taken at a certain intermediate place $\tilde{w}$ between v and w . Often the sign of A is known, for instance $A \geqq 0$. Then one has to test whether

(19) $$L\phi - \phi A \geqq 0 \text{ in } B \ , \ U_\mu \phi = 0 \text{ on } \Gamma_\mu \ , \ A \geqq 0$$

implies $\phi \geqq 0$. If this is true, the operator T is monotonic. The discussion of the nonlinear problem (10) is thus reduced to the discussion of the linear inequalities (19). Many types of linear and nonlinear boundary value problems with elliptic and parabolic differential equations were treated with these methods [1] [13].

BIBLIOGRAPHY

1. L. Collatz, Aufgaben monotoner Art. , Arch d. Math. 3(1952) pp. 366-376.

2. L. Collatz, Numerische Behandlung von Differentialgleichungen, Berlin-Göttingen-Heidelberg, 2. ed. 1955, 526 p.

3. L. Collatz, Fehlerabschätzungen bei Randwertaufgaben partieller Differentialgleichungen mit unendlichem Grundgebiet, Z. angew. Math. Physik. 9a(1958), pp. 118-128.

4. G. Fichera, Methods of functional linear analysis in mathematical physics, Proc. Internat. Congress of Math., Amsterdam Bd. 3(1956), pp. 220-232.

5. Ph. Hartman, On the local behavior of solutions of $\Delta u = g(x, u, \nabla u)$, Comm. pure and Appl. Math. 9(1956), pp. 435-445.

6. J. Leray, J. Schauder, Topologie et équations fonctionelles, Ann. Sci. de l'École norm. sup., Vol. 51(1934), pp. 45-78.

7. J. Schauder, Der Fixpunktsatz in Funktionalräumen, Std. Math. II, (1930), pp. 171-182.

8. J. Schröder, Nichtlineare Majoranten beim Verfahren der schrittweisen Näherung, Arch. Math. 7 (1956), pp. 471-484.

9. J. Schröder, Anwendung funktionalanalytischer Methoden zur numerischen Behandlung von Gleichungen, Z. angew. Math. Mech. 36 (1956), pp. 260-261.

10. J. Schröder, Fehlerabschätzungen bei gewöhnlichen und partiellen Differentialgleichungen, Arch.Rat. Mech. Math. Analysis, to appear.

11. J. Schröder, Über das Differenzenverfahren bei nichtlinearen Randwertaufgaben I, II, Z. angew. Math. Mech. 36 (1956), pp. 319-331 and 443-455.

12. L. Collatz - J. Schröder, Einschliessen der Lösungen von Randwertaufgaben, Numerische Mathematik, 1(1959), pp. 61-72.

13. J. Szarski, Sur la limitation et l'unicité des solutions d'une système non linéaire d'équations paraboliques aux dérivées partielles du second ordre, Annales Polonici Mathematici II. 2(1955), pp. 237-249.

J. B. DIAZ

Upper and Lower Bounds for Quadratic Integrals, and at a Point, for Solutions of Linear Boundary Value Problems

§1. Introduction.

In many problems of mathematical physics it is desired to find either the numerical value of a quadratic integral of a function, or the numerical value of a function at a given point, where the (a priori unknown) function is a solution of a boundary value problem consisting of a linear partial differential equation plus linear boundary conditions. The quadratic integral is usually the quadratic form associated with a bilinear integral which occurs in a Green's identity for the boundary value problem.

For example, consider the determination of the capacity of a "ring shaped" plane domain D bounded externally by a smooth simple closed curve C_0 and internally by another simple closed curve C_1. Here it is desired to evaluate the integral

$$\iint_D (v_x^2 + v_y^2)\,dx\,dy ,$$

where the unknown function v is the solution of the Dirichlet problem:

$$\Delta v = 0 , \quad \text{on } D ,$$

$$v = 1 , \text{ on } C_1 ; \; v = 0, \text{ on } C_0 ,$$

and

$$\Delta = \frac{\partial^2}{\partial x^2} + \frac{\partial^2}{\partial y^2}$$

is the Laplacian. Still another example is the determination of the torsional rigidity, or stiffness, S, of a bounded plane domain D whose boundary is C. Consider the formula (Lamé's constant μ is taken to be unity, and P is the polar moment of inertia of D with respect to its centroid)

$$S = P - \iint_D (v_x^2 + v_y^2)\,dx\,dy ,$$

which has been given by J. B. Diaz and A. Weinstein [2], and is valid for simply or multiply connected D. In this formula, v is the warping function, and the evaluation of the torsional rigidity S is seen to be equivalent to the evaluation of the integral

$$\iint_D (v_x^2 + v_y^2)\, dx\, dy ,$$

where the warping function v is a single valued solution of the Neumann problem

$$\Delta v = 0 , \quad \text{on } D ,$$

$$\frac{\partial v}{\partial u} = \frac{\partial}{\partial s}\left[\tfrac{1}{2}(x^2 + y^2)\right] , \quad \text{on } C ,$$

and $\frac{\partial}{\partial n}$, $\frac{\partial}{\partial s}$ denote differentiation in the direction of the outer normal to C, and along C, respectively. In both these examples, the bilinear integral associated with the quadratic integral to be evaluated is

$$\iint_D (\phi_x \psi_x + \phi_y \psi_y)\, dx\, dy ,$$

which occurs in Green's identity

$$\iint_D \phi \Delta \psi\, dx\, dy + \iint_D (\phi_x \psi_x + \phi_y \psi_y)\, dx\, dy = \int_C \phi \frac{\partial \psi}{\partial n}\, ds .$$

An example of when the value of a function at a particular point is desired is the determination of the deflection at the center (say at the origin) of the deflection at the center of a clamped plane square plate. Here one seeks to find the number $w(0, 0)$, where the deflection $w(x, y)$ is the solution of the boundary value problem

$$\Delta\Delta w = P , \qquad \text{on } D ,$$

$$w = \frac{\partial w}{\partial n} = 0 , \qquad \text{on } C ,$$

where P is a given function (the "load" normal to the "thin plate" D), and D is the interior of a square with center at the origin.

The present paper is intended as a quick introduction to several methods for obtaining reliable, precise, numerically computable upper and lower bounds for a large class of problems of this general nature. For definiteness, only certain specific boundary value problems will be considered in detail, although the same procedures can be easily seen to be applicable in more general situations.

Section 2 treats the determination of upper and lower bounds for Dirichlet's integral in the exterior Dirichlet problem in three dimensional Euclidean space. The starting point for the general approach (based on Schwarz's inequality) were the papers by J. B. Diaz and A. Weinstein [1], [2], which dealt with upper and lower bounds for the Dirichlet integral in Dirichlet's and Neumann's problems in the plane.

The rôle of Bessel's inequality in the successive improvement of the upper and lower bounds has been emphasized in J. B. Diaz [1], [2]. In a book review (Bull. Amer. Math. Soc., vol. 59, 1953, pp. 588-602) of the book "Isoperimetric Inequalities", by G. Pólya and G. Szegö [1], it was pointed out that Schwarz's inequality can be used to derive, and to clarify the interrelation of, various principles for the capacity; a detailed account of this is also included in section 2. Section 3 is devoted to the determination of pointwise bounds in the interior Dirichlet problem in three dimensional Euclidean space; the approach employed is patterned after that of J. B. Diaz and H. J. Greenberg [1] for the first biharmonic boundary value problem in the plane (for a generalization of this procedure see P. C. Rosenbloom [1, pp. 145-146], and for an alternative method see L. E. Payne and H. F. Weinberger [1, pp. 300-303]). The determination of the capacity furnishes a curious link between the considerations of sections 2 and 3 (see item (h) of section 3). Finally, in section 4, a direct derivation is given of the algorithm of L. E. Payne and H. F. Weinberger [1, pp. 292-296] for the estimation of the capacity.

The bibliography lists a number of essential relevant references, directly concerned with the subject matter, which have come to the writer's attention, but is not meant to be exhaustive. A discussion of some of the references in the bibliography is to be found in J. B. Diaz [2, section 4].

It is hoped that the present brief survey will serve to stimulate renewed interest and activity in this field.

§2. Upper and lower bounds for Dirichlet's integral in the exterior Dirichlet problem in three dimensional Euclidean space

(a) Formulation of the problem. Let S be a bounded, smooth closed surface in three dimensional Euclidean space, and ext S be the exterior of S. Let $u(x, y, z)$ be a sufficiently smooth real valued function defined on S + ext S and satisfying the relations

$$\left.\begin{aligned} \Delta u \equiv u_{xx} + u_{yy} + u_{zz} &= 0 , \quad \text{on ext } S , \\ u &= f , \quad \text{on } S , \end{aligned}\right\} \tag{2.1}$$

where f is a given smooth real valued function on S and Δ is the Laplacian operator. It is also supposed that u is "regular at infinity", i.e. that

$$u(x, y, z) = O(r^{-1}) , \qquad \text{as } r \to \infty , \tag{2.2}$$

where $r = \sqrt{x^2 + y^2 + z^2}$ is the Euclidean distance from the origin. Under general hypotheses on S and f it is known that there exists one and only one such function $u(x, y, z)$, "the solution of the exterior Dirichlet problem for S with boundary values f". The problem to be considered in this section is the determination of numerically computable upper and lower bounds (in terms of certain known functions to be specified precisely) for the a priori unknown real number, the volume integral

$$\iiint_{\text{ext } S} [u_x^2 + u_y^2 + u_z^2]d\tau = \iiint_{\text{ext } S} |\text{grad } u|^2 d\tau \ , \qquad (2.3)$$

which is called the Dirichlet integral of the (a priori unknown) function $u(x, y, z)$.

(b) <u>Schwarz's inequality.</u> Let ϕ be a smooth vector field, with real valued components $\phi_1(x, y, z)$, $\phi_2(x, y, z)$, $\phi_3(x, y, z)$, defined on $S + \text{ext } S$, which will be denoted briefly by $\phi = [\phi_1, \phi_2, \phi_3]$. If $\psi = [\psi_1, \psi_2, \psi_3]$ is another vector field, the scalar product will be denoted, as usual, by

$$\phi\cdot\psi = \phi_1\psi_1 + \phi_2\psi_2 + \phi_3\psi_3 = \sum_{i=1}^{3} \phi_i\psi_i \ , \qquad (2.4)$$

and the non-negative length of ϕ will be denoted by $|\phi| = (\phi, \phi)^{\frac{1}{2}}$. Further, the sum of ϕ and ψ is

$$\phi + \psi = [\phi_1 + \psi_1, \ \phi_2 + \psi_2, \ \phi_3 + \psi_3] \ , \qquad (2.5)$$

and

$$\lambda\phi = [\lambda\phi_1, \ \lambda\phi_2, \ \lambda\phi_3] \ , \qquad (2.6)$$

for any real number λ .

All the triple integrals involved being assumed convergent, one has, for λ <u>any</u> real number, that

$$0 \leq \iiint_{\text{ext } S} (\phi+\lambda\psi)\cdot(\phi+\lambda\psi)d\tau = \iiint_{\text{ext } S} \phi\cdot\phi d\tau + 2\lambda\iiint_{\text{ext } S} \phi\cdot\psi d\tau + \lambda^2\iiint_{\text{ext } S} \psi\cdot\psi d\tau. \ (2.7)$$

If $\iiint_{\text{ext } S} \psi\cdot\psi d\tau > 0$, (i.e. ψ is not the identically zero fector field) then (2.7) may be rewritten

$$0 \leq \left[\iiint_{\text{ext } S} \phi\cdot\phi d\tau - \frac{\left(\iiint_{\text{ext } S} \phi\cdot\psi d\tau\right)^2}{\iiint_{\text{ext } S} \psi\cdot\psi d\tau}\right] + \left(\iiint_{\text{ext } S} \psi\cdot\psi d\tau\right)\left(\lambda + \frac{\iiint_{\text{ext } S} \phi\cdot\psi d\tau}{\iiint_{\text{ext } S} \psi\cdot\psi d\tau}\right)^2, \ (2.8)$$

which implies, since λ is any real number, that

$$\left(\iiint_{\text{ext } S} \phi\cdot\psi d\tau\right)^2 \leq \left(\iiint_{\text{ext } S} \phi\cdot\phi d\tau\right)\left(\iiint_{\text{ext } S} \psi\cdot\psi d\tau\right) \ ; \qquad (2.9)$$

this is Schwarz's inequality. In the seemingly excluded case,

$\iiint\limits_{\text{ext } S} \psi\cdot\psi d\tau = 0$, then ψ must be the zero vector field, hence $\iiint\limits_{\text{ext } S} \phi\cdot\psi d\tau = 0$ and (2.9) still holds.

(c) Upper bounds for the Dirichlet integral (Dirichlet's principle). Let $w(x, y, z)$ be a real valued function defined on $S + \text{ext } S$ and satisfying the same "boundary conditions" (see (2.1) and (2.2)) as the a priori unknown function $u(x, y, z)$, namely

$$w = u = f, \qquad \text{on } S, \tag{2.10}$$

and

$$w(x, y, z) = O(r^{-1}), \quad \text{as } r \to \infty \quad . \tag{2.11}$$

Putting $\phi = \text{grad } u$ and $\psi = \text{grad } w$ in Schwarz's inequality (2.9), it follows that

$$\Big(\iiint\limits_{\text{ext } S} \text{grad } u\cdot \text{grad } w \, d\tau\Big)^2 \leq \iiint\limits_{\text{ext } S} |\text{grad } u|^2 d\tau \iiint\limits_{\text{ext } S} |\text{grad } w|^2 d\tau . \tag{2.12}$$

On the other hand, from the boundary conditions (2.2) for u and (2.11) for w , it follows that

$$\lim_{R\to\infty} \iint w \frac{\partial u}{\partial n} d\sigma = 0 , \tag{2.13}$$

where the surface integral is extended over any sufficiently large sphere with center at the origin and radius R . (Notice that, since u is harmonic on ext S , (2.2) implies that $u_x, u_y, u_z = O(r^{-2})$ as $r \to \infty$). Hence, by Green's identity and the boundary condition (2.1) for u (with $\frac{\partial}{\partial n_e}$ denoting differentiation in the direction of the exterior normal to S);

$$\left.\begin{aligned} \iiint\limits_{\text{ext } S} \text{grad } u\cdot \text{grad } w \, d\tau &= -\iiint\limits_{\text{ext } S} w \,\Delta u d\tau - \iint\limits_{S} w \frac{\partial u}{\partial n_e} d\sigma , \\ &= -\iint\limits_{S} u \frac{\partial u}{\partial n_e} d\sigma = \iiint\limits_{\text{ext } S} |\text{grad } u|^2 d\tau . \end{aligned}\right\} \tag{2.14}$$

In view of (2.14), Schwarz's inequality (2.12) becomes just Dirichlet's principle

$$\iiint\limits_{\text{ext } S} |\text{grad } u|^2 d\tau \leq \iiint\limits_{\text{ext } S} |\text{grad } w|^2 d\tau . \tag{2.15}$$

Formulated in variational form, Dirichlet's principle (2.15) states that the minimum of the Dirichlet integral $\iiint\limits_{\text{ext } S} |\text{grad } w|^2 d\tau$, over the class of all functions w satisfying the same boundary conditions ((2.10) and (2.11)) as the solution $u(x, y, z)$ of the exterior Dirichlet boundary value problem (2.1), (2.2), is precisely the Dirichlet integral $\iiint_{\text{ext } S} |\text{grad } u|^2 d\tau$ of the solution $u(x, y, z)$. So that any chosen function w , satisfying (2.10) and (2.11), furnishes, by means of (2.15), a numerically computable upper bound for the number $\iiint_{\text{ext } S} |\text{grad } u|^2 d\tau$.

(d) Lower bounds for the Dirichlet integral (Thomson's principle). Let $\phi(x, y, z)$ be a real valued, non-zero, vector field defined on $S + \text{ext } S$ (with $\iiint_{\text{ext } S} \phi \cdot \phi d\tau$ finite), such that

$$\text{div } \phi \equiv \frac{\partial \phi_1}{\partial x_1} + \frac{\partial \phi_2}{\partial x_2} + \frac{\partial \phi_3}{\partial x_3} = 0 \text{ , on ext } S \text{ ,} \tag{2.16}$$

and satisfying the "boundary condition at ∞"

$$\phi_1, \phi_2, \phi_3 = O(r^{-2}) \text{ ,} \qquad \text{as } r \to \infty \text{ .} \tag{2.17}$$

(In a certain sense, the vector field ϕ "approximates" the vector field grad u . Notice that, in view of (2.1), the vector field grad u satisfies

$$\text{div grad } u = 0 \text{ ,} \tag{2.18}$$

which is to be compared with (2.16) above. Also, in view of (2.2), since u is harmonic on ext S , the components of the vector field grad u satisfy

$$\frac{\partial u}{\partial x}, \frac{\partial u}{\partial y}, \frac{\partial u}{\partial z} = O(r^{-2}) \text{ ,} \qquad \text{as } r \to \infty \text{ ,} \tag{2.19}$$

which is to be compared with (2.17) above.)

Putting $\psi = \text{grad } u$, and letting ϕ be as just specified, Schwarz's inequality (2.9) yields

$$\frac{\left(\iiint_{\text{ext } S} \phi \cdot \text{grad } u \, d\tau\right)^2}{\iiint_{\text{ext } S} |\phi|^2 d\tau} \leq \iiint_{\text{ext } S} |\text{grad } u|^2 d\tau \text{ .} \tag{2.20}$$

On the other hand, from the condition (2.2) imposed on $u(x, y, z)$ and the conditions (2.16) and (2.17) imposed on ϕ , it follows that

$$\lim_{r \to \infty} \iint u \, \phi \cdot n_e \, d\sigma = 0 \text{ ,} \tag{2.21}$$

where the surface integral is extended over any sufficiently large sphere with center at the origin and radius R . Hence, by Green's identity

$$\iiint_{\text{ext } S} \phi\cdot \operatorname{grad} u \, d\tau = \iiint_{\text{ext } S} [\phi_1 \frac{\partial u}{\partial x} + \phi_2 \frac{\partial u}{\partial y} + \phi_3 \frac{\partial u}{\partial z}] \, d\tau \ ,$$

$$= \iiint_{\text{ext } S} [\frac{\partial}{\partial x}(\phi_1 u) + \frac{\partial}{\partial y}(\phi_2 u) + \frac{\partial}{\partial z}(\phi_3 u) - u(\frac{\partial \phi_1}{\partial x} + \frac{\partial \phi_2}{\partial y} + \frac{\partial \phi_3}{\partial z})] d\tau,$$

$$= \iiint_{\text{ext } S} \operatorname{div}(u\phi) d\tau = - \iint_S u\phi\cdot n_e d\sigma \ . \tag{2.22}$$

In view of (2.22), Schwarz's inequality (2.20) becomes just Thomson's principle:

$$\frac{\left[\iint_S u\phi\cdot n_e \, d\sigma\right]^2}{\iiint_{\text{ext } S} |\phi|^2 d\tau} \leqq \iiint_{\text{ext } S} |\operatorname{grad} u|^2 d\tau \ . \tag{2.23}$$

Formulated in variational form, Thomson's principle states that the maximum of the quotient

$$\frac{\left[\iint_S u\phi\cdot n_e \, d\sigma\right]^2}{\iiint_{\text{ext } S} |\phi|^2 \, d\tau} \ ,$$

over the set of all non-zero "admissible" vector fields ϕ with $\operatorname{div} \phi = 0$ on ext S, is precisely the Dirichlet integral $\iiint_{\text{ext } S} |\operatorname{grad} u|^2 \, d\tau$ of the solution $u(x, y, z)$. So that any chosen admissible vector field furnishes, by means of (2.23), a numerically computable lower bound for the number $\iiint_{\text{ext } S} |\operatorname{grad} u|^2 \, d\tau$.

(e) Lower bounds for the Dirichlet integral in terms of harmonic functions (Trefftz). If, in particular, the vector field ϕ of (2.16) is equal to $\operatorname{grad} v$, where $v(x, y, z)$ is a non-zero harmonic function on ext S, and $v = O(r^{-1})$ as $r \to \infty$, then (2.17) holds. In this particular case, the inequality (2.23) becomes

$$\frac{\left(\iint_S u \frac{\partial v}{\partial n_e} \, d\sigma\right)^2}{\iiint_{\text{ext } S} |\operatorname{grad} v|^2 d\tau} \leq \iiint_{\text{ext } S} |\operatorname{grad} u|^2 \, d\tau \ ; \tag{2.24}$$

so that any function $v(x, y, z)$ which is harmonic on ext S and regular at ∞ furnishes a lower bound for the Dirichlet integral of $u(x, y, z)$.

(f) Lower bounds for the Dirichlet integral in terms of an "arbitrary" vector field. The condition (2.16) on ϕ :

$$\operatorname{div} \phi = 0 , \qquad \text{on ext } S , \tag{2.16}$$

can always be replaced by the equivalent condition

$$\phi = \operatorname{curl} \theta , \qquad \text{on ext } S ; \tag{2.16'}$$

where the vector field θ has components $\theta_1, \theta_2, \theta_3$, i.e.

$$\phi_1 = \frac{\partial \theta_3}{\partial y} - \frac{\partial \theta_2}{\partial z} , \quad \phi_2 = \frac{\partial \theta_1}{\partial z} - \frac{\partial \theta_3}{\partial x} , \quad \phi_3 = \frac{\partial \theta_2}{\partial x} - \frac{\partial \theta_1}{\partial y} , \tag{2.16''}$$

and the three functions $\theta_1(x, y, z)$, $\theta_2(x, y, z)$, $\theta_3(x, y, z)$ need not be single valued on ext S , but their gradients are. In terms of the "arbitrary" vector field θ , inequality (2.23) becomes

$$\frac{\left[\iint_S u(\operatorname{curl} \theta) \cdot n_e \, d\sigma\right]^2}{\iiint_{\text{ext } S} |\operatorname{curl} \theta|^2 \, d\tau} \leq \iiint_{\text{ext } S} |\operatorname{grad} u|^2 d\tau . \tag{2.25}$$

(g) Remarks concerning two inequalities, analogous to (e) and (f) above, in the two dimensional interior Dirichlet problem. The interior boundary value problem in question, in two dimensions, is (compare (2.1)):

$$\left.\begin{aligned} \Delta u \equiv u_{xx} + u_{yy} &= 0 , \qquad \text{on int } C , \\ u &= f , \qquad \text{on } C , \end{aligned}\right\} \tag{2.26}$$

where C is a smooth simple closed curve, f is a given smooth real valued function on C , and Δ is the two dimensional Laplacian operator.

In the present plane problem, an inequality analogous to (2.24) in item (e) above was given by E. Trefftz [1]. It reads as follows:

$$\frac{\left(\int_C u \frac{\partial v}{\partial n_e} ds\right)^2}{\iint_{\text{int } C} (v_x^2 + v_y^2) dx\, dy} \leq \iint_{\text{int } C} (u_x^2 + u_y^2) dx\, dy , \tag{2.27}$$

where $v(x, y)$ is any non-constant harmonic function defined on

C + int C , and $\frac{\partial}{\partial n_e}$ denotes differentiation in the direction of the exterior normal to C . For a derivation of (2.27) see, e.g., J. B. Diaz and A. Weinstein [1].

In the present plane interior problem, an inequality analogous to (2.25) in item (f) above was given by J. B. Diaz [2, p. 31]. It reads as follows

$$\frac{\left(\int_C u \frac{\partial v}{\partial s} ds\right)^2}{\iint_{\text{int } C} (v_x^2 + v_y^2)\, dx\, dy} \leq \iint_{\text{int } C} (u_x^2 + u_y^2) dx\, dy \ , \tag{2.28}$$

where $v(x, y)$ is any non-constant function on C + int C , not necessarily single valued, but such that v_x and v_y are single valued on C + int C , and $\frac{\partial}{\partial s}$ denotes differentiation along the curve C. (Notice that, formally, one passes from (2.27) to (2.28) merely by replacing $\frac{\partial}{\partial n_e}$ by $\frac{\partial}{\partial s}$ on the left hand side of (2.27).) For a discussion of the connection between (2.28) and some earlier results of K. O. Friedrichs [1], see J. B. Diaz [2, pp. 42-43].

(h) Lower bounds for the Dirichlet integral in terms of an arbitrary mass distribution on the surface S (Gauss' principle). Just like the Trefftz lower bound (2.24) for the Dirichlet integral of u in terms of an arbitrary harmonic function, which was mentioned in item (e) above, the principle of Gauss is also a particular case of Thomson's principle (2.20), mentioned in item (d) above. Suppose, in particular, that the harmonic function $v(x, y, z)$ appearing in (2.24) is the potential of a single layer distribution, with density μ , on the surface S, i.e., (in an obvious notation)

$$v(p) = \iint_S \mu(q) \frac{1}{r_{pq}} d\sigma_q \ . \tag{2.29}$$

Notice that, given the continuous density distribution μ on S , (2.29) defines v as a continuous function throughout three dimensional space, and that v is harmonic both on the interior and on the exterior of S .

In order to rewrite the inequality (2.24) in terms of the density μ , use will be made of the known "jump condition", across the surface S , which is

$$\frac{\partial v}{\partial n_e} + \frac{\partial v}{\partial n_i} = -4\pi\mu \ ,$$

where $\frac{\partial}{\partial n_e}$ and $\frac{\partial}{\partial n_i}$ denote differentiation in the direction of the outer and the inner normal to S, respectively. In view of this, Green's identity yields

$$\iiint_{\text{ext } S} |\text{grad } v|^2 d\tau = -\iint_S v \frac{\partial v}{\partial n_e} d\sigma ,$$

$$= -\iint_S v \left[-4\pi\mu - \frac{\partial v}{\partial n_i}\right] d\sigma$$

$$= 4\pi \iint_S v \mu \, d\sigma + \iint_S v \frac{\partial v}{\partial n_i} d\sigma ,$$

$$= 4\pi \iint_S v \mu \, d\sigma - \iiint_{\text{int } S} |\text{grad } v|^2 d\tau ,$$

and also

$$\iint_S u \frac{\partial v}{\partial n_e} d\sigma = \iint_S u\left[-4\pi\mu - \frac{\partial v}{\partial n_i}\right] d\sigma ;$$

so that the inequality (2.24) becomes

$$\frac{\left(4\pi \iint_S u\mu \, d\sigma - \iint_S u \frac{\partial v}{\partial n_i} d\sigma\right)^2}{4\pi \iint_S v\mu \, d\sigma - \iiint_{\text{int } S} |\text{grad } v|^2 \, d\tau} \leqq \iiint_{\text{ext } S} |\text{grad } u|^2 d\tau . \tag{2.30}$$

This inequality remains valid, a fortiori, if the denominator of the left hand side is simply replaced by $4\pi \iint_S v\mu \, d\sigma$. Supposing this to be done, and considering <u>the special case</u> when the given function f of (2.1) is identically one (and the Dirichlet integral of u is 4π times the <u>capacity</u> of the surface S), it follows that

$$\frac{4\pi \left(\iint_S \mu d\sigma\right)^2}{\iint_S v\mu d\sigma} \leqq \iiint_{\text{ext } S} |\text{grad } u|^2 d\tau , \tag{2.31}$$

(see G. Pólya and G. Szegö [1, p. 56]); or, alternatively, (recall the definition (2.29) of v as the potential of a single layer with density μ over S):

$$\frac{4\pi \left(\iint_S \mu d\sigma\right)^2}{\iint_S \left\{\left[\iint_S \frac{\mu(p_2)}{r_{12}} d\sigma_2\right] \mu(p_1)\right\} d\sigma_1} \leqq \iiint_{\text{ext } S} |\text{grad } u|^2 d\tau , \tag{2.32}$$

(see G. Szegö [1, p. 772]).

(i) Successive improvement of the lower bounds for the Dirichlet integral of u. Connection with Bessel's inequality. Consider, for example, inequality (2.20) of item (d) above. Any "admissible" vector field ϕ furnishes a lower bound for the Dirichlet integral of u. The question of successively improving the lower bounds will now be treated.

Let $\phi_1, \phi_2, \ldots, \phi_n$ be n linearly independent admissible vector fields such that $\operatorname{div} \phi_j = 0$, $j = 1, 2, \ldots, n$, and write $\phi_{j1}, \phi_{j2}, \phi_{j3}$ for the three components of the vector field ϕ_j. Then, for any n real numbers $a_1, \ldots, a_n$, not all zero, the vector field $\sum_{j=1}^{n} a_j \phi_j$ has divergence zero and furnishes a lower bound for the Dirichlet integral of u:

$$\frac{\left[\sum_{j=1}^{n} a_j \iint_S u \phi_j \cdot n_e d\sigma\right]^2}{\sum_{j,k=1}^{n} a_j a_k \iiint_{\text{ext } S} \phi_j \cdot \phi_k d\tau} \leqq \iiint_{\text{ext } S} |\text{grad } u|^2 d\tau . \tag{2.33}$$

Maximizing the left hand side quotient in (2.33) with respect to the a_j's (notice that this quotient is homogeneous of degree zero with respect to the a_j's, so that one need only consider its values on an ellipsoid $\sum_{j,k=1}^{n} a_j a_k \iiint_{\text{ext } S} \phi_j \cdot \phi_k d\tau = \text{const.}$) one obtains that the critical values of the a_j's must satisfy the system of n linear equations

$$\lambda \frac{\partial}{\partial a_\ell}\left[\sum_{j,k=1}^{n} a_j a_k \iiint_{\text{ext } S} \phi_j \cdot \phi_k d\tau\right] = \frac{\partial}{\partial a_\ell}\left[\sum_{j=1}^{n} a_j \iint_S u\phi_j \cdot n_e d\sigma\right]^2 ,$$

$\ell = 1, \ldots, n$, that is

$$\sum_{k=1}^{n} a_k^n \iiint_{\text{ext } S} \phi_k \cdot \phi_\ell d\tau = \iint_S u \phi_\ell \cdot n_e d\sigma , \tag{2.34}$$

$\ell = 1, \ldots, n$, where the critical values of the a_k's have been denoted by a_k^n, to indicate their explicit dependence on n, and the Lagrange multiplier λ on the left hand side has been replaced by unity, without loss, in view of the homogeneity with respect to the a_k's of the quotient being minimized. From (2.34) one has that

$$\sum_{k=1}^{n} a_k^n \iiint_{\text{ext } S} \phi_k \cdot \phi_j \, d\tau = \iint_S u\phi_j \cdot n_e \, d\sigma \ , \tag{2.35}$$

$j = 1, \ldots, n$, and that

$$\sum_{j=1}^{n} \sum_{k=1}^{n} a_j^n a_k^n \iiint_{\text{ext } S} \phi_k \cdot \phi_j \, d\tau = \sum_{j=1}^{n} a_j^n \iint_S u\phi_j \cdot n_e \, d\sigma \ . \tag{2.36}$$

Thus the final (optimum) inequality obtainable from (2.33) may be written in either of the equivalent forms

$$\sum_{j=1}^{n} a_j^n \iint_S u\phi_j \cdot n_e \, d\sigma \leqq \iiint_{\text{ext } S} |\text{grad } u|^2 \, d\tau \ , \tag{2.37}$$

and

$$\sum_{j=1}^{n} \sum_{k=1}^{n} a_j^n a_k^n \iiint_{\text{ext } S} \phi_k \cdot \phi_j \, d\tau \leqq \iiint_{\text{ext } S} |\text{grad } u|^2 \, d\tau \ . \tag{2.38}$$

If, in particular, the n vector fields $\phi_1, \ldots, \phi_n$ are orthonormal, i.e. that

$$\iiint_{\text{ext } S} \phi_j \cdot \phi_k \, d\tau = \begin{cases} 1 \ , & \text{if } j = k \ , \\ 0 \ , & \text{if } j \neq k \ , \end{cases} \tag{2.39}$$

for $j, k = 1, \ldots, n$, it follows from (2.35) that (recall (2.16)):

$$a_j^n = \iint_S u\phi_j \cdot n_e \, d\sigma = \iiint_{\text{ext } S} (\text{grad } u) \cdot (\phi_j) \, d\tau \ , \tag{2.40}$$

$j = 1, \ldots, n$, and (2.37) may then be rewritten

$$\sum_{j=1}^{n} \left[\iiint_{\text{ext } S} (\text{grad } u) \cdot (\phi_j) \, d\tau \right]^2 \leqq \iiint_{\text{ext } S} |\text{grad } u|^2 \, d\tau \ . \tag{2.41}$$

This is just Bessel's inequality

$$\sum_{j=1}^{n} (\text{grad } u, \ \phi_j)^2 \leqq (\text{grad } u, \ \text{grad } u) \ , \tag{2.42}$$

with respect to the "scalar product" (ϕ, ψ) of two vector fields defined as follows:

$$(\phi, \psi) = \iiint_{\text{ext } S} (\text{grad } \phi) \cdot (\text{grad } \psi) \, d\sigma \quad . \tag{2.43}$$

(In this connection, see J. B. Diaz [1].)

Now consider the inequality (2.24) of item (e) above. Putting $\phi_j = \text{grad } v_j$ in what has just been said, where $v_1, \ldots, v_n$ are harmonic on ext S and regular at ∞, one obtains (replacing the real constants a_j by b_j, for ease of reference) that

$$\sum_{j=1}^{n} b_j^n \iint_S u \frac{\partial v_j}{\partial n_e} \, d\sigma \leq \iiint_{\text{ext } S} |\text{grad } u|^2 d\tau \quad , \tag{2.37'}$$

and

$$\sum_{j=1}^{n} \sum_{k=1}^{n} b_j^n b_k^n \iint_S v_k \frac{\partial v_j}{\partial n_e} \, d\sigma \leq \iiint_{\text{ext } S} |\text{grad } u|^2 d\tau \quad , \tag{2.38'}$$

where the (optimum) real numbers $b_1^n, \ldots, b_n^n$ solve the system of linear equations

$$\sum_{k=1}^{n} b_k^n \iint_S v_k \frac{\partial v_j}{\partial n_e} \, d\sigma = \iint_S u \frac{\partial v_j}{\partial n_e} \, d\sigma \quad , \tag{2.35'}$$

$j = 1, \ldots, n$.

(j) Successive improvement of the upper bounds for the Dirichlet integral of u . Connection with Bessel's inequality. Consider inequality (2.15) of item (c) above. Any "admissible" function w furnishes an upper bound for the Dirichlet integral of u . The question of successively improving the upper bounds will now be treated (this is the "Rayleigh-Ritz method").

Let $w_1, w_2, \ldots, w_m$ be m functions defined on ext S and satisfying the "boundary conditions" (compare (2.10) and (2.11)):

$$w_j = 0 \quad , \qquad \text{on } S \quad , \tag{2.10'}$$

$$w_j(x, y, z) = O(r^{-1}) \quad , \quad \text{as } r \to \infty \quad , \tag{2.11'}$$

for $j = 1, \ldots, m$. Then, for any real numbers $c_1, c_2, \ldots, c_m$, the function $w - \sum_{j=1}^{n} c_j w_j$ furnishes an upper bound for the Dirichlet integral of u :

$$\iiint_{\text{ext } S} |\text{grad } u|^2 d\tau \leq \iiint_{\text{ext } S} |\text{grad } (w - \sum_{j=1}^{m} c_j w_j)|^2 d\tau \quad . \tag{2.44}$$

Minimizing the right hand size of (2.44) with respect to the c_j's , one obtains that the critical value of the c_j's must satisfy the system of m linear equations

$$\frac{\partial}{\partial c_\ell}\left[\iiint_{\text{ext }S}\left\{\text{grad}\left(w-\sum_{j=1}^{m}c_j w_j\right)\cdot\text{grad}\left(w-\sum_{k=1}^{m}c_k w_k\right)\right\}d\tau\right] \tag{2.45}$$

$$=\frac{\partial}{\partial c_\ell}\left[\iiint_{\text{ext }S}\left\{|\text{grad } w|^2-2\sum_{k=1}^{m}c_k\,\text{grad } w\cdot\text{grad } w_k+\sum_{j=1}^{m}\sum_{k=1}^{m}c_k c_j\,\text{grad } w_k\cdot\text{grad } w_j\right\}d\tau\right]=0\ ,$$

for $\ell = 1,\dots,m$; that is

$$\sum_{k=1}^{m} c^m_k \iiint_{\text{ext }S} (\text{grad } w_\ell)\cdot(\text{grad } w_k)d\tau = \iiint_{\text{ext }S} (\text{grad } w)\cdot(\text{grad } w_\ell)d\tau\ , \tag{2.46}$$

for $\ell = 1,\dots,m$, where the critical values of the c_k's have been denoted by c^m_k , to denote their explicit dependence on m . From (2.46) one has that

$$\sum_{k=1}^{m} c^m_k \iiint_{\text{ext }S} (\text{grad } w_j)\cdot(\text{grad } w_k)d\tau = \iiint_{\text{ext }S} (\text{grad } w)\cdot(\text{grad } w_j)d\tau\ , \tag{2.47}$$

$j = 1,\dots,m$, and that

$$\sum_{j=1}^{m}\sum_{k=1}^{m} c^m_j c^m_k \iiint_{\text{ext }S} (\text{grad } w_j)\cdot(\text{grad } w_k)d\tau = \sum_{j=1}^{m} c^m_j \iiint_{\text{ext }S} (\text{grad } w)\cdot(\text{grad } w_j)\,d\tau\ . \tag{2.48}$$

Thus the final (optimum) inequality obtainable from (2.44) may be written in either of the equivalent forms

$$\iiint_{\text{ext }S} |\text{grad } u|^2 d\tau \le \iiint_{\text{ext }S} |\text{grad } w|^2 d\tau - \sum_{j=1}^{m} c^m_j \iiint_{\text{ext }S} (\text{grad } w)\cdot(\text{grad } w_j)d\tau\ , \tag{2.49}$$

and

$$\iiint_{\text{ext }S} |\text{grad } u|^2 d\tau \le \iiint_{\text{ext }S} |\text{grad } w|^2 d\tau - \sum_{j=1}^{m}\sum_{k=1}^{m} c^m_j c^m_k \iiint_{\text{ext }S} (\text{grad } w_j)\cdot(\text{grad } w_k)\,d\tau\ . \tag{2.50}$$

If, in particular, the m functions $w_1, w_2, \dots, w_m$ are orthonormal, i.e. that

$$\iiint_{\text{ext }S} (\text{grad } w_j)\cdot(\text{grad } w_k)d\tau = \begin{cases} 1\ , & \text{if } j = k\ ,\\ 0\ , & \text{if } j \ne k\ ,\end{cases} \tag{2.51}$$

For $j, k = 1, \ldots, m$, it follows from (2.47) that

$$c_j^m = \iiint_{\text{ext } S} (\text{grad } w) \cdot (\text{grad } w_j) d\tau \quad , \tag{2.52}$$

for $j = 1, \ldots, m$, and (2.49) may then be rewritten

$$\iiint_{\text{ext } S} |\text{grad } u|^2 d\tau + \sum_{j=1}^{m} \iiint_{S} (\text{grad } w) \cdot (\text{grad } w_j) d\tau \leq \iiint_{\text{ext } S} |\text{grad } w|^2 d\tau . \tag{2.53}$$

When $\iiint_{\text{ext } S} |\text{grad } u|^2 d\tau = 0$, inequality (2.53) is just Bessel's inequality,

$$\sum_{j=1}^{m} (\text{grad } w, \text{ grad } w_j)^2 \leq (\text{grad } w, \text{ grad } w) \quad , \tag{2.54}$$

with respect to the scalar product (ϕ, ψ) of two vector fields defined as follows

$$(\phi, \psi) \equiv \iiint_{\text{ext } S} (\text{grad } \phi) \cdot (\text{grad } \psi) d\tau \quad . \tag{2.55}$$

But, <u>even when</u> $\iiint_{\text{ext } S} |\text{grad } u|^2 d\tau > 0$, inequality (2.53) is just Bessel's inequality (compare J. B. Diaz [2, especially pages 43-44]), with respect to the scalar product defined by (2.55):

$$\left(\text{grad } w, \frac{\text{grad } u}{\left[\iiint_{\text{ext } S} |\text{grad } u|^2 d\tau\right]^{\frac{1}{2}}}\right) + \sum_{j=1}^{m} (\text{grad } w, \text{ grad } w_j)^2 \leq (\text{grad } w, \text{ grad } w), \tag{2.56}$$

since the $m + 1$ vector fields

$$\frac{\text{grad } u}{\left[\iiint_{\text{ext } S} |\text{grad } u|^2 d\tau\right]^{\frac{1}{2}}} , \text{ grad } w_1, \ldots, \text{ grad } w_m , \tag{2.57}$$

are orthonormal with respect to the scalar product (2.55).

(k) <u>Capacity of the "conductor"</u> S . The capacity C of the surface S (see item (a) above) is defined to be

$$C = \frac{1}{4\pi} \iiint_{\text{ext } S} |\text{grad } u|^2 d\tau \quad , \tag{2.58}$$

where the function u is the solution of the <u>exterior</u> Dirichlet problem (compare (2.1) and (2.2) above)

$$\left.\begin{aligned} \Delta u \equiv u_{xx} + u_{yy} + u_{zz} = 0 \ , &\quad \text{on ext } S \ , \\ u = 1 \ , &\quad \text{on } S \ , \\ u(x,y,z) = O(r^{-1}) \ , &\quad \text{as } r \to \infty \ . \end{aligned}\right\} \tag{2.59}$$

Since the capacity C is $\frac{1}{4\pi}$ times the Dirichlet integral of the solution u of (2.59), it is clear that the earlier considerations of the present section furnish algorithms for the computation of upper and lower bounds for the capacity of the surface S. For more detailed information concerning the capacity, reference is made to G. Pólya and G. Szegö [1, especially chapters 2 and 3].

§3. Upper and lower bounds for the value of a solution (and for the partial derivatives), at a given point, of the interior Dirichlet problem in three dimensional Euclidean space.

(a) Formulation of the problem. Let S be a bounded, smooth, closed surface in three dimensional Euclidean space, and int S be the interior of S. Let $u(x,y,z)$ be a sufficiently smooth real-valued function defined on S + int S and satisfying the relations

$$\left.\begin{aligned} \Delta u \equiv u_{xx} + u_{yy} + u_{zz} = p(x,y,z) \ , &\quad \text{on int } S \ , \\ u = f \ , &\quad \text{on } S \ , \end{aligned}\right\} \tag{3.1}$$

where p and f are given smooth real-valued functions on int S and S, respectively, and Δ is the Laplacian operator. Under general hypotheses on S, f and p it is known that there exists one and only one such function $u(x,y,z)$, "the solution of the interior Dirichlet problem (for Poisson's equation $\Delta u = p$) for S, with boundary values f". Let (x_0, y_0, z_0) be a point of int S, which will be regarded as fixed throughout the discussion. The problem to be considered in this section is the determination of numerically computable upper and lower bounds (in terms of certain known functions to be specified precisely) for the a priori unknown real number

$$u(x_0, y_0, z_0) \ , \tag{3.2}$$

which is the functional value at the given point (x_0, y_0, z_0) of the a priori unknown function u.

(b) Scalar product. Schwarz's inequality. Green's first identity. In this section the following definition of the scalar product (F, G) of two functions $F(x,y,z)$ and $G(x,y,z)$ will be employed:

$$(F, G) \equiv \iiint_{\text{int } S} (F_x G_x + F_y G_y + F_z G_z) d\tau = \iiint_{\text{int } S} (\text{grad } F) \cdot (\text{grad } G) d\tau \quad . \quad (3.3)$$

As in (b) of section 2, one has, for any real numbers α and β that

$$0 \leq (\alpha F + \beta G, \alpha F + \beta G) = \alpha^2 (F, F) + 2\alpha\beta (F, G) + \beta^2 (G, G), \quad (3.4)$$

and Schwarz's inequality

$$(F, G)^2 \leq (F, F)(G, G) \quad . \quad (3.5)$$

The following identity, known as "Green's first identity for Laplace's operator" (in the terminology of O. D. Kellogg [1, pp. 211-212])

$$(F, G) = \begin{cases} -\iiint_{\text{int } S} F \Delta G d\tau + \iint_S F \dfrac{\partial G}{\partial n_e} d\sigma , \\ -\iiint_{\text{int } S} G \Delta F d\tau + \iint_S G \dfrac{\partial F}{\partial n_e} d\sigma , \end{cases} \quad (3.6)$$

will be employed repeatedly.

(c) <u>Orthogonality of any two functions, one satisfying the homogeneous partial differential equation and the other the homogeneous boundary conditions. An inequality.</u> Suppose that

$$\Delta F = F_{xx} + F_{yy} + F_{zz} = 0 , \quad \text{on int } S , \quad (3.7)$$

and that

$$G = 0 , \quad \text{on } S . \quad (3.7')$$

Then (3.6) implies that F and G are orthogonal, i.e. that

$$(F, G) = 0 . \quad (3.8)$$

Now, let w be a function satisfying the boundary conditions of the boundary value problem (3.1), i.e. such that

$$w = u , \quad \text{on } S , \quad (3.9)$$

and let v be a function satisfying the partial differential equation of the boundary value problem (3.1), i.e. such that

$$\Delta v = \Delta u , \quad \text{on int } S . \quad (3.10)$$

Then the following inequality holds

$$\left.\begin{matrix}(v-u,\ v-u)\\ \\ (w-u,\ w-u)\end{matrix}\right\} \leqq (v-w,\ v-w) \ . \tag{3.11}$$

This inequality is easily verified, as follows:

$$\begin{aligned}(v-w,\ v-w) &= ([v-u] + [u-w],\ [v-u] + [u-w])\ , \\ &= (v-u,\ v-u) + 2(v-u,\ v-w) + (u-w,\ u-w)\ , \qquad (3.12)\\ &= (v-u,\ v-u) + (w-u,\ w-u)\ ;\end{aligned}$$

since the Laplacian of $v-u$ vanishes on int S, the function $w-u$ vanishes on S, and hence $(v-u,\ u-w) = 0$ by (3.8).

(d) Regular part of Green's function. Green's third identity. Together with the function $u(x, y, z)$ of (3.1), it will be convenient to consider the function $\overline{u}(x, y, z)$, which is the solution of the following boundary value problem:

$$\begin{aligned}\Delta\overline{u} &= 0\ , &&\text{on int } S\ ,\\ \overline{u} &= -1/r &&\text{on } S\ ,\end{aligned} \tag{3.13}$$

where $r = \sqrt{(x-x_0)^2 + (y-y_0)^2 + (z-z_0)^2}$ denotes the Euclidean distance from the given point $(x_0,\ y_0,\ z_0)$. The function $\overline{u}(x, y, z)$ is the "regular part of Green's function with pole at $(x_0,\ y_0,\ z_0)$". (Recall that Green's function $g(x, y, z;\ x_0, y_0, z_0)$ is defined by

$$g(x, y, z;\ x_0, y_0, z_0) = 1/r + \overline{u}(x, y, z)\ .) \tag{3.14}$$

It is emphasized that, in finding upper and lower bounds for the number $u(x_0, y_0, z_0)$ by the method to be explained here, a knowledge of the function $\overline{u}(x, y, z)$ is not required. However, one requires, besides a knowledge of the two functions v and w of (3.9) and (3.10) (which are related to the function u of (3.1)), the knowledge of two functions $\overline{v}$ and $\overline{w}$, which are related to the function $\overline{u}$ of (3.13) as follows:

$$\overline{w} = \overline{u} = -1/r\ , \qquad \text{on } S\ , \tag{3.15}$$

and

$$\Delta\overline{v} = 0\ , \qquad \text{on int } S\ , \tag{3.16}$$

In other words, the function $\overline{w}$ satisfies the same boundary conditions as the function $\overline{u}$, while the function $\overline{v}$ satisfies the same partial differential equation as $\bar{u}$. The following inequality, analogous to (3.11), holds:

$$\left.\begin{array}{l}(\bar{v}-\bar{u},\ \bar{v}-\bar{u})\\ \\ (\bar{w}-\bar{u},\ \bar{w}-\bar{u})\end{array}\right\}\leqq (\bar{v}-\bar{w},\ \bar{v}-\bar{w})\ . \tag{3.17}$$

The final ingredient needed in order to obtain upper and lower bounds for the number $u(x_0, y_0, z_0)$ is Green's third identity (see O. D. Kellogg [1, p.219]):

$$4\pi\, u(x_0, y_0, z_0) = -\iiint\limits_{\text{int } S} \frac{1}{r}\Delta u\, d\tau + \iint\limits_{S}\left(\frac{1}{r}\frac{\partial u}{\partial n_e} - u\frac{\partial \frac{1}{r}}{\partial n_e}\right)d\sigma \ , \tag{3.18}$$

which expresses the sought number $u(x_0, y_0, z_0)$ as "the sum of three potentials, one of area distribution over int S , and the other two of a single and a double layer over the surface S ".

(e) Upper and lower bounds for $u(x_0, y_0, z_0)$. Two sets of upper and lower bounds will now be given, in terms of the four (chosen) functions v, w, $\bar{v}$, $\bar{w}$ of (3.10), (3.9), (3.16) and (3.15) respectively.

The first set of upper and lower bounds for $u(x_0, y_0, z_0)$ follows from Schwarz's inequality:

$$(w-u,\ \bar{w}-\bar{u})^2 \leq (w-u,\ w-u)\ (\bar{w}-\bar{u},\ \bar{w}-\bar{u})\ , \tag{3.19}$$

together with the inequalities (3.11) and (3.17). Because (3.19), (3.11) and (3.17) imply that

$$(w-u,\ \bar{w}-\bar{u})^2 \leq (v-w,\ v-w)\ (\bar{v}-\bar{w},\ \bar{v}-\bar{w})\ ; \tag{3.20}$$

while, from (3.8), Green's first identity (3.6), and Green's third identity (3.18) it follows that

$$\begin{aligned}(w-u, \bar{w}-\bar{u}) &= (w, \bar{w}) - (w, \bar{u}) - (u, \bar{w}) + (u, \bar{u})\ ,\\ &= (w, \bar{w}) - (u, \bar{w}) + (u-w, \bar{u})\ ,\\ &= (w, \bar{w}) - \Big[-\iiint\limits_{\text{int } S} \bar{w}\ \Delta u\ d\tau + \iint\limits_{S} \bar{w}\ \frac{\partial u}{\partial n_e}\ d\sigma\Big]\ , \qquad (3.21)\\ &= (w, \bar{w}) + \iiint\limits_{\text{int } S} \bar{w}\,\Delta u\ d\tau - \iint\limits_{S} \bar{w}\ \frac{\partial u}{\partial n_e}\, d\sigma\ ,\\ &= (w, \bar{w}) + \iiint\limits_{\text{int } S} \bar{w}\Delta u\ d\tau + \iiint\limits_{\text{int } S} \frac{1}{r}\ \Delta u\, d\tau + \iint\limits_{S} u\frac{\partial\frac{1}{r}}{\partial n_e}\, d\sigma + 4\pi u(x_0, y_0, z_0)\end{aligned}$$

Thus the left hand side of inequality (3.20) is just the square of a difference: $4\pi u(x_0, y_0, z_0)$ minus several known terms, while the right hand side of (3.20) is just the known "error term" $(v-w, v-w)(\bar{v}-\bar{w}, \bar{v}-\bar{w})$. It is to be noticed that, while the "error term" $(v-w, v-w)(\bar{v}-\bar{w}, \bar{v}-\bar{w})$ involves all four functions $v, w, \bar{v}, \bar{w}$, the "approximation" to $4\pi u(x_0, y_0, z_0)$ given by (3.21) involves only the functions w and $\bar{w}$ which are required to satisfy certain boundary conditions (see (3.9) and (3.15)).

The second set of upper and lower bounds for $u(x_0, y_0, z_0)$ follows from Schwarz's inequality

$$(v-u, \bar{v}-\bar{u})^2 \leq (v-u, v-u)(\bar{v}-\bar{u}, \bar{v}-\bar{u}) , \tag{3.22}$$

together with the inequalities (3.11) and (3.17). Because (3.22), (3.11) and (3.17) imply that

$$(v-u, \bar{v}-\bar{u})^2 \leq (v-w, v-w)(\bar{v}-\bar{w}, \bar{v}-\bar{w}) ; \tag{3.23}$$

while, from Green's first identity (3.6), and Green's third identity (3.18), it follows that

$$\begin{aligned}(v-u, \bar{v}-\bar{u}) &= (v,\bar{v}) - (u,\bar{v}) - (v,\bar{u}) + (u,\bar{u}) ,\\ &= (v,\bar{v}) - (u,\bar{v}) + (u-v, \bar{u}) ,\\ &= (v,\bar{v}) - \iint_S u \frac{\partial \bar{v}}{\partial n_e} d\sigma + \iint_S \bar{u} \frac{\partial (u-v)}{\partial n_e} d\sigma ,\\ &= (v,\bar{v}) - \iint_S u \frac{\partial \bar{v}}{\partial n_e} d\sigma + \iint_S \frac{1}{r} \frac{\partial v}{\partial n_e} d\sigma - \iint_S \frac{1}{r} \frac{\partial u}{\partial n_e} d\sigma ,\\ &= (v,\bar{v}) - \iint_S u \frac{\partial \bar{v}}{\partial n_e} d\sigma + \iint_S \frac{1}{r} \frac{\partial v}{\partial n_e} d\sigma - \iiint_{\text{int } S} \frac{1}{r} \Delta u d\tau - \iint_S u \frac{\partial \frac{1}{r}}{\partial n_e} d\sigma - 4\pi u(x_0, y_0, z_0).\end{aligned} \tag{3.24}$$

Thus the left hand side of inequality (3.23) is just the square of a difference: $4\pi u(x_0, y_0, z_0)$ minus several known terms, while the right hand side of (3.23) is just the same known "error term" $(v-w, v-w)(\bar{v}-\bar{w}, \bar{v}-\bar{w})$ which occurs in (3.20). It is to be noticed that, while the "error term" $(v-w, v-w)(\bar{v}-\bar{w}, \bar{v}-\bar{w})$ involves all four functions $v, w, \bar{v}, \bar{w}$, the "approximation" to $4\pi u(x_0, y_0, z_0)$ given by (3.24) involves only the functions v and $\bar{v}$ which are required to satisfy certain partial differential equations (see (3.10) and (3.16)).

(f) Successive improvement of the upper and lower bounds for $u(x_0, y_0, z_0)$. The present considerations are similar to those of items (i) and (j) of section 2. Let m and n be non-negative integers (if either $m = 0$ or $n = 0$ then the corresponding functions below are supposed to be absent). Let $v_1, \ldots, v_m$ be m functions satisfying the homogeneous partial differential equation, that is

$$\Delta v_i = 0 \qquad \text{on int } S\ , \tag{3.25}$$

$i = 1,\ldots,m$; and let $w_1,\ldots,w_n$ be n functions satisfying the homogeneous boundary conditions

$$w_j = 0\ , \qquad \text{on } S\ , \tag{3.26}$$

$j = 1,\ldots,n$. Given <u>any</u> $2(m+n)$ real numbers a_i, b_j, c_i, d_j , where $i = 1,\ldots,m$ and $j = 1,\ldots,n$, the four functions $v, w, \overline{v}, \overline{w}$ may be replaced, respectively, by the four functions

$$v - \sum_{i=1}^{m} a_i v_i\ ,\ w - \sum_{j=1}^{n} b_j w_j\ ,\ \overline{v} - \sum_{i=1}^{m} c_i v_i\ ,\ \overline{w} - \sum_{j=1}^{n} d_j w_j\ , \tag{3.27}$$

in (3.20), (3.21) (and in (3.23), (3.24)) , to obtain upper and lower bounds for $u(x_0, y_0, z_0)$. What is the "best possible" choice of the real numbers a_i, b_j, c_i, d_j ? Minimizing the (identical) "error terms" in (3.20) and (3.23), one obtains systems of linear equations for the "optimum values" a_i^m , b_j^n , c_i^m , d_j^n . Notice that, for example, in view of (3.8) ,

$$\begin{aligned}
&\Big(v - \sum_{i=1}^{m} a_i v_i - [w - \sum_{j=1}^{n} b_j w_j]\ ,\ v - \sum_{k=1}^{m} a_k v_k - [w - \sum_{\ell=1}^{n} b_\ell w_\ell]\Big) \\
&= \Big(v-u- \sum_{i=1}^{m} a_i v_i - [w-u - \sum_{j=1}^{n} b_j w_j],\ v-u - \sum_{k=1}^{m} a_k v_k - [w-u - \sum_{\ell=1}^{n} b_\ell w_\ell]\Big), \\
&= \Big(v-u - \sum_{i=1}^{m} a_i v_i\ ,\ v-u - \sum_{k=1}^{m} a_k v_k\Big) + \Big(w-u - \sum_{j=1}^{n} b_j w_j,\ w-u - \sum_{\ell=1}^{m} b_\ell w_\ell\Big)\ .
\end{aligned} \tag{3.28}$$

Thus the optimum values a_i^m satisfy the systems of linear equations

$$\sum_{i=1}^{m} a_i^m (v_i, v_k) = (v-u,\ v_k) = (v-w,\ v_k)\ , \tag{3.29}$$

for $k = 1, \ldots, m$ while the optimum values b_j^n satisfy the system of linear equations

$$\sum_{j=1}^{n} b_j^n (w_j,\ w_\ell) = (w-u,\ w_\ell) = (w-v,\ w_\ell)\ , \tag{3.30}$$

for $\ell = 1, \ldots, n$. Similarly, the optimum values c_i^m satisfy the system of linear equations

$$\sum_{i=1}^{n} c_i^m (v_i, v_k) = (\overline{v}-\overline{u},\ v_k) = (\overline{v}-\overline{w},\ v_k)\ , \tag{3.31}$$

for $k = 1, \ldots, m$, while the optimum values d_j^n satisfy the system of linear equations

$$\sum_{j=1}^{n} d_j^n (w_j, w_\ell) = (\overline{w} - \overline{u}, w_\ell) = (\overline{w} - \overline{v}, w_\ell) , \tag{3.32}$$

for $\ell = 1, \ldots, n$.

If, in particular, the v_i's and the w_j's are orthonormal, i.e.

$$(v_i, v_k) = \begin{cases} 1, & \text{if } i = k , \\ 0, & \text{if } i \neq k , \end{cases} \tag{3.33}$$

for $i, k = 1, \ldots, m$, and

$$(w_j, w_\ell) = \begin{cases} 1, & \text{if } j = \ell , \\ 0, & \text{if } j \neq \ell , \end{cases} \tag{3.34}$$

for $j, \ell = 1, \ldots, n$, then one has simply, from (3.29), (3.31), (3.30), and (3.32), that

$$a_k^m = (v - w, v_k) \; ; \; c_k^m = (\overline{v} - \overline{w}, v_k) , \tag{3.35}$$

for $k = 1, \ldots, m$ and

$$b_\ell^n = (w - v, w_\ell) \; ; \; d_\ell^n = (\overline{w} - \overline{v}, w_\ell) , \tag{3.36}$$

for $\ell = 1, \ldots, n$.

(g) Upper and lower bounds for the partial derivatives of u at (x_0, y_0, z_0). Let p, q, and s be non-negative integers, and suppose that the partial derivative

$\dfrac{\partial^{p+q+s} u}{\partial x_0^{\,p} \partial y_0^{\,q} \partial z_0^{\,s}} (x_0, y_0, z_0)$ exists (notice that, in general, this partial derivative need not exist, it depends upon how smooth Δu happens to be, compare (3.18)). Then, from Green's third identity (3.18) it follows that (since the single and double layer potentials over S have derivatives of all orders inside S):

$$4\pi \frac{\partial^{p+q+s} u}{\partial x_0^{\,p} \partial y_0^{\,q} \partial z_0^{\,s}} (x_0, y_0, z_0) = -(-1)^{p+q+s} \iiint_{\text{int } S} \left[\frac{\partial^{p+q+s}}{\partial x^p \partial y^p \partial z^s} \left(\frac{1}{r}\right) \right] \Delta u \, d\tau \tag{3.37}$$

$$+ \iint_S \left\{ \left[(-1)^{p+q+s} \frac{\partial^{p+q+s} \left(\frac{1}{r}\right)}{\partial x^p \partial y^p \partial z^s} \right] \frac{\partial u}{\partial n_e} - u \frac{\partial \left[(-1)^{p+q+s} \dfrac{\partial^{p+q+s} \left(\frac{1}{r}\right)}{\partial x^p \partial y^q \partial z^s} \right]}{\partial n_e} \right\} d\sigma ,$$

since $r = \sqrt{(x-x_0)^2 + (y-y_0)^2 + (z-z_0)^2}$, and, e.g.

$$\frac{\partial}{\partial x_0}\left(\frac{1}{r}\right) = -\frac{\partial}{\partial x}\left(\frac{1}{r}\right) . \tag{3.38}$$

It is now quite clear how to proceed in order to estimate $\frac{\partial^{p+q+s} u}{\partial x_0{}^p \partial y_0{}^q \partial z_0{}^s}(x_0, y_0, z_0)$ using (3.37), instead of (3.18) as was done for $u(x_0, y_0, z_0)$ in (d) and (e) of the present section. Instead of the auxiliary function $\bar{u}$ of (3.13) one considers an auxiliary function, call it $\bar{u}_{p,q,s}$, which is the solution of the following boundary value problem:

$$\begin{aligned} \Delta \bar{u}_{p,q,s} &= 0 , && \text{on int } S , \\ \bar{u}_{p,q,s} &= -(-1)^{p+q+s} \frac{\partial^{p+q+s}\left(\frac{1}{r}\right)}{\partial x^p \partial y^q \partial z^s} , && \text{on } S , \end{aligned} \tag{3.39}$$

where $r = \sqrt{(x-x_0)^2 + (y-y_0)^2 + (z-z_0)^2}$ denotes the Euclidean distance from the given point (x_0, y_0, z_0) . It is emphasized that an explicit knowledge of the function $\bar{u}_{p,q,s}$ is not required. What is required, besides a knowledge of the two functions v and w of (3.9) and (3.10) (which are related to the function u of (3.1)), is the knowledge of two functions $\bar{v}$ and $\bar{w}_{p,q,s}$, which are related to the function $\bar{u}_{p,q,s}$ of (3.39) as follows:

$$\bar{w}_{p,q,s} = \bar{u}_{p,q,s} = -(-1)^{p+q+s} \frac{\partial^{p+q+s}\left(\frac{1}{r}\right)}{\partial x^p \partial y^q \partial z^s} , \text{ on } S , \tag{3.40}$$

and

$$\Delta \bar{v} = 0 , \qquad \text{on int } S , \tag{3.41}$$

The determination of upper and lower bounds for $\frac{\partial^{p+q+s} u}{\partial x_0{}^p \partial y_0{}^q \partial z_0{}^s}(x_0, y_0, z_0)$ is now immediate. The two pertinent (initial) inequalities (compare (3.20) and (3.23) of the present section) are

$$(w-u, \bar{w}_{p,q,s} - \bar{u}_{p,q,s})^2 \leqq (v-w, v-w)(\bar{v}-\bar{w}_{p,q,s}, \bar{v}-\bar{w}_{p,q,s}), \tag{3.42}$$

and

$$(v-u, \bar{v}-\bar{u}_{p,q,s})^2 \leqq (v-w, v-w)(\bar{v}-\bar{w}_{p,q,s}, \bar{v}-\bar{w}_{p,q,s}) . \tag{3.43}$$

(h) An algorithm for the computation of the capacity, based on the determination of upper and lower bounds for the value of a solution of an interior Dirichlet problem at a given point. It was indicated before that the capacity C of the surface S is

$$C = \frac{1}{4\pi} \iiint_{\text{ext } S} |\text{grad } u|^2 \, d\tau = -\frac{1}{4\pi} \iint_S \frac{\partial u}{\partial n_e} \, d\sigma \,, \tag{3.44}$$

where the function u is the solution of the exterior Dirichlet problem:

$$\begin{aligned} \Delta u = u_{xx} + u_{yy} + u_{zz} &= 0 \,, && \text{on ext } S \,, \\ u &= 1 \,, && \text{on } S \,, \\ u(x, y, z) &= O(r^{-1}) \,, && \text{as } r \to \infty \,. \end{aligned} \tag{3.45}$$

Near infinity, the potential $u(x, y, z)$ may be expanded in the form

$$u(x, y, z) = X_0 r^{-1} + X_1 r^{-2} + X_2 r^{-3} \ldots \,, \tag{3.46}$$

where $X_0, X_1, X_2, \ldots$ are surface harmonics of degree 0, 1, 2, ... respectively. It follows from (3.44) and (3.46) that

$$C = -\frac{1}{4\pi} \iint_S \frac{\partial u}{\partial n_e} \, d\sigma = X_0 \,. \tag{3.47}$$

(Notice the essential rôle played here by the boundary condition on S , (3.44), satisfied by u . The present method may be used to find upper and lower bounds for $\iint_S \frac{\partial u}{\partial n_e} d\sigma$ for the general exterior Dirichlet problem (2.1), (2.2). But when u = f on S one will not have, in general, that the Dirichlet integral of u is a known constant multiple of $\iint_S \frac{\partial u}{\partial n_e} d\sigma$.)

Suppose now, which is really not an essential restriction, that the origin 0 = (0, 0, 0) lies inside the surface S . As is well known, by a Kelvin inversion, with pole at the origin, with respect to the unit sphere (see O. D. Kellogg [1, p. 232]), the exterior Dirichlet problem (3.45) is equivalent to the following interior Dirichlet problem:

$$\begin{aligned} \Delta U &= 0 \,, && \text{on int } S^* \,, \\ u &= \frac{1}{r} = \frac{1}{\sqrt{x^2 + y^2 + z^2}} \,, && \text{on } S^* \,, \end{aligned} \tag{3.48}$$

where S^* is the surface obtained from S by Kelvin inversion, and the function $U(x, y, z)$ is defined in terms of $u(x, y, z)$ by

$$U(x,y,z) = \frac{1}{r} u\left(\frac{x}{r^2}, \frac{y}{r^2}, \frac{z}{r^2}\right) , \tag{3.49}$$

with $r = \sqrt{x^2 + y^2 + z^2}$, whenever the point $\left(\frac{x}{r^2}, \frac{y}{r^2}, \frac{z}{r^2}\right)$ is in ext S .

The considerations of the present section are applicable, as a particular case, to the interior Dirichlet problem (3.48), for finding upper and lower bounds for the value of U at any point interior to S^* . But from (3.46) and (3.49) it follows, for the value of U at the origin, that

$$U(0,0,0) = C , \tag{3.50}$$

thus yielding an algorithm for the computation of upper and lower bounds for the capacity. It would appear to be of some interest to actually carry out numerical computations, by this method, for the capacity of a cube.

§4. Upper and lower bounds for the capacity of surfaces which are star shaped with respect to a point

(a) A new formula for the capacity C . A new formula for the capacity C , which was given by L. E. Payne and H. F. Weinberger [1, p. 293] will now be derived. In the notation of (h) of section 3, one has

$$u(x,y,z) = C/r + O(r^{-2}) , \qquad \text{as } r \to \infty , \tag{4.1}$$

where the capacity C is given by

$$C = \frac{1}{4\pi} \iiint_{\text{ext } S} |\text{grad } u|^2 d\tau = -\frac{1}{4\pi} \iint_S u \frac{\partial u}{\partial n_e} d\sigma = -\frac{1}{4\pi} \iint_S \frac{\partial u}{\partial n_e} d\sigma . \tag{4.2}$$

Now, from (4.1)

$$\frac{\partial u}{\partial r} = - Cr^{-2} + O(r^{-3}) , \qquad \text{as } r \to \infty , \tag{4.3}$$

and

$$r\frac{\partial u}{\partial r} = - Cr^{-1} + O(r^{-2}) , \qquad \text{as } r \to \infty , \tag{4.4}$$

Further, since $\Delta u = 0$, on ext S , and $r\frac{\partial u}{\partial r} = x\frac{\partial u}{\partial x} + y\frac{\partial u}{\partial y} + z\frac{\partial u}{\partial z}$, it is true that

$$\Delta\, r\frac{\partial u}{\partial r} = 0 , \qquad \text{on ext } S . \tag{4.5}$$

Let Σ be a "large sphere", with center at the origin, and containing the surface S in its interior. Green's (second) identity, applied to the domain bounded internally by S and externally by Σ , yields

$$\iint_{S+\Sigma} u \frac{\partial}{\partial n_e}\left(r \frac{\partial u}{\partial r}\right) d\sigma - \iint_{S+\Sigma} r \frac{\partial u}{\partial r} \frac{\partial u}{\partial n_e} d\sigma = \iiint_{(\mathrm{int}\Sigma)-(S+\mathrm{int}\, S)} \left[u \Delta\left(r \frac{\partial u}{\partial r}\right) - r \frac{\partial u}{\partial r} \Delta u\right] d\tau = 0, \quad (4.6)$$

where n_e is the unit outward normal relative to the domain in question. Letting the radius of Σ increase indefinitely, and using the boundary condition $u = 1$ on S, (4.6) yields

$$\iint_S \frac{\partial}{\partial n_e}\left(r \frac{\partial u}{\partial r}\right) d\sigma = \iint_S r \frac{\partial u}{\partial r} \frac{\partial u}{\partial n_e} d\sigma , \quad (4.7)$$

where n_e is now the unit outward normal to the surface S. In view of (4.5) and (4.4), one then obtains, using again a "large sphere" Σ, that the integral on the left hand side of (4.7) has the value $-4\pi C$, since

$$-\iint_S \frac{\partial}{\partial n_e}\left(r \frac{\partial u}{\partial r}\right) d\sigma + \iint_\Sigma \frac{\partial}{\partial n_e}\left(r \frac{\partial u}{\partial r}\right) d\sigma = \iiint_{(\mathrm{int}\Sigma)-(S+\mathrm{int}\, S)} \Delta\left(r \frac{\partial u}{\partial r}\right) d\tau = 0 , \quad (4.8)$$

where, in each case, n_e is the unit outward normal to the surface in question. Moreover, the integrand on the right hand side of (4.7) is

$$r \frac{\partial u}{\partial r} \frac{\partial u}{\partial n_e} = r[(\mathrm{grad}\, u)\cdot(\mathrm{grad}\, r)][(\mathrm{grad}\, u)\cdot n_e] . \quad (4.9)$$

But S is a level surface of u, therefore

$$\mathrm{grad}\, u = [(\mathrm{grad}\, u)\cdot n_e] n_e = \frac{\partial u}{\partial n_e} n_e , \quad (4.10)$$

on S. Consequently, (4.9) may be rewritten

$$\begin{aligned} r \frac{\partial u}{\partial r} \frac{\partial u}{\partial n_e} &= r[(\mathrm{grad}\, u)\cdot n_e][n_e \cdot \mathrm{grad}\, r][(\mathrm{grad}\, u)\cdot n_e] , \\ &= r[n_e \cdot \mathrm{grad}\, r][(\mathrm{grad}\, u)\cdot n_e]^2 , \quad (4.11) \\ &= r \frac{\partial r}{\partial n_e} \left(\frac{\partial u}{\partial n_e}\right)^2 . \end{aligned}$$

The final result obtained from (4.7) is the following formula for the capacity C:

$$C = \frac{1}{4\pi} \iint_S r \frac{\partial r}{\partial n_e} \left(\frac{\partial u}{\partial n_e}\right)^2 d\sigma = \frac{1}{4\pi} \iint_S h \left(\frac{\partial u}{\partial n_e}\right)^2 d\sigma , \quad (4.12)$$

where, by definition

$$h \equiv r\frac{\partial r}{\partial n_e} = r\,[n_e \cdot \text{grad } r] = \frac{\partial}{\partial n_e}(\tfrac{1}{2}r^2) \ . \tag{4.13}$$

(b) A variational principle for the capacity of a star shaped surface S . As a first application of formula (4.12), suppose that the surface S is a star shaped with respect to the origin, i.e. that the origin is in the interior of S and that every ray issuing from the origin intersects the surface S in exactly one point. Then $[n_e \cdot \text{grad } r] > 0$ at each point of S , and hence, from (4.13)

$$h > 0 \ , \qquad \text{on } S \ . \tag{4.14}$$

The inequality (4.14) is essential in all the subsequent considerations, since it will enable one to apply Schwarz's inequality, as will be seen immediately.

Let v be any non-zero function, defined on $S + \text{ext } S$, harmonic on ext S , and regular at ∞ (i.e., $v = O(r^{-1})$ as $r \to \infty$). Then, if u is the solution of the boundary value problem (3.45), Green's (second) identity yields:

$$\iint_S v\frac{\partial u}{\partial n_e}\,d\sigma = \iint_S u\frac{\partial v}{\partial n_e}\,d\sigma = \iint_S \frac{\partial v}{\partial n_e}\,d\sigma \ . \tag{4.15}$$

But, using (4.14), from Schwarz's inequality:

$$\left(\iint_S FG\,d\sigma\right)^2 \leq \left(\iint_S F^2 d\sigma\right)\left(\iint_S G^2 d\sigma\right) , \tag{4.16}$$

one has that

$$\left[\iint_S v\frac{\partial v}{\partial n_e}\,d\sigma\right]^2 = \left[\iint_S \left(\frac{v}{\sqrt{h}}\right)\left(\sqrt{h}\,\frac{\partial u}{\partial n_e}\right)d\sigma\right]^2 \leq \left(\iint_S h^{-1}v^2\,d\sigma\right)\left(\iint_S h\left(\frac{\partial u}{\partial n_e}\right)^2 d\sigma\right) \tag{4.17}$$

where the function h is given by (4.13). The importance of the formula (4.12) for the capacity C is now clear from the last term occurring on the extreme right hand side of (4.17). From (4.15) and (4.17), together with the formula (4.12) for the capacity C , it follows that

$$\frac{\left(\iint_S \frac{\partial v}{\partial n_e}\,d\sigma\right)^2}{\iint_S h^{-1}v^2\,d\sigma} \leq 4\pi C \ . \tag{4.18}$$

In view of (4.12), inequality (4.18), in words, states that the maximum of the quotient

$$\frac{1}{4\pi}\ \frac{\left(\iint_S \frac{\partial v}{\partial n_e}\, d\sigma\right)^2}{\iint_S h^{-1} v^2\, d\sigma}\ , \tag{4.19}$$

over the class of functions v harmonic on ext S and regular at ∞, is precisely the capacity C of the surface S. (Inequality (4.19) is to be compared with inequality (2.24) of item (e) of section 2, the "Trefftz lower bound".)

A simple consequence of (4.18) is of some interest. Since the function u is itself an admissible function, one may take $v = u$ in (4.18). The result is, from (4.12) and (compare (4.2))

$$4\pi C = -\iint_S \frac{\partial u}{\partial n_e}\, d\sigma\ , \tag{4.20}$$

that

$$\frac{[4\pi C]^2}{\iint_S h^{-1}\, d\sigma} \leqq 4\pi C\ ; \tag{4.21}$$

i.e.

$$4\pi C \leq \iint_S h^{-1} d\sigma\ . \tag{4.22}$$

This upper bound for the capacity C given by (4.22) occurs already in G. Pólya and G. Szegö [1, p. 68, eq. (5)].

(c) Upper and lower bounds for the capacity of a star shaped surface S. A direct derivation of an algorithm for the computation of the capacity, which was first given by L. E. Payne and H. F. Weinberger [1, pp. 293-295] as an application of their formula (4.12) for the capacity, will now be presented.

Let ϕ and ψ be functions defined on S + ext S, harmonic on ext S, and regular at ∞. In view of Green's identity one has that (compare (4.2)):

$$\begin{aligned}\iint_S (u-\phi)\left(\frac{\partial u}{\partial n_e} - h^{-1}\psi\right) d\sigma &= \iint_S u\frac{\partial u}{\partial n_e} d\sigma - \iint_S \phi\frac{\partial u}{\partial n_e} d\sigma - \iint_S u h^{-1}\psi d\sigma + \iint_S \phi h^{-1}\psi d\sigma\ ,\\ &= \iint_S \frac{\partial u}{\partial n_e} d\sigma - \iint_S u \frac{\partial \phi}{\partial n_e} d\sigma + \iint_S h^{-1}(1-\phi)\psi d\sigma\ , \qquad (4.23)\\ &= -4\pi C - \iint_S \frac{\partial \phi}{\partial n_e} d\sigma + \iint_S h^{-1}(1-\phi)\psi d\sigma\ .\end{aligned}$$

But, from Schwarz's inequality (4.16) one has that

$$\left[\iint_S (u-\phi)\left(\frac{\partial u}{\partial n_e} - h^{-1}\psi\right)d\sigma\right]^2 = \left[\iint_S \left(\frac{u-\phi}{\sqrt{h}}\right)\sqrt{h}\left(\frac{\partial u}{\partial n_e} - h^{-1}\psi\right)d\sigma\right]^2 \leq \left(\iint_S h\left(\frac{\partial u}{\partial n_e} - h^{-1}\psi\right)^2 d\sigma\right)\left(\iint_S h^{-1}(1-\phi)^2 d\sigma\right), \tag{4.24}$$

since $u = 1$ on S. It will now be shown that, on account of (4.23) and (4.12), inequality (4.24) furnishes upper and lower bounds for C in terms of the harmonic functions ϕ and ψ. Because, using (4.23) and (4.12), plus

$$\iint_S \frac{\partial u}{\partial n_e}\psi\, d\sigma = \iint_S u\frac{\partial \psi}{\partial n_e}d\sigma = \iint_S \frac{\partial \psi}{\partial n_e}d\sigma \quad , \tag{4.25}$$

the inequality (4.24) may be rewritten

$$\left[4\pi C + \iint_S \frac{\partial \phi}{\partial n_e}d\sigma - \iint_S h^{-1}(1-\phi)\psi\, d\sigma\right]^2 \leq \left[4\pi C - 2\iint_S \frac{\partial \psi}{\partial n_e}d\sigma + \iint_S h^{-1}\psi^2 d\sigma\right]\left[\iint_S h^{-1}(1-\phi)^2 d\sigma\right], \tag{4.26}$$

i.e.

$$(4\pi C)^2 + (4\pi C)\left[2\left(\iint_S \frac{\partial \phi}{\partial n_e}d\sigma - \iint_S h^{-1}(1-\phi)\psi d\sigma\right) - \iint_S h^{-1}(1-\phi)^2 d\sigma\right] \tag{4.27}$$

$$\leq -\left(\iint_S \frac{\partial \phi}{\partial n_e}d\sigma - \iint_S h^{-1}(1-\phi)\psi d\sigma\right)^2 + \left(-2\iint_S \frac{\partial \psi}{\partial n_e}d\sigma + \iint_S h^{-1}\psi^2 d\sigma\right)\left(\iint_S h^{-1}(1-\phi)^2 d\sigma\right).$$

"Completing the square" on the left hand side of (4.27) yields finally the desired result:

$$\left[4\pi C + \left(\iint_S \frac{\partial \phi}{\partial n_e}d\sigma - \iint_S h^{-1}(1-\phi)\psi d\sigma\right) - \tfrac{1}{2}\iint_S h^{-1}(1-\phi)^2 d\sigma\right]^2 \tag{4.28}$$

$$\leq \tfrac{1}{4}\left(\iint_S h^{-1}(1-\phi)^2 d\sigma\right)\left(\iint_S h^{-1}(1-\phi)^2 d\sigma - 4\left[\iint_S \frac{\partial \phi}{\partial n_e}d\sigma - \iint_S h^{-1}(1-\phi)\psi d\sigma\right]\right.$$

$$\left. + 4\left[-2\iint_S \frac{\partial \psi}{\partial n_e}d\sigma + \iint_S h^{-1}\psi^2 d\sigma\right]\right).$$

Now, let m be a positive integer, and $v_1, \ldots, v_m$ be m linearly independent functions, defined on S + ext S, harmonic on ext S, and regular at ∞. Then the functions ϕ and ψ appearing in (4.24) may be chosen to be

$$\phi = \sum_{i=1}^{m} a_i v_i \quad , \qquad \psi = \sum_{j=1}^{m} b_j v_j \quad ,$$

with real coefficients a_i and b_j.

Taking (4.23) into account, the resulting inequality is

$$\left[4\pi C + \iint_S \frac{\partial\left(\sum_{i=1}^{n} a_i v_i\right)}{\partial n_e} d\sigma - \iint_S h^{-1}\left(1-\sum_{i=1}^{m} a_i v_i\right)\left(\sum_{j=1}^{m} b_j v_j\right) d\sigma\right]^2 \tag{4.29}$$

$$\leq \left[\iint_S h^{-1}\left(1-\sum_{i=1}^{m} a_i v_i\right)^2 d\sigma\right]\left[\iint_S h\left(\frac{\partial u}{\partial n_e} - h^{-1}\sum_{j=1}^{m} b_j v_j\right)^2 d\sigma\right].$$

Regarding the right hand side of (4.29) as an "error term", the a_i's and the b_j's may now be chosen so as to minimize the factors on the right hand side of (4.29). The "optimum" values of the a_i's (denote them by a_i^m) will satisfy the system of linear equations

$$\iint_S h^{-1}\left(1 - \sum_{i=1}^{m} a_i^m v_i\right) v_k \, d\sigma = 0 , \tag{4.30}$$

for $k = 1,\ldots,m$, that is

$$\sum_{i=1}^{m} a_i^m \iint_S h^{-1} v_i v_k \, d\sigma = \iint_S h^{-1} v_k \, d\sigma , \tag{4.31}$$

for $k = 1,\ldots,m$. The optimum values of the b_j's (denote them by b_j^m) will satisfy the system of linear equations

$$\iint_S h\left(\frac{\partial u}{\partial n_e} - h^{-1}\sum_{j=1}^{m} b_j^m v_j\right)(h^{-1} v_k) d\sigma = 0 , \tag{4.32}$$

for $k = 1,\ldots,m$, that is

$$\sum_{j=1}^{m} b_j^m \iint_S h^{-1} v_j v_k d\sigma = \iint_S v_k \frac{\partial u}{\partial n_e} d\sigma = \iint_S \frac{\partial v_k}{\partial n_e} d\sigma , \tag{4.33}$$

for $k = 1,\ldots, m$. With these optimum values of the a_i's and the b_j's one has

$$\iint_S h^{-1}\left(1-\sum_{i=1}^{m} a_i^m v_i\right)^2 d\sigma = \iint_S h^{-1}\left(1-\sum_{i=1}^{m} a_i^m v_i\right) d\sigma = \iint_S h^{-1}\left[1-\left(\sum_{i=1}^{m} a_i^m v_i\right)^2\right] d\sigma, \tag{4.34}$$

and

$$\iint_S h\left(\frac{\partial u}{\partial n_e} - h^{-1}\sum_{j=1}^m b_j^m v_j\right)^2 d\sigma = \iint_S h\left(\frac{\partial u}{\partial n_e}\right)^2 d\sigma - \sum_{j=1}^m b_j^m \iint_S u \frac{\partial v_j}{\partial n_e} d\sigma \ , \tag{4.35}$$

$$= \iint_S h\left(\frac{\partial u}{\partial n_e}\right)^2 d\sigma - \iint_S h^{-1}\left(\sum_{j=1}^m b_j^m v_j\right)^2 d\sigma \ .$$

Using (4.34) and (4.35), inequality (4.29) becomes (notice that the last term inside the square bracket on the left hand side of (4.29) is zero, by virtue of the system of linear equations (4.30) for the a_i^m):

$$[4\pi C + \sum_{i=1}^m a_i^m \iint_S \frac{\partial v_i}{\partial n_e} d\sigma]^2 \tag{4.36}$$

$$\leq \left[\iint_S h^{-1} d\sigma - \sum_{i=1}^m a_i^m \iint_S h^{-1} v_i d\sigma\right]\left[4\pi C - \sum_{j=1}^m b_j^m \iint_S \frac{\partial v_j}{\partial n_e} d\sigma\right],$$

from which follows (by the same "completing the square" procedure just used in deriving (4.28) from (4.26)) the final result:

$$\left[4\pi C + \sum_{i=1}^m a_i^m \iint_S \frac{\partial v_i}{\partial n_e} d\sigma - \frac{1}{2}\left(\iint_S h^{-1} d\sigma - \sum_{i=1}^m a_i^m \iint_S h^{-1} v_i \, d\sigma\right)\right]^2 \tag{4.37}$$

$$\leq \frac{1}{4}\left[\iint_S h^{-1} d\sigma - \sum_{i=1}^m a_i^m \iint_S h^{-1} v_i d\sigma\right]\left[\left(\iint_S h^{-1} d\sigma - \sum_{i=1}^m a_i^m \iint_S h^{-1} v_i d\sigma\right) - 4\left(\sum_{i=1}^m a_i^m \iint_S \frac{\partial v_i}{\partial n_e} d\sigma + \sum_{j=1}^m b_j^m \iint_S \frac{\partial v_j}{\partial n_e} d\sigma\right)\right]$$

The final (optimum) inequality (4.37) is of some interest when only one harmonic function is used. Writing $m = 1$, and also writing v instead of v_1, one has from (4.31) that

$$a_1' = \frac{\iint_S h^{-1} v \, d\sigma}{\iint_S h^{-1} v^2 \, d\sigma} \ ; \tag{4.38}$$

and from (4.33) that

$$b_1' = \frac{\iint_S \frac{\partial v}{\partial n_e} d\sigma}{\iint_S h^{-1} v^2 d\sigma} \ . \tag{4.39}$$

Replacing these values in (4.37) yields

$$\left[4\pi C+\frac{\left(\iint_S h^{-1}v\,d\sigma\right)\left(\iint_S \frac{\partial v}{\partial n_e}\,d\sigma\right)}{\iint_S h^{-1}v^2\,d\sigma}-\frac{1}{2}\left\{\iint_S h^{-1}\,d\sigma-\frac{\left(\iint_S h^{-1}v\,d\sigma\right)^2}{\iint_S h^{-1}v^2\,d\sigma}\right\}\right]^2 \tag{4.40}$$

$$\leq \frac{1}{4}\left[\iint_S h^{-1}\,d\sigma-\frac{\left(\iint_S h^{-1}v\,d\sigma\right)^2}{\iint_S h^{-1}v^2\,d\sigma}\right]\left[\left\{\iint_S h^{-1}\,d\sigma-\frac{\left(\iint_S h^{-1}v\,d\sigma\right)^2}{\iint_S h^{-1}v^2\,d\sigma}\right\}-4\left(\iint_S \frac{\partial v}{\partial n_e}\,d\sigma\right)\left(\frac{\iint_S h^{-1}v\,d\sigma+\iint_S \frac{\partial v}{\partial n_e}\,d\sigma}{\iint_S h^{-1}v^2\,d\sigma}\right)\right]$$

(d) <u>Upper and lower bounds for the capacity of a cube</u>. Consider the special case of the cube, i.e. when the surface S is a cube with center at the origin, and edge length a. G. Pólya and G. Szegö [1, p. 76], obtained that

$$0.632\,a < C < 0.71055\,a\ , \tag{4.41}$$

where C denotes the capacity of the cube. J. McMahon [1], employing a method suggested by J. L. Synge, gave the lower bound

$$0.639\,a < C\ . \tag{4.42}$$

L. Daboni [1], following a suggestion of Gaetano Fichera, obtained

$$0.654\,a < C < 0.676\,a\ . \tag{4.43}$$

W. Gross [1], obtained approximations to C, but was unable to give rigorous bounds, through lack of the formula (4.12) for C. After obtaining (4.12), L. E. Payne and H. F. Weinberger [1], essentially by employing the inequality (4.37), plus the computations of W. Gross [1], arrived at the result

$$0.627\,a < C < 0.668\,a\ ; \tag{4.44}$$

while by employing the inequality (4.40), plus L. Daboni's [1] "third" harmonic function, they found that

$$0.653\,a < C < 0.672\,a\ . \tag{4.45}$$

Thus the best inequality that can be written at present is

$$0.654\,a < C < 0.668\,a\ , \tag{4.46}$$

where the lower bound was given by L. Daboni [1], and the upper bound by L. E. Payne and H. F. Weinberger [1].

This research was supported by the United States Air Force through the Air Force Office of Scientific Research of the Air Research and Development Command under Contract No. AF 49(638)-228.

BIBLIOGRAPHY

Bertolini, F., 1. Sulla capacità di un condensatore sferico, Nuovo Cimento, Vol. 9, 1952.

Courant, R., 1. Variational methods for the solution of problems of equilibrium and vibrations, Bulletin of the American Mathematical Society, vol. 49, (1943), pp. 1-23.

Courant, R. and Hilbert, D., 1. Methods of mathematical physics, Vol. 1, First English edition. New York, 1953 (specially pp. 252-257).

Collatz, L., 1. Numerische Behandlung von Differentialgleichungen, second edition, Berlin, 1955.

Cooperman, P., 1. An extension of the method of Trefftz for finding local bounds on the solutions of boundary value problems, and on their derivatives, Quarterly of Applied Mathematics, Vol. 10, 1952, pp. 359-373.

Diaz, J. B., 1. Upper and lower bounds for quadratic functionals, Proceedings of the Symposium on Spectral Theory and Differential Problems, Oklahoma Agricultural and Mechanical College, Stillwater, Oklahoma, 1951, pp. 279-289.

2. Upper and lower bounds for quadratic functionals, Collectanea Mathematica, Seminario Matemático de Barcelona, Vol. 4, 1951, pp. 1-50.

3. On the estimation of torsional rigidity and other physical quantities, Proceedings of the First National Congress of Applied Mechanics, American Society of Mechanical Engineers, 1952, pp. 259-263.

Diaz, J. B. and Greenberg, H. J., 1. Upper and lower bounds for the solution of the first biharmonic boundary value problem, Journal of Mathematics and Physics, Vol. 27, 1948, pp. 193-201.

2. Upper and lower bounds for the solution of the first boundary value problem of elasticity, Quarterly of Applied Mathematics, Vol. 6, 1948, pp. 326-331.

Diaz, J. B. and Weinstein, A., 1. Schwarz' inequality and the methods of Rayleigh-Ritz and Trefftz, Journal of Mathematics and Physics, Vol. 26, 1947, pp. 133-136.

2. The torsional rigidity and variational methods, American Journal of Mathematics, Vol. 70, 1948, pp. 107-116.

Daboni, L., 1. Applicazione al caso del cubo di un metodo per ecceso e per difetto della capacità elettrostatica di un conduttore, Rendiconti Accademia Nazionale dei Lincei, ser. VIII, Vol. XIV, 1953, pp. 461-466.

2. Capacità elettrostatica di un condensatore sferico con apertura circolare, Atti della Accademia delle Scienze di Torino, Vol. 89, 1954-55, 1-10.

Duffin, R.J., 1. Distributed and lumped networks, Technical Report No. 37, Research Project: Mathematical Analysis of Electrical and Mechanical Systems, Department of Mathematics, Carnegie Institute of Technology, February 1, 1958.

Fichera, Gaetano, 1. Sulla maggiorazione dell'errore di approssimazione nei procedimenti di integrazione numerica delle equazioni della Fisica Matematica, Rendiconti dell'Accademia delle Scienze e Matematiche di Napoli, Ser 4, Vol. XVII, 1950, pp. 1-8.

2. Risultati concernenti la risoluzione delle equazioni funzionali dovuti all'Istituto Nazionale per le applicazioni del Calcolo, Memorie dell'Accademia Nazionale dei Lincei, serie VIII, Vol. 3, 1950, pp. 3-81.

3. On some general integration methods employed in connection with linear differential equations, Journal of Mathematics and Physics, Vol. 29, 1950, pp. 59-68.

4. Methods of linear functional analysis in mathematical physics, Proceedings of the International Congress of Mathematicians, Amsterdam, 1954, Vol. III, 216-228.

5. Formule di maggiorazione connesse ad una classe di trasformazioni lineari, Annali di Matematica, serie IV, Vol. 36, 1954, pp. 273-296.

Friedrichs, K.O., 1. Ein Verfahren der Variationsrechnung das Minimum eines Integrals als das Maximum eines anderen Ausdruckes darzustellen, Göttingen Nachrichten, 1929, 13-20.

2. Die Ramdwert und Eigenwert Probleme aus der Theorie der Elastischen Platten (Anwendung der Direkten Methoden der Variationsrechnung), Mathematische Annalen, Vol. 98, 1927, 205-247.

Funk, P. and Berger, E., 1. Eingrenzung für die grösste Durchbiegung einer gleichmàssig belasteten eigespannten quadratischen Plätte, Federhofer-Girkman Festschrift, F. Deuticke, Vienna, 1950, 199-204.

Golomb, M. and Weinberger, H.F., 1. Optimal approximation and error bounds, Proceedings of a Symposium on Numerical Approximation, conducted by the Mathematics Research Center, U. S. Army, University of Wisconsin, Madison, April 21-23, 1958, University of Wisconsin Press, Madison, 1959, pp. 117-191.

Gross, W., 1. Sul calcolo della capacità elettrostatica di un conduttore, Rend. Accad. Naz. Lincei, serie VIII, Vol. XII, 1952, pp. 496-506.

Greenberg, H. J., 1. The determination of upper and lower bounds for the solutions of the Dirichlet problem, Journal of Mathematics and Physics, Vol. 27, 1948, 161-182.

Greenberg, H. J. and Prager, W., 1. Direct determination of bending and twisting moments in thin elastic plates, American Journal of Mathematics, vol. 70, 1948, pp. 749-763.

Kellogg, O. D., 1. Foundations of Potential Theory, Berlin, Springer, 1929.

Kato, Tosio, 1. On some approximate methods concerning the operators T^*T, Mathematische Annalen, Vol. 126, 1953, 253-262.

Maple, C. G., 1. The Dirichlet Problem: Bounds at a point for the solution and its derivatives, Quarterly of Applied Mathematics, 8, 1950, 213-228.

Mihlin, S. G., 1. Direct methods in mathematical physics, Moscow, 1950.

2. The problem of the minimum of a quadratic functional, Moscow, 1952.

McMahon, J., 1. Lower bounds for the electrostatic capacity of a cube, Proceedings of the Royal Irish Academy, 55A, 1953, 133-167.

Nehari, Z., 1. On the numerical solution of the Dirichlet problem, Proceedings of the conference on differential equations (dedicated to A. Weinstein) pp. 157-178, University of Maryland Book Store, College Park, Maryland, 1956.

Nicolovius, R., 1. Abschätzung der Lösung der ersten Platten-Randwertaufgabe nach der Methode von Maple-Synge, Zeitschrift für Angenwandte Mathematik und Mechanik, vol. 37, 1957, 344-349.

2. Beiträge zur Diaz-Greenberg-Methode, Zeitschrift für Angewandte Mathematik und Mechanik, Vol. 37, 1957, 449-457.

Payne, L. and Weinberger, H. F., 1. New bounds in harmonic and biharmonic problems, Journal of Mathematics and Physics, Vol. 33, 1955, 291-307.

2. New bounds for solutions of second order elliptic partial differential equations, Pacific Journal of Mathematics, Vol. 8, 1958, 551-573.

Picone, M. and Fichera, G., 1. Neue Funktionalanalytische Grundlagen für die Existenzprobleme und Losungsmethoden von Systemen

Linearer Partieller Differentialgleichungen, Monatshefte fur Mathematik, 1950.

Pólya, G., 1. Estimating electrostatic capacity, American Mathematical Monthly, Vol. 54, 1947, 201-206.

Pólya, G. and Szegö, G., 1. Isoperimetric inequalities in mathematical physics, Annals of Mathematics Studies, no. 27, Princeton University Press, 1951 (see also the book review in Bulletin of the American Mathematical Society, Vol. 59, 1953, pp. 588-602).

Pólya, G. and Weinstein, A., 1. On the torsional rigidity of multiply connected cross-sections, Annals of Mathematics, (2) 52, 1950, 154-163.

Prager, W. and Synge, J.L., 1. Approximations in elasticity based on the concept of function space, Quarterly of Applied Mathematics, Vol. 5, 1947, 241-269.

Reitan, D.K. and Higgins, T.J., 1. Calculation of the electrical capacitance of a cube, Journal of Applied Physics, Vol. 22, 1951, 223-226.

Rosenbloom, P.C., 1. Numerical Analysis and Partial Differential Equations, by G. E. Forsythe and P. C. Rosenbloom (Vol. 5 of Surveys in Applied Mathematics) New York, 1958 (see, in particular, pages 145-146).

Slobodyanskii, M.G., 1. Estimate of the error of the quantity sought for in the solution of linear problems by a variational method, Doklady Akademia Nauk SSSR (N.S.), 86, 1952, 243-246.

Synge, J.L., 1. The hypercircle in mathematical physics, Cambridge University Press, 1957 (see also the book review in Bulletin of the American Mathematical Society, vol. 65, 1959).

Szegö, G., 1. Chapter 17 in P. Frank and R. von Mises, Die Differentialgleichungen der Physik, Vol. I, New York, 1943.

Topolyanskii, D.B., 1. On bounds for Dirichlet's integral, Prikladnia Matematika i Mehanika, Vol. 11, 1947.

Trefftz, E., 1. Ein Gegenstuck zum Ritzchen Verfahren, Proceedings of the Second International Congress for Applied Mechanics, Zürich, 1926, pp. 131-137.

2. Konvergenz und Fehlerschàtzung beim Ritzchen Verfahren, Mathematische Annalen, Vol. 100, 1928.

Washizu, K., 1. Bounds for solutions of boundary value problems in elasticity, Journal of Mathematics and Physics, Vol. 32, 1953, pp. 117-128.

Weber, C., 1. Eigengrenzung von Verschiebungen mit Hilfe der

Minimalsàtze, Zeitschrift fur Angewandte Mathematik und Mechanik, 22, 1942, 126-130.

Weinberger, H. F., 1. Upper and lower bounds for torsional rigidity, Journal of Mathematics and Physics, Vol. 32, 1953, 54-62.

Weinstein, A., 1. New methods for the estimation of the torsional rigidity, Proceedings of the Third Symposium in Applied Mathematics of the American Mathematical Society (1949). McGraw-Hill, New York (1950), pp. 141-161.

JOHANN SCHRÖDER

Error Estimates for Boundary Value Problems Using Fixed-Point Theorems

Let a differential equation

$$M[u] = f_0(x, u) \qquad \text{on } \mathfrak{B} \qquad (0.1a)$$

and boundary conditions

$$U_i[u] = f_i(x, u) \qquad \text{on } \Gamma_i \quad (i = 1, 2, \ldots) , \qquad (0.1b)$$

$$V_j[u] = \delta_j(x) \qquad \text{on } \Gamma^j \quad (j = 1, 2, \ldots) \qquad (0.1c)$$

be given, where $\mathfrak{B}$ denotes a domain of the p-dimensional Euclidean space with points x , and Γ_i and Γ^j are parts of the boundary Γ of $\mathfrak{B}$. M and the U and V denote formal linear differential operators. The functions $f_i(x, y)$ may depend on y in a nonlinear way. The δ_j are defined on Γ^j . All functions are assumed to be real.

In this paper we prove error estimates of the type

$$|u^*(x) - u_0(x)| \leqq \eta(x) ,$$

where $u^*(x)$ denotes an exact solution of (0.1) and $u_0(x)$ is an approximation for it. $u_0(x)$ must satisfy only the boundary conditions (0.1c) exactly. One gets the error bound $\eta(x)$ by solving a so-called comparison problem, which contains inequalities in place of the equations (0.1a), (0.1b), and starts from the defects of these equations corresponding to $u_0(x)$. The existence of u^* is also proved.

We suggest a way to evaluate $u_0(x)$ and $\eta(x)$ numerically. This uses the difference method and linear approximation methods, and seems to be suitable for electronic computers. In this way one need not solve any differential equation exactly.

We write the given problem as an equation $u = Tu$ in a linear topological space $\mathfrak{R}$. For our investigations we need three essential assumptions: A fixed-point theorem must be true for the operator T ; the linear operators M , U and V must have some monotonic character, and there must exist majorants $\tilde{f}_i(x, y)$ of the functions $f_i(x, y)$. In most cases it is easy to find these majorants. In No. 2 we give two examples of boundary value problems, for which the other two assumptions are also satisfied.

To explain the suggested method there are two simple numerical examples in No. 3, an ordinary and a partial differential equation.

§1. General Results

1.1. The functions $f_i(x, y)$ and their derivatives $f_{i_y}(x, y)$ are to be continuous in points (x, y) with

$$x \in \begin{cases} \overline{\mathfrak{B}} = \mathfrak{B} + \Gamma & \text{for } i = 0 \\ \Gamma_i & \text{for } i \neq 0 \end{cases} \quad \text{and} \quad \phi(x) \underset{(=)}{<} y \underset{(=)}{<} \psi(x) \quad . \qquad (1.1)$$

$\phi(x)$ and $\psi(x)$ need not be finite. Let $\mathfrak{G}$ be the set of points with

$$x \in \overline{\mathfrak{B}} \;, \; \phi(x) \underset{(=)}{<} y \underset{(=)}{<} \psi(x) \quad .$$

If $\mathfrak{M}$ is a linear set of functions u, we denote by $\dot{\mathfrak{M}}$ the subset of all $u \in \mathfrak{M}$ with $(x, u(x)) \in \mathfrak{G}$ for $x \in \overline{\mathfrak{B}}$.

We ask for solutions $u^* \in \dot{\mathfrak{A}}$ of the given problem, where $\mathfrak{A}$ is a linear set of functions u with properties depending on the special problem. $\mathfrak{A}$ shall be a part of a linear topological function-space $\mathfrak{R}$, the topological structure of which is compatible with the ordering relation $u(x) \leq v(x)$.

There shall exist a linear set $\mathfrak{C}$ with $\mathfrak{A} \subset \mathfrak{C} \subset \mathfrak{R}$, such that the problem

$$M[v] = f_0(x, u) \quad \text{on} \quad \mathfrak{B} \;,$$

$$U_i[v] = f_i(x, u) \quad \text{on} \quad \Gamma_i \quad (i=1, 2, \ldots) \;, \; V_j[u] = \delta_j \text{ on } \Gamma^j \; (j=1, 2, \ldots)$$

has a unique* solution $v \in \mathfrak{A}$, if u is a fixed but arbitrary function $\in \dot{\mathfrak{C}}$. By $\hat{T} u = v$ we define an operator $\hat{T}$ on $\hat{\mathfrak{D}} = \dot{\mathfrak{C}}$. It shall be possible to continue $\hat{T}$ to an operator T, which maps $\mathfrak{D} = \dot{\mathfrak{R}}$ in $\mathfrak{C}$. Then the given problem is equivalent with

$$u = Tu \;.$$

We suppose moreover, that $\hat{T}$ is continued to T in such a way that the following is true. If u is an element $\in \mathfrak{D}$ which is not contained in $\mathfrak{C}$, and $x \in \dot{\mathfrak{A}}$ with $x \leq u$, then there exists a sequence $\{u_n\} \subset \hat{\mathfrak{D}}$ with $x \leq u_n \leq u$ and $\lim T u_n = Tu$.

By $u_0(x) \in \mathfrak{D}$ we denote a suitably chosen approximation for a solution $u^*(x)$, which satisfies the conditions (0.1c)

$$V_j[u_0] = \delta_j \quad \text{on} \quad \Gamma^j \; (j = 1, 2, \ldots) \;.$$

For short we write

$$d_0(x) = d_0[u_0] = -M[u_0] + f_0(x, u_0)$$

and

$$d_i(x) = d_i[u_0] = -U_i[u_0] + f_i(x, u_0) \quad (i = 1, 2, \ldots) .$$

1.2. To prove the existence of a solution $u^*(x)$ and to get an error estimation we need furthermore the following three essential assumptions.

a. Each set $\mathbb{K}$, which consists of all functions u with $\Phi(x) \leq u(x) \leq \Psi(x)$ and arbitrary functions $\Phi, \Psi \in \dot{\mathfrak{A}}$, contains a solution $u^* = Tu^*$, if $T\,\mathbb{K} \subset \mathbb{K}$.

To establish whether a given operator T has this property, one will examine whether the assumptions of one of the known fixed-point theorems are satisfied.

b. It is

$$u(x) \geqq 0 \tag{1.2a}$$

if $u \in \mathfrak{A}$ and

$$\left.\begin{aligned} &M[u] \geqq \text{ on } \mathfrak{B} , \\ &U_i[u] \geqq \text{ on } \Gamma_i \ (i = 1, 2, \ldots) , \ V_j[u] = 0 \text{ on } \Gamma_j^{\,j} \ (j = 1, 2, \ldots) \end{aligned}\right\} \tag{1.2b}$$

(In [1] one finds several examples of problems with monotonic character.)

c. There are functions $\widetilde{f}_i(x, y)$ $(i = 0, 1, 2, \ldots)$, called majorants of $f_i(x, y)$, with the following properties. The function $\widetilde{f}_i(x, y)$ and its derivative $\widetilde{f}_{i_y}(x, y)$ are defined and continuous in points (x, y) with

$$x \in \begin{cases} \overline{\mathfrak{B}} & \text{for } i = 0 \\ \Gamma_i & \text{for } i \neq 0 \end{cases} \quad \text{and } 0 \leq y < \infty . \tag{1.3}$$

One has

$$\widetilde{f}_i(x, 0) \equiv 0 , \tag{1.4a}$$

$$|f_{i_y}(x, u_0(x) + z)| \leq \widetilde{f}_{i_y}(x, |z|) , \tag{1.4b}$$

insofar as the arguments are points (x, y) with (1.1) and (1.3) respectively.

1.3. If the assumptions of No. 1.1 and 1.2 are satisfied, one has the

Theorem. If there exists a function $\eta(x)$ with the following properties:

$$\eta(x) \geqq 0 \ , \tag{1.5}$$

$$|d_0[u_0]| \leqq M[\eta] - \tilde{f}_0(x,\eta) \quad \text{on } \mathfrak{B} \ , \tag{1.6a}$$

$$|d_i[u_0]| \leqq U_i[\eta] - \tilde{f}_i(x,\eta) \quad \text{on } \Gamma_i \quad (i=1,2,\ldots) \ , \tag{1.6b}$$

$$V_j[\eta] = 0 \quad \text{on } \Gamma^j \quad (j=1,2,\ldots) \ , \tag{1.6c}$$

$$\phi(x) + \eta(x) \underset{(=)}{<} u_0(x) \underset{(=)}{<} \psi(x) - \eta(x) \ , \tag{1.7}$$

the given problem has a solution $u^*(x)$ for which

$$|u^*(x) - u_0(x)| \leqq \eta(x) \ . \tag{1.8}$$

Proof. Let $\mathfrak{K}$ be the set of functions $u \in \mathfrak{R}$ with $|u-u_0| \leqq \eta$. We have $\mathfrak{K} \subset \mathfrak{D}$ as a consequence of (1.7). If $\hat{\mathfrak{D}} = \mathfrak{D}$, then it follows from (1.4) and (1.6) for $u \in \mathfrak{K}$:

$$\begin{aligned}
|M[Tu-u_0]| &\leqq |M[Tu] - M[Tu_0]| + |M[Tu_0] - M[u_0]| \\
&= |f_0(x,u) - f_0(x,u_0)| + |f_0(x,u_0) - M[u_0]| \\
&\leqq \int_0^1 |f_{0_y}(x, u_0 + t(u-u_0))| \, |u-u_0| \, dt + |d_0[u_0]| \\
&\leqq \int_0^1 \tilde{f}_{0_y}(x, t|u-u_0|) \, |u-u_0| \, dt + |d_0[u_0]| \\
&= \tilde{f}_0(x, |u-u_0|) + |d_0[u_0]| \leqq \tilde{f}_0(x,\eta) + |d_0[u_0]|
\end{aligned}$$

and in the same way

$$|U_i[Tu-u_0]| \leqq U_i[\eta] \qquad (i = 1,2,\ldots)$$

and

$$V_j[Tu-u_0] = V_j[\eta] = 0 \qquad (j = 1,2,\ldots).$$

Because of (1.2) one gets $|Tu-u_0| \leqq \eta$, hence $T\,\mathfrak{K} \subset \mathfrak{K}$. Therefore $\mathfrak{K} \subset \mathfrak{D}$ contains a solution $u^* = Tu^*$. If $\hat{\mathfrak{D}} \neq \mathfrak{D}$, one also gets $|Tu-u_0| \leqq \eta$ for $u \in \mathfrak{K}$, because there exists for each $u \in \mathfrak{D} \cap \mathfrak{K}$ a sequence $\{u_n\} \subset \hat{\mathfrak{D}} \cap \mathfrak{K}$ $(n = 1,2,3,\ldots)$ with $|\hat{T}u_n - u_0| \leqq \eta$ and $\lim Tu_n = Tu$.

A similar theorem can be proved using iteration procedures. One needs, however, the additional assumption that $f_{i_y}(x,y)$ is a monotonic increasing function of y. By this means one gets a uniqueness theorem, too. (See [6], where a special case is treated.)

Remark. In many cases one can replace (1.4b) for a certain number or several numbers $i = i_k$ by

$$f_{i_y}(x, u_0(x) + z) \leqq \tilde{f}_{i_y}(x, |z|) \quad . \tag{1.9}$$

This is possible if the assumptions a., b. of 1.2 and those of 1.1 are also satisfied with

$$\left.\begin{array}{llll} \hat{M}[u] = M[u] + C_0 u & \text{instead of} & M[u] & \text{for } i_k = 0 \\ \hat{U}_{i_k}[u] = U_{i_k}[u] + C_{i_k} u & \text{instead of} & U_{i_k}[u] & \text{for } i_k \neq 0 \end{array}\right\} \tag{1.10a}$$

and the functions

$$\hat{f}_{i_k}(x, y) = f_{i_k}(x, y) + C_{i_k} y \quad \text{instead of} \quad f_{i_k}(x, y) \tag{1.10b}$$

with arbitrary constants $C_{i_k} \geqq 0$.

This remark can be proved if the theorem is applied to the problem (0.1) modified by adding $C_{i_k} u$ on both sides of the corresponding equation, where C_{i_k} is large enough. (See [6], where a special case is treated.)

If, for example, $f_{0_y}(x, y) \leqq 0$ on $\mathfrak{G}$, (1.9) is satisfied for $i = 0$ with $\tilde{f}_0(x, y) \equiv 0$.

§2. Application of the results

In 2.1 and 2.2 we state for example two simple classes of boundary value problems, for which the assumptions of No. 1 are satisfied. In No. 2.3 we suggest a way to evaluate $u_0(x)$ and $\eta(x)$ practically.

2.1. Ordinary differential equations. We consider the problem

$$\left.\begin{array}{ll} -u'' = f(x, u) & \text{for } 0 \leqq x \leqq 1 , \\ au(0) - bu'(0) = \gamma_1(u(0)) , & cu(1) + du'(1) = \gamma_2(u(1)) \end{array}\right\} \tag{2.1}$$

with $a, b, c, d \geqq 0$, $ac + ad + bc > 0$. This can be written in the form (0.1) with

$$M[u] = -u'' , \quad f_0(x, y) = f(x, y) , \quad \mathfrak{B} = [0, 1] ,$$

$$U_1[u] = au - bu' , \quad f_1(x, y) = \gamma_1(y) , \quad \Gamma_1 = \{0\} ,$$

$$U_2[u] = cu + du' , \quad f_2(x, y) = \gamma_2(y) , \quad \Gamma_2 = \{1\} .$$

$\mathfrak{A}$ shall be the set of functions $u(x)$ which have a continuous second order derivative $u''(x)$, $\mathfrak{R}$ the Banach space of continuous functions with $\|u\| = \max |u(x)|$. One can choose $\mathfrak{C} = \mathfrak{R}$ and gets

$$Tu = g_1(x)\gamma_1(u(0)) + g_2(x)\gamma_2(u(1)) + \int_0^1 G(x,\xi) f(\xi, u(\xi)) d\xi$$

where $M[g_k] = 0$, $U_i[g_k] = \delta_{ik}$ and $G(x, \xi)$ is a Green's function.

One proves assumption a. of 1.2 to be satisfied using the fixed-point theorem of Schauder [4]. (1.2a) is a consequence of (1.2b) because the functions g_1, g_2 and G are $\geqq 0$.

All the required assumptions are also satisfied with the operators $\hat{M}[u]$, $\hat{U}_i[u]$ $(i = 1, 2)$ and the functions $\hat{f}_i(x, y)$ $(i=0, 1, 2)$ (see (1.10)). Therefore the majorants $\widetilde{f}_i(x, y)$ $(i=0, 1, 2)$ can be evaluated by (1.9).

The comparison problem is

$$|u_0'' + f(x, u_0)| \leqq -\eta'' - \widetilde{f}(x, \eta) \qquad \text{for } 0 \leqq x \leqq 1 ,$$

$$|au_0(0) - bu_0'(0)| \leqq a\eta(0) - b\eta'(0) - \widetilde{\gamma}_1(\eta(0)) ,$$

$$|cu_0(1) + du_0'(1)| \leqq c\eta(1) + d\eta'(1) - \widetilde{\gamma}_1(\eta(1))$$

with

$$\widetilde{f}(x, y) = \widetilde{f}_0(x, y) , \quad \widetilde{\gamma}_1(y) = \widetilde{f}_1(x, y) , \quad \widetilde{\gamma}_2(y) = \widetilde{f}_2(x, y) .$$

2.2. Partial differential equations. As a simple example, we consider the problem

$$\left.\begin{aligned} (M[u] =)\quad & -\Delta u = f(x, u) \quad (=f_0(x, u)) \quad \text{on } \mathfrak{B} , \\ (U_1[u] =)\quad & u = \gamma_1(x) \quad (=f_1(x, u)) \quad \text{on } \Gamma \end{aligned}\right\} \tag{2.2}$$

in the plane $(x = (x_1, x_2))$. $\mathfrak{B}$ denotes a bounded, simply connected open domain. $\gamma_1(x)$ is a given function, which is defined on Γ and does not depend on y. Γ and γ_1 shall have suitable properties. These properties are explained and the following statements are proved in [3]. The function $f(x, y)$ may have continuous first order derivatives and satisfy the conditions given above.

We ask for solutions which are continuous on $\overline{\mathfrak{B}}$ and have continuous first and second order derivatives on $\mathfrak{B}$. The set of functions with these properties will be denoted by $\mathfrak{A}$.

As $\mathfrak{R}$ we chose the Banach space of functions $u(x)$ which are continuous on $\overline{\mathfrak{B}}$ $(\|u\| = \max |u(x)|)$ and as $\mathfrak{C}$ the set of functions which are H-continuous on $\overline{\mathfrak{B}}$. Then we have

$$\hat{T}u = g(x) + \int_{\mathfrak{B}} G(x, \xi)\, f(\xi, u(\xi))d\xi \quad \text{for } u \in \hat{\mathfrak{D}} = \dot{\mathfrak{C}} ,$$

where $g(x)$ is defined by $\Delta g = 0$ on $\mathfrak{B}$ and $g = \gamma_1$ on Γ and $G(x, \xi)$ denotes a Green's function. Tu has the same form for $u \in \mathfrak{D} = \mathfrak{R}$. Each function $v = Tu (u \in \mathfrak{D})$ is H-continuous and therefore contained in $\mathfrak{C}$.

The assumption a. of 1.2 is satisfied because of the fixed-point theorem of Schauder [4], as the set $T\mathfrak{R}$ is compact. The monotonic character of the linear operators M and U_1 can be proved using known theorems about the Dirichlet problem. The comparison problem is

$$|\Delta u_0 + f(x, u_0)| \leqq -\Delta\eta - \tilde{f}(x, \eta) \quad \text{on } \mathfrak{B} ,$$

$$|u_0 - \gamma_1| \leqq \eta \quad \text{on } \Gamma$$

with $\tilde{f}(x, y) = \tilde{f}_0(x, y)$ $(\tilde{f}_1(x, y) \equiv 0)$.

2.3. It would be desirable to have a systematical method to solve a given boundary value problem approximately and to estimate the error of the approximation. Here we suggest a way of computation which seems to be useful in many cases of problems treated in this paper.

1. If (0.1) is a nonlinear problem one computes approximate values $v(x_k)$ of $u^*(x_k)$ by the difference method in several points $x_k \in \bar{\mathfrak{B}}$.
2. One tries to get an approximation $u_0(x)$ of the form

$$u_0(x) = w_0(x) + \sum_{\gamma=1}^{m} a_\gamma w_\gamma(x)$$

with suitably chosen functions $w_\gamma(x)$, such that $V_j[u_0] = \delta_j (j=1, 2, \ldots)$ for all values of the parameters a_γ . The a_γ will be fixed by the requirement, that the linear approximate defects

$$\tilde{d}_0(x) = \tilde{d}_0[u_0] = -M[u_0] + f_0(x, v) + f_{0_y}(x, v)(u_0 - v)$$

and

$$\tilde{d}_i(x) = \tilde{d}_i[u_0] = -U_i[u_0] + f_i(x, v) + f_{i_y}(x, v)(u_0 - v) \quad (i=1, 2, \ldots)$$

are "small" in those points x_k which are contained in $\mathfrak{B}$ or Γ_i respectively. (One can use the method of least squares, Tschebycheff approximation, collocation method, etc.)

If $f_i(x, y)$ is a linear function of y , one has $\tilde{d}_i = d_i$ and can choose the corresponding points x_k arbitrarily.

3. One evaluates the defects $d_i[u_0]$ $(i = 0, 1, 2, \ldots)$.
4. One selects majorants $\tilde{f}_i(x, y)$ with respect to a suitably chosen domain $\mathfrak{G}$ (See [5]).
5. One computes a solution $\eta(x)$ of the comparison problem to have the estimation $|u^*(x) - u_0(x)| \leqq \eta(x)$.

Of course one can compute $u_0(x)$ in some other way instead of using 1. and 2. But this procedure has some advantages which will now be explained. In many cases the nonlinear difference equations (of step 1) can be solved by an iteration procedure corresponding to the iteration method

$$\left.\begin{aligned} M[u_{n+1}] &= f(x, u_n) \\ U_i[u_{n+1}] = f_i(x, u_n) , \quad V_j[u_{n+1}] &= \delta_j \quad (n=0, 1, 2, \ldots) \end{aligned}\right\} \qquad (2.3)$$

Generally this procedure will be convergent, if the comparison problem (1.6) has a solution $\eta(x) \geqq 0$. However this need not be true, if the $\widetilde{f}_i(x,y)$ are evaluated using (1.9) instead of (1.4b) for several i_k . In this case one can try an iteration procedure corresponding to (2.3) with $\hat{M}$ instead of M (for $i_k = 0$), $\hat{U}_{i_k}$ instead of U_{i_k} (for $i_k \neq 0$) and $\hat{f}_{i_k}$ instead of f_{i_k} , where the C_{i_k} are suitably chosen.

Each iteration step in 1. necessitates the solution of a system of linear equations. In 2. one has to solve an approximation problem which is linear, too. These steps of computation can be done by a computer. A computer will also be useful to accomplish the other steps of the procedure.

If one is concerned with a partial differential equation and the domain $\mathfrak{B}$ is not very simple, finding a good approximation by step 2 seems to be the most difficult part of the procedure.

§3. Numerical examples

3.1. An ordinary differential equation. We consider the problem

$$-u'' = \tfrac{1}{2} + x u^2 \qquad \text{for } 0 \leq x \leq 1 \;,$$

$$-u'(0) = \tfrac{1}{4} u^2(0) \qquad u(1) = 0$$

of the type (2.1), and try to solve it with the method of No. 2.3.

1. Using the approximations

$$u''(x_k) \approx \frac{1}{h^2} \{ u(x_{k-1}) - 2u(x_k) + u(x_{k+1}) \} \;,$$

$$-u'(0) \approx \frac{1}{h}(u(0) - u(x_1)) - \frac{h}{6}(2u''(0) + u''(x_1))$$

with $x_k = kh$ and $h = \frac{1}{4}$ one gets difference equations, which can easily be solved. The approximate values $v_k \approx u^*(x_k)\,(k=0,1,\ldots,4)$ are contained in column 2 of the table.

2. As u_0 we chose a polynomial

$$u_0(x) = a + bx + cx^2 \;.$$

The approximate defects are

$$\widetilde{d}_0(x) = u_0'' + \tfrac{1}{2} + x(2vu_0 - v^2) \;,$$

$$\widetilde{d}_1(0) = u_0'(0) + \tfrac{1}{4}(2v_0 u_0(0) - v_0^2) \;,$$

$$\widetilde{d}_2(1) = u_0(1) \;.$$

Demanding

$$\tilde{d}_1(0) = \tilde{d}_2(1) = 0$$

one gets

$$u_0(x) = -\tfrac{1}{4}\,\frac{v_0^{\,2}}{2-v_0}\,(1-x) + a(1-x)(1+(1-\frac{v_0}{2})\,x) \quad (a = \frac{2b}{2-v_0})\,.$$

The requirement

$$\tilde{d}_0(0) = -\tilde{d}_0(\tfrac{1}{2}) \qquad \text{(it is } \tilde{d}_0(0) = \tilde{d}_0(1) \text{ for all } a\text{)}$$

leads to $a = 0,296$.

3. We have (see columns 3 and 4 of the table)

$$u_0(x) = (1-x)\ (0,27377 + 0,25503\,x)\ ,$$

$$d_0(x) = -0,01006 + x(1-x)^2\ (0,27377 + 0,25503\,x)^2$$

$$d_1(0) = 0,000\,025$$

and

$$d_2(1) = 0\ .$$

4. Because of

$$|f_{0_y}(x, u_0 + z)| = 2x\,|u_0 + z| \leqq 2x(u_0 + |z|)\ ,$$

$$|f_{1_y}(x, u_0 + z)| = \tfrac{1}{2}|u_0 + z| \leqq \tfrac{1}{2}(u_0 + |z|)\ ,$$

the functions

$$\tilde{f}_0(x, y) = x(2u_0y + y^2)\ ,\ \tilde{f}_1(x, y) = \tfrac{1}{4}(2u_0y + y^2),\ \tilde{f}_2(x, y) \equiv 0$$

are majorants of the $f_i(x, y)$ for all values of y , so that we can choose $\phi(x) = -\infty$, $\psi(x) = +\infty$.

5. The comparison problem is

$$|d_0(x)| \leqq -\eta''(x) - x(2u_0(x)\,\eta(x) + \eta^2(x)) \qquad \text{for } 0 \leqq x \leqq 1\ ,$$

$$|d_1(0)| \leqq -\eta'(0) - \tfrac{1}{4}(2u_0(0)\,\eta(0) + \eta^2(0))\ ,$$

$$0 \leqq \eta(1)\ .$$

With

$$\eta(x) = A\cdot\zeta(x)\ ;\ \zeta(x) = (1-x)(1 + (1-\epsilon)\,x)\ ;\ \mu = \epsilon - \tfrac{1}{2}u_0(0)\ ;$$

$$A,\ \mu = \text{const.}$$

one gets the condition

$$|d_0(x)| \leqq A\{2 - u_0(0) - 2\mu - x\zeta(x)(2u_0(x) + A\zeta(x))\} , \qquad (3.1)$$

$$|d_1(0)| \leqq A\{\mu - \tfrac{1}{4}A\} . \qquad (3.2)$$

Neglecting A and μ, which can be supposed small, everywhere within the braces of (3.1), one evaluates $A = 0{,}0068$. Then (3.2) leads to $\mu = 0{,}00208$. Finally one proves that (3.1) is satisfied exactly with these values of A and μ.

As a consequence there exists a solution $u^*(x)$, for which

$$|u^*(x) - u_0(x)| \leqq 0{,}0068\,(1-x)(1+0{,}139\,x) .$$

The approximation $u_0(x)$ and the bound $\eta(x)$ can be improved using more general functions. In this case one may apply a more systematical method in order to have small $\widetilde{d}_i$ (see [6] where another problem is solved with much higher accuracy using the computer IBM 650 at the University of Hamburg).

3.2. A partial differential equation of the type (2.2):

$$-\Delta u = (1 + r^2)u \qquad \text{for } 0 \leqq r < 1 , \qquad r = \sqrt{x_1^2 + x_2^2} ,$$

$$u = 1 \qquad \text{for } r = 1 .$$

With

$$u_0 = 1 + (1 - r^2)(\alpha + \beta r^2)$$

one gets

$$d_0(x) = (1 + r^2) - \alpha(3 + r^4) + \beta(4 - 15 r^2 - r^6) = d_0\langle r\rangle .$$

For simplicity we use the collocation method to obtain a small d_0 and demand

$$d_0\langle 0\rangle = d_0\langle 1\rangle = 0 .$$

This leads to

$$u_0 = 1 + \frac{1}{26}(1-r^2)(10 + r^2) \quad \text{and} \quad d_0 = \frac{1}{26} r^2 (1-r^2)(11 + r^2) .$$

With

$$\widetilde{f}(x, y) \equiv f(x, y) = (1 + r^2)y$$

the comparison problem is

$$\frac{1}{26} r^2(1-r^2)(11+r^2) \leqq -\Delta\eta - (1+r^2)\eta \qquad \text{for } 0 \leqq r < 1 ,$$

$$0 \leqq \eta \qquad \text{for } r = 1 .$$

Trying with

$$\eta = A\zeta , \quad \zeta = 1 - r^2 , \quad A = \text{const.}$$

we get for A :

$$\frac{1}{26} r^2(1-r^2)(11+r^2) \leqq A(3+r^4) . \tag{3.3}$$

Because of

$$r^2(1-r^2) \leqq \frac{1}{4} , \quad 11 + r^2 \leqq 12 , \quad 3 + r^4 \geqq 3$$

(3.3) is true for $A = \frac{1}{26}$.

We have the estimation

$$|u^* - u_0| \leqq \frac{1}{26}(1-r^2) .$$

A more complicated example is in preparation.

Generalizations

One can easily prove corresponding results for more general problems, for example, for systems of equations

$$A_i[u] = f_i(x,u) \qquad \text{on} \quad \mathfrak{B}_i \quad (i = 1, 2, \ldots) ,$$

$$B_j[u] = \delta_j(x) \qquad \text{on} \quad \mathfrak{B}^j \quad (j = 1, 2, \ldots) ,$$

Here $u(x)$ denotes a vector, the A_i and B_j are formal linear differential operators and the $\mathfrak{B}_i$ and the $\mathfrak{B}^j$ are subsets of a domain $\mathfrak{B}$ (for example $\mathfrak{B}$ itself or parts of its boundary).

The theorem contains estimates of the type $|u^*-u_0| \leqq \eta$. In a similar way one can get upper and lower bounds of u^*-u_0 , which do not differ only in the sign. One has to ask for functions v, w such that T maps the set $\mathfrak{K} = \{u : v \leqq u \leqq w\}$ into itself. In this way one gets a large class of error estimates. This class contains several known estimates, for example, those which can be proved in connection with the iteration procedure $u_{n+1} = Tu_n$ in a metric space [2] or a generalized metric space [5], furthermore the estimates for those procedures with monotonic operators (see [3] and the paper of L. Collatz in these proceedings). All these special estimates need special investigations to make them useful for numerical application. Therefore we have treated in this paper only one special method of estimation. But in view of practical application this method seems to be one of the most important of the general class mentioned above.

TABLE

x	v	u_0	$d_0[u_0]$
0	0,275	0,27377	-0,01006
0,25	0,255	0,25315	0,00596
0,5	0,202	0,20064	0,01007
0,75	0,117	0,11626	0,00008
1	0	0	-0,01006

NOTE

*The uniqueness of v is a consequence of assumption b. in 1.2.

REFERENCES

1. Collatz, L., Aufgaben monotoner Art., Arch. Math. 3 (1952) pp. 366-376.

2. Collatz, L., Numerische Behandlung von Differentialgleichungen, 2. Aufl., Berlin-Göttingen-Heidelberg 1955.

3. Collatz, L. and J. Schröder, Einschliessen der Lösungen von Randwertaufgaben, Numer. Math. 1 (1959), pp. 61-72.

4. Schauder, J., Der Fixpunktsatz in Funktionalräumen, Stud. Math. 2, (1930), pp. 171-182.

5. Schröder, J., Fehlerabschätzungen bei gewöhnlichen und partiellen Differentialgleichungen, Arch. Rat. Mech. Anal. 2 (1958-59), 367-392.

6. Schröder, J., Vom Defekt ausgehende Fehlerabschätzungen bei Differentialgleichungen, Arch. Rat. Mech. Anal. 3(1959), 219-228.

GAETANO FICHERA

On a Unified Theory of Boundary Value Problems for Elliptic-Parabolic Equations of Second Order

The present lecture is concerned with the theory of boundary value problems for linear partial differential equations of second order. It consists of a proposal for a unified theory of boundary value problems for second order linear equations of elliptic-parabolic type, including the classical cases of totally elliptic equations, heat equation, and first order equations.

The theory does not claim to be complete at this time. Nevertheless it opens, in my opinion, many attractive fields for further research and, therefore, the results obtained up to the present time deserve to be expounded here.

The first results of this theory were obtained by the writer in 1956 [4]. A more complete treatment can be found in the mimeographed notes containing the lectures the writer delivered at the Istituto Italiano di Alta Matematica in Rome in 1957 [5].

In 1958, K. O. Friedrichs published a paper [7] on boundary value problems for linear differential equations independent of type. The Friedrichs theory covers equations that may be hyperbolic in one subregion of the domain where the problem is considered and elliptic in a different subregion. However, it does not seem possible to include in the class of equations considered by Friedrichs every elliptic-parabolic equation, since Friedrichs assumes a symmetry condition, that is not needed in the present treatment.

A comparison between the Friedrichs theory and the present one would be --in the opinion of the writer--very interesting.

§1. Hypotheses and statement of the general boundary value problem for second order linear elliptic-parabolic equations

Let us denote by $X^{(r)}$ the r-dimensional real Cartesian space. Let $x \equiv (x_1, \dots, x_r)$ be a point in $X^{(r)}$ and B a connected open set in $X^{(r)}$.

A function is said to belong to $C^m(B)$ (m nonnegative integer) if it is continuous in B together with its partial derivatives of order $h \leq m$. Let $a^{ij}(x)$ $(i, j = 1, \dots, r)$, $b^i(x)$ $(i = 1, \dots, r)$, $c(x)$ be real functions of $C^2(B)$, $C^1(B)$, $C^0(B)$ respectively.

We shall consider the following second order linear differential operator:

$$L(u) \equiv a^{ij} u_{x_i x_j} + b^i u_{x_i} + cu \qquad (1) \qquad (a^{ij} \equiv a^{ji})$$

and suppose that for any $x \in B$ the quadratic form $a^{ij}(x) \lambda_i \lambda_j$ is positive definite or semi-definite, that is to say that L is a positive elliptic-parabolic operator in B. The case that perhaps for some points of B, $a^{ij}(x) \lambda_i \lambda_j \equiv 0$ is not excluded.

This means that in some subset of B --possibly coinciding with B --the differential operator might degenerate to a first order operator.

Let A be a bounded open set contained in B such that its boundary Σ coincides with the boundary of its closure $\bar{A}$.

In order to state the exact hypotheses to be assumed on Σ, we shall define first what we mean by a regular (r-1)-cell in $X^{(r)}$.

Let $x = x(t)$ be a function, defined in a closed domain D of the Cartesian (r-1)-space and with range in $X^{(r)}$, satisfying the following conditions: (a.) D is homeomorphic to an (r-1)-sphere, (b.) $x(t)$ maps D one-to-one onto a subset of $X^{(r)}$, (c.) the rank of the Jacobian matrix $\frac{\partial(x)}{\partial(t)}$ is r-1 at any point of D, (d.) the (r-1)-Lebesgue measure of the boundary of D is zero.

The range Σ_0 of $x(t)$ is an (r-1)-regular cell of $X^{(r)}$. The image of the boundary of D is called the border of Σ_0.

We shall suppose that Σ can be decomposed in a finite number of regular (r-1)-cells: $\Sigma = \Sigma_1 \cup \ldots \cup \Sigma_m$ such that any two of them have at most points of their borders in common.

In addition we shall suppose that the Green-Gauss identity, that transforms an r-integral over A into an (r-1)-integral over Σ, can be applied to $A \cup \Sigma$.

Let us denote by Σ'_h the subset of Σ_h $(h = 1, \ldots, m)$ such that at any point x of Σ'_h the tangent hyperplane to Σ_h is characteristic with respect to the operator L. This means that the direction cosines $n_1, \ldots, n_r$ of the normal to Σ_h at x satisfy the equation: $a^{ij}(x) n_i n_j = 0$. At any point x of Σ_h, not lying on the border of Σ_h, the function,

$$b(x) = (b^i - a^{ij}_{x_j}) n_i ,$$

is well defined, where $n_1, \ldots, n_r$ are the direction cosines of the inner normal to A at the point x of Σ_h.

For any fixed h we can extend the definition of $b(x)$ by continuity over all Σ_h [2]. Let $\Sigma_h^{(1)}$ be the subset of Σ'_h defined by the condition $b(x) \geq 0$. Let us set:

$$\Sigma^{(1)} = \Sigma_1^{(1)} \cup \Sigma_2^{(1)} \cup \ldots \cup \Sigma_m^{(1)}$$

$$\Sigma^{(2)} = (\Sigma'_1 \cup \Sigma'_2 \cup \ldots \cup \Sigma'_m) - \Sigma^{(1)}$$

$$\Sigma^{(3)} = \Sigma - (\Sigma^{(1)} \cup \Sigma^{(2)}) .$$

The set Σ is decomposed in three disjoint subsets $\Sigma^{(1)}$, $\Sigma^{(2)}$, $\Sigma^{(3)}$. It must be observed that someone of these sets might be empty.

Let $\Sigma_D^{(3)}$ and $\Sigma_N^{(3)}$ be two disjoint sets such that

$$\Sigma^{(3)} = \Sigma_D^{(3)} \cup \Sigma_N^{(3)} .$$

The set $\Sigma_D^{(3)}$ or $\Sigma_N^{(3)}$ may be assumed to be empty. Of course both these sets are empty when $\Sigma^{(3)}$ is empty.

Let $f(x)$, $g(x)$, $h(x)$ be given functions defined respectively on A, on $\Sigma^{(2)} \cup \Sigma_D^{(3)}$ and on $\Sigma_N^{(3)}$.

The boundary value problem that we shall consider for a general elliptic-parabolic equation is the following:

$$\begin{array}{ll} L(u) = f & \text{in } A , \\ u = g & \text{on } \Sigma^{(2)} \cup \Sigma_D^{(3)} , \\ a^{ij}(x)\, u_{x_i} n_j = h & \text{on } \Sigma_N^{(3)} . \end{array} \tag{1.1}$$

§2. Particular cases and examples

Let us suppose $a^{ij}(x)\lambda_i\lambda_j$ positive definite in any point of B, that is to say that L is a totally elliptic operator. In this particular case $\Sigma^{(1)}$ and $\Sigma^{(2)}$ are both empty. If $\Sigma_N^{(3)}$ is assumed empty the boundary value problem (1.1) is the classical Dirichlet problem. If $\Sigma_D^{(3)}$ is empty we have the Neumann problem for a general elliptic operator. In the case that $\Sigma_D^{(3)}$ and $\Sigma_N^{(3)}$ are not empty, problem (1.1) reduces to the mixed Dirichlet-Neumann boundary value problem for an elliptic operator.

Let us now assume:

$$L(u) \equiv L_0(u) - u_{x_r}$$

where L_0 is an elliptic operator in the r-1 variables: $x_1, \ldots, x_{r-1}$. In this case L is the well known parabolic heat equation operator.

$\Sigma^{(1)}$ is the part of Σ where the inner normal n is parallel and opposite in direction to the x_r-axis (hatched line in Fig. 1), $\Sigma^{(2)}$ the part of Σ where n is parallel to the x_r-axis and oriented as this axis. $\Sigma^{(3)}$ is the part of the boundary where n and x_r form an angle different from 0 and π.

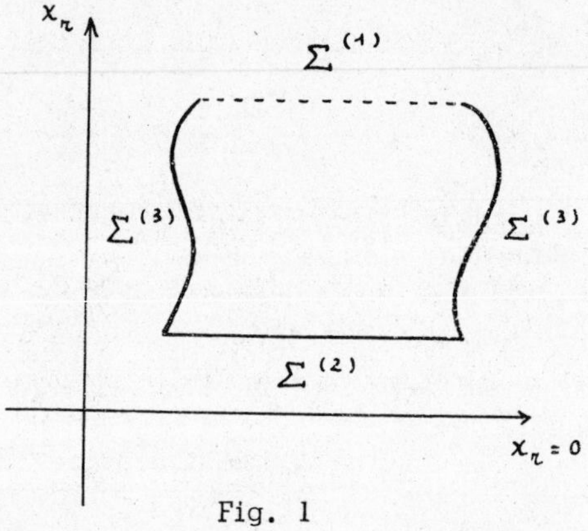

Fig. 1

Let us consider the more general parabolic operator:

$$L(u) \equiv L_0(u) - b^r(x)\, u_{x_r}$$

where L_0 is defined as above (elliptic operator in the variables $x_1, \ldots, x_{r-1}$) and $b^r(x)$ is an arbitrary function, not necessarily of fixed sign, in $A \cup \Sigma$. We do not exclude that the coefficients of L_0 may depend also on the variable x_r.

Let W^+ (W^-) be the part (possibly empty) of Σ where the inner normal n is parallel and equiverse (opposite) to the x_r-axis. $W^+_1(W^-_1)$ be the subset of $W^+(W^-)$ where $b_r(x) \geq 0$ ($b_r(x) \leq 0$) and $W^+_2(W^-_2)$ the remaining part. We have:

$\Sigma^{(1)} \supset W^+_1 \cup W^-_1$; $\Sigma^{(2)} \supset W^+_2 \cup W^-_2$. It is easy to see how to distribute the points of Σ where the tangent hyperplane is not defined.

As an example consider the parabolic equation

$$\frac{\partial^2 u}{\partial x_1^2} - \sin x_1 \frac{\partial u}{\partial x_2} = f(x_1, x_2) ,$$

in the domain indicated in fig. 2.

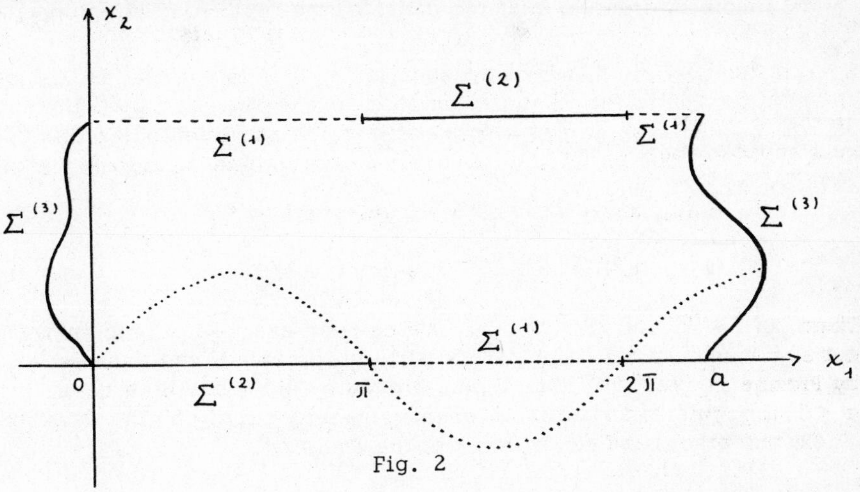

Fig. 2

The hatched line denotes the part $\Sigma^{(1)}$ of Σ where one must not prescribe any boundary condition.

As very simple and elementary examples consider the two first order equations:

$$u_{x_1} + c(x)\,u = f(x)\ , \quad x_1 u_{x_1} + x_2 u_{x_2} + c(x)u = f(x)\ .$$

In fig. 3 and fig. 4 the parts $\Sigma^{(1)}$ and $\Sigma^{(2)}$ of Σ are, respectively, shown ($\Sigma^{(1)} \equiv$ hatched line, $\Sigma^{(2)} \equiv$ continuous line):

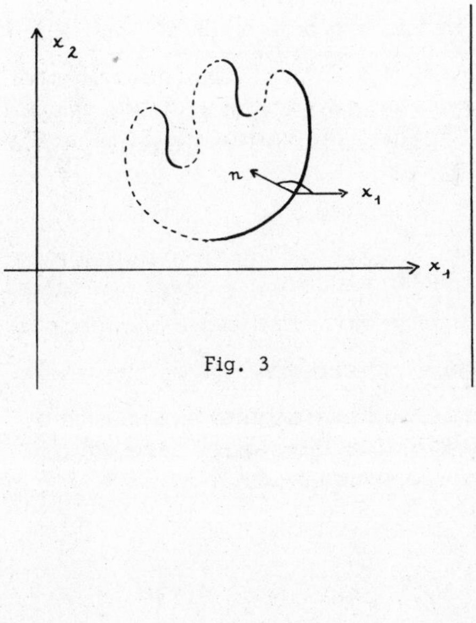

Fig. 3

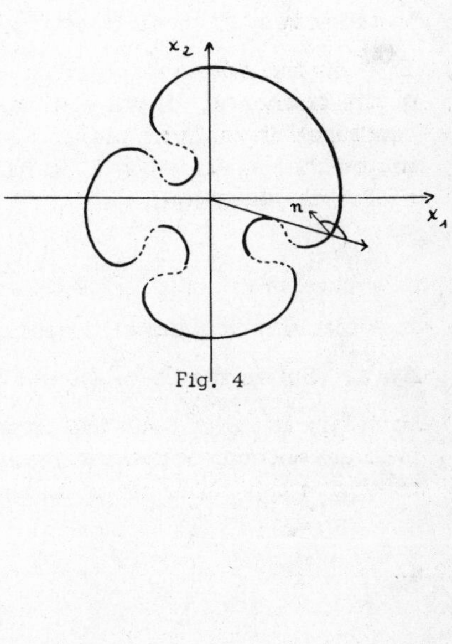

Fig. 4

As a more interesting example consider the first order equation,

$$b_1 u_{x_1} + b_2 u_{x_2} + cu = f ,$$

in the interval $-a_1 \leq x_1 \leq a_1$, $-a_2 \leq x_2 \leq a_2$ $(a_1 > 0, a_2 > 0)$ and suppose that

$$b_1(-a_1, x_2) \geq 0 , \qquad b_1(a_1, x_2) \leq 0$$

$$b_2(x_1, -a_2) \geq 0 , \qquad b_2(x_1, a_2) \leq 0 .$$

Then $\Sigma^{(2)} \equiv \emptyset$ and $\Sigma \equiv \Sigma^{(1)}$. We have an example of problem without any boundary condition. This particular problem was considered by Picone in 1928 [14], and it was proved by him that in the case $c < 0$ a <u>regular</u> solution is determined by only satisfying the equation.

On the other hand if we consider the equation,

$$-b_1 u_{x_1} - b_2 u_{x_2} + cu = f$$

with b_1 and b_2 satisfying the above inequalities on Σ strictly, then $\Sigma \equiv \Sigma^{(2)}$ and $\Sigma^{(1)} \equiv \emptyset$. That is to say the value of u must be prescribed on the whole boundary.

Let us now consider some other examples concerning parabolic equations of second order. First we consider the equation,

$$(x_1^2 + x_2^2 - 1)u_{x_1x_2} + x_2(x_1^2 + 2x_2^2 - 2)u_{x_2} + cu = f .$$

Let A be the domain defined by the condition:

$$x_1^2 + x_2^2 > 1 , \quad 0 < x_1 < 2 , \quad -1 < x_2 < 1 .$$

In this case $\Sigma^{(1)}$ is constituted by the two points $(0, 1)$ and $(0, -1)$; $\Sigma^{(3)}$ is the segment $x_1 = 2$, $-1 < x_2 < 1$, $\Sigma^{(2)}$ the remaining part of the boundary. If we assume as A the part of the previous domain contained in the half plane $x_2 > 0$, then the part of the boundary lying on the x_1-axis is $\Sigma^{(1)}$ (fig. 5).

For the equation:

$$x_2^2 u_{x_1x_1} - 2x_1x_2 u_{x_1x_2} + x_1^2 u_{x_1x_2} - 2x_1 u_{x_1} - 2x_2 u_{x_2} + cu = f$$

in a circular domain with center at the origin, the whole boundary is $\Sigma^{(1)}$. But in the star-shaped domain indicated in fig. 6, the whole boundary is $\Sigma^{(3)}$. In the first case we have another example of a problem without boundary conditions and in the second case we can prescribe the value of u on the whole boundary.

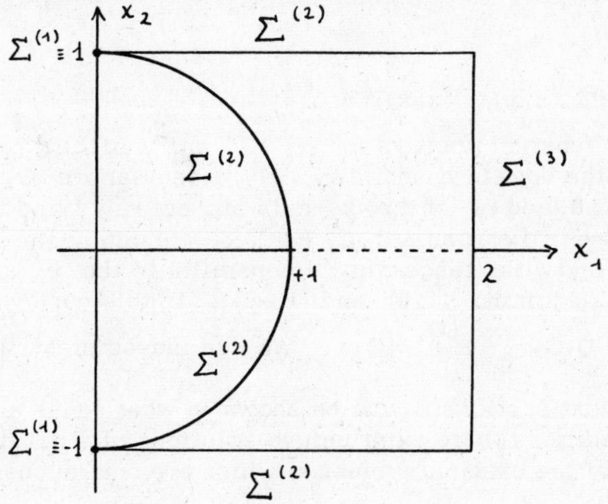
x_2
$\Sigma^{(2)}$
$\Sigma^{(1)} \equiv 1$
$\Sigma^{(2)}$
$\Sigma^{(3)}$
x_1
+1
2
$\Sigma^{(2)}$
$\Sigma^{(1)} \equiv -1$
$\Sigma^{(2)}$

Fig. 5

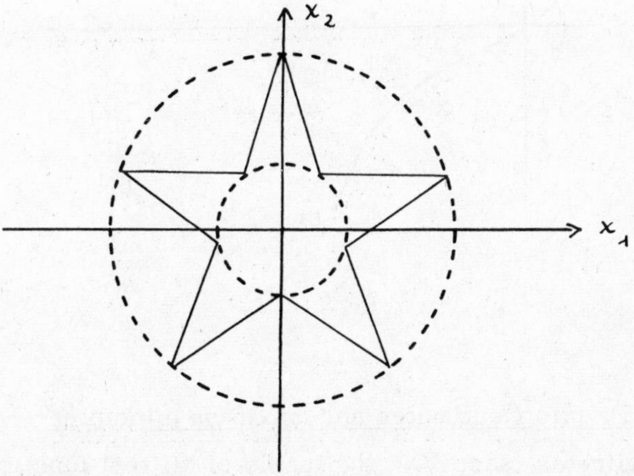
x_2
x_1

Fig. 6

As last example let us consider the mixed elliptic-parabolic equation:

$$k(x_2)\, u_{x_1x_1} + u_{x_2x_2} = f \;;$$

$k(x_2)$ is a function positive for $x_2 > 0$ and vanishing for $x_2 \leq 0$. Let A be the domain bounded by: (1.) a regular arc C_1 joining the two points 0 and 1 of the x_1-axis and entirely lying in the half-plane $x_2 > 0$; (2.) an arc C_2 (with $x_2 < 0$) joining the origin with the point $(1,-1)$ and with a tangent nowhere parallel to the x_2-axis; (3.) the segment C_3 joining $(1,0)$ and $(1,-1)$. In this case we have $\Sigma^{(3)} = C_1 \cup C_2$, $\Sigma^{(1)} = C_3$. We can indeed prescribe u on C_1 and C_2.

In the next sections it will be shown in what sense and under what further conditions there exist unique solutions of (1.1) (in particular, solutions of the example problems) which are continuously dependent on the data.

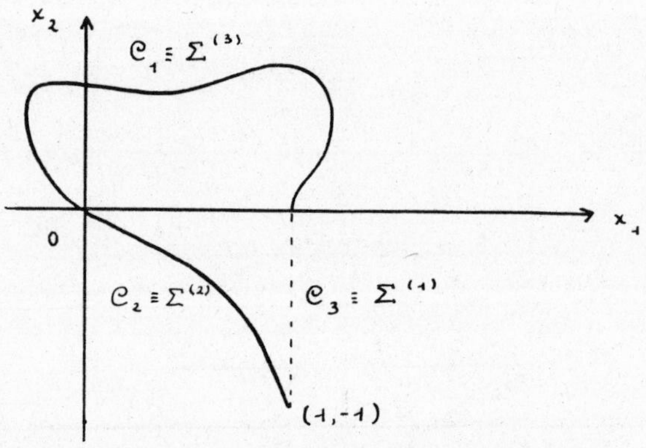

Fig. 7

§3. Integral a priori estimates and maximum principles

Let us define as class C_L the family of all real functions u satisfying the following conditions:

a. u is continuous with its first derivatives in $A \cup \Sigma$, $[u \in C^1(A \cup \Sigma)]$,

b. u has continuous second derivatives in A, $[u \in C^2(A)]$,

c. the function $L(u)$ is bounded in A.

We shall denote by L^* the formal adjoint of the operator L :

$$L^*(u) = (a^{ij}u)_{x_i x_j} - (b^i u)_{x_i} + cu$$

$$\equiv a^{ij} u_{x_i x_j} + b^{*i} u_{x_i} + c^* u ,$$

where

$$b^{*i} = 2a^{ij}_{x_j} - b^i , \quad c^* = a^{ij}_{x_i x_j} - b^i_{x_i} + c .$$

I. Let p be a real number such that $1 \leq p < +\infty$ and let a function w exist belonging to $C^2(A \cup \Sigma)$ and satisfying the condition

(3.1) $$w \leq 0 , \quad L^*(w) + (p-1)\, cw > 0 \text{ in } A \cup \Sigma .$$

For any function u of C_L vanishing almost everywhere on $\Sigma^{(2)} \cup \Sigma^{(3)}$, the following inequality holds:

(3.2) $$\left(\int_A |u|^p dx\right)^{\frac{1}{p}} \leq p \, \frac{\max\limits_{A \cup \Sigma} |w|}{\min\limits_{A \cup \Sigma} [L^*(w) + (p-1)cw]} \left(\int_A |L(u)|^p dx\right)^{\frac{1}{p}} .$$

Let δ denote an arbitrary positive number. By using Green's integral theorem the following identity is shown:

(3.3) $$\int_A \{(u^2+\delta)^{\frac{p}{2}} L^*(w) - w \left(p[(p-1)u^2+\delta](u^2+\delta)^{\frac{p}{2}-2} a^{hk} u_{x_h} u_{x_k} + p(u^2+\delta)^{\frac{p}{2}-1} uL(u) + c(u^2+\delta)^{\frac{p}{2}-1} [(1-p)u^2+\delta]\right)\} dx$$

$$= \int_{\Sigma^{(1)} \cup \Sigma^{(2)}} w(u^2+\delta)^{\frac{p}{2}} b\, d\sigma + \int_{\Sigma^{(3)}} [p^2(u^2+\delta)^{\frac{p}{2}-1} wua^{hk} u_{x_h} n_k - (u^2+\delta)^{\frac{p}{2}} (a^{hk} w_{x_h} n_k - bw)] d\sigma .$$

Since a.e. on $\Sigma^{(1)}$, $b \geq 0$; and $a^{hk} u_{x_h} u_{x_k} \geq 0$, $w \leq 0$ in $A \cup \Sigma$, by the assumed hypotheses on u, it follows:

$$\int_A (u^2+\delta)^{\frac{p}{2}} \{L^*(w) - cw(u^2+\delta)^{-1}[(1-p)u^2+\delta]\}dx$$

$$\leq p\int_A (u^2+\delta)^{\frac{p}{2}-1} uwL(u)dx + \delta^{\frac{p}{2}}[\int_{\Sigma^{(2)}} wbd\sigma - \int_{\Sigma^{(3)}} (a^{hk}w_{x_h}n_k - bw)d\sigma] .$$

We observe that

$$\lim_{\delta\to 0} (u^2+\delta)^{\frac{p}{2}} \{L^*(w) - cw(u^2+\delta)^{-1}[(1-p)u^2+\delta]\} = (u^2)^{\frac{p}{2}} \{L^*(w)-(1-p)cw\} ,$$

$$\lim_{\delta\to 0} (u^2+\delta)^{\frac{p}{2}-1} u = (u^2)^{\frac{p}{2}-1} u ,$$

uniformly with respect to x in $A \cup \Sigma$.

From (3. 3) it follows

$$(3.4)\qquad \int_A |u|^p dx \leq p \frac{\max_{A\cup\Sigma} |w|}{\min_{A\cup\Sigma} [L^*(w) + (p-1)cw]} \int_A |u|^{p-1} |L(u)| dx .$$

This coincides with (3. 2) for $p = 1$. For $p > 1$, (3. 2) follows from (3. 4) by applying the Schwarz-Hölder inequality to the integral on the right hand side.

II. <u>If</u> $c < 0$ <u>in</u> $A \cup \Sigma$, <u>or</u> $c^* < 0$ <u>in</u> $A \cup \Sigma$, p <u>and</u> w <u>exist satisfying (3. 1).</u>

In the first case $(c < 0)$ we can assume $w \equiv -1$ and p large enough, that

$$\min_{A\cup\Sigma} [-a^{hk}_{x_h x_k} + b^h_{x_h} - pc] > 0 \qquad \text{in } A \cup \Sigma .$$

In the second case $(c^* < 0)$ we assume $w \equiv -1$ and p so small that $\min_{A\cup\Sigma} [(1-p)c - c^*] > 0$ (in particular $p = 1$) .

It is obvious that

III. <u>If</u> $c < 0$ <u>and</u> $c^* < 0$ <u>in</u> $A \cup \Sigma$, <u>then for any</u> $p \geq 1$ <u>the condition (3. 1) is satisfied by assuming</u> $w \equiv -1$.

IV. <u>Let</u> c <u>be negative in</u> $A \cup \Sigma$. <u>Let</u> w <u>denote an arbitrary function of</u> $C^2(A\cup\Sigma)$ <u>negative in</u> $A \cup \Sigma$ <u>and</u> p_0 <u>a real number such that</u> $L^*(w) + (p_0 - 1)cw \geq 0$ <u>in</u> $A \cup \Sigma$. <u>For any</u> p <u>such that</u> $p > p_0$, $p \geq 1$, <u>and for any</u> $u \in C_L$, <u>vanishing a. e. on</u>

$\Sigma^{(2)} \cup \Sigma^{(3)}$, the following inequality holds:

$$(3.5)\qquad \left(\int_A |u|\, cw\, dx\right)^{\frac{1}{p}} \leq \frac{p}{p-p_0}\left(\int_A \left|\frac{L(u)}{c}\right|^p cw\, dx\right)^{\frac{1}{p}} .$$

Since w satisfies for $p > p_0$ the conditions (3.1), from (3.3) for $p > p_0$, $p \geq 1$, it follows (for $\delta \to 0$) that

$$\int_A (u^2)^{\frac{p}{2}} [L^*(w) - (1-p)cw]dx \leq p\int_A (u^2)^{\frac{p}{2}-1} u\, w\, L(u)dx .$$

Since $L^*(w) - (1-p)cw \geq (p-p_0)w$, from the previous inequality it follows that

$$(3.6)\qquad \int_A |u|^p cwdx \leq \frac{p}{p-p_0} \int_A |u|^{p-1} |w|\, |L(u)|\, dx$$

which coincides with (3.5) for $p = 1$. In the case $p > 1$ we have

$$(3.7)\qquad \int_A |u|^{p-1} |L(u)|\, |w| dx \leq \left(\int_A \left[\cdot |u|^{p-1} |c|^{\frac{p-1}{p}}\right]^{\frac{p}{p-1}} |w| dx\right)^{\frac{p-1}{p}} .$$

$$\cdot\left(\int_A \left[|L(u)|\, |c|^{\frac{1-p}{p}}\right]^p |w| dx\right)^{\frac{1}{p}} = \left(\int_A |u|^p |c|\, |w| dx\right)^{\frac{p-1}{p}} \left(\int_A \left|\frac{L(u)}{c}\right|^p |c|\, |w| dx\right)^{\frac{1}{p}} =$$

$$= \left(\int_A |u|^p cwdx\right)^{\frac{p-1}{p}} \left(\int_A \left|\frac{L(u)}{c}\right|^p cwdx\right)^{\frac{1}{p}} .$$

From (3.6) and (3.7), the inequality (3.5) follows.

From (3.5) we deduce the following maximum principle:

V. Let c be negative in $A \cup \Sigma$. For any $u \in C_L$ vanishing almost everywhere on $\Sigma^{(2)} \cup \Sigma^{(3)}$ the inequality holds:

$$(3.8)^{(3)}\qquad \max_{A \cup \Sigma} |u| \leq \underset{A}{\ell.u.b.} \left|\frac{L(u)}{c}\right|$$

This follows from (3.5) for $p \to +\infty$.

VI. When hypotheses of theorems III or V are satisfied, a uniqueness theorem holds for the problem (1.1) with $\Sigma_N = \emptyset$ in the class C_L .

It is evident that for particular classes of elliptic-operators L (as an instance first order operators) theorems I - VI remain valid with the same proof, assuming C_L to be defined in a more general way (not necessarily requiring the existence and the continuity of all the derivatives of u in A .)

We want now to consider some estimates in connection with problem (1.1) in the general case (i.e., Σ_N not empty).

VII. Let p be a real number: $1 \leq p < +\infty$ and w a function of $C^2(A \cup \Sigma)$ such that:

$$(3.1) \quad w \leq 0 \ , \ L^*(w) + (p-1)cw > 0 \ \text{on} \ A \cup \Sigma$$

$$a^{hk} w_{x_h} n_k - bw \geq 0 \quad \text{a.e. on} \ \Sigma^{(3)} - \overline{\Sigma_D^{(3)}} \ . \qquad (4)$$

For any $u \in C_L$ satisfying a.e. the conditions

$$u = 0 \ \text{on} \ \Sigma^{(2)} \cup \overline{\Sigma_D^{(3)}} \ , \ a^{hk} u_{x_h} n_k = 0 \ \text{on} \ \Sigma^{(3)} - \overline{\Sigma_D^{(3)}}$$

the inequality (3.2) holds.

The proof is analogous to the proof of theorem I [5].

VIII. Let c be negative in $A \cup \Sigma$ and a negative function w in $A \cup \Sigma$ exist such that $a^{hk} w_{x_h} n_k - bw \geq 0$ on $\Sigma_N^{(3)}$. Then $p \geq 1$ exists such that (3.1) is satisfied.

The proof is obvious.

IX. For the same hypotheses of the previous theorem, let p_0 be a real number such that $L^*(w) + (p_0 - 1)cw \geq 0$. For $p > p_0$, $p \geq 1$ and for any u satisfying the conditions of theorem VII, the inequality (3.5) holds.

This theorem is proved as theorem IV.

X. For the same hypotheses of theorem VIII, the inequality (3.8) holds for any u satisfying the conditions of theorem VII.

From theorems VII and IX uniqueness theorems follow for the problem (1.1) in the class C_L .

XI. For a fixed p $(1 \leq p < +\infty)$ let a function $w \in C^2(A \cup \Sigma)$ exist satisfying the following conditions:

$w \leq 0$, $L^*(w) + (p-1)\,cw > 0$ in $A \cup \Sigma$,

$w = 0$ a.e. on $\overline{\Sigma_D^{(3)}}$, $a^{hk} w_{x_h} n_k - bw \geq 0$ a.e. on $\Sigma^{(3)} - \overline{\Sigma_D^{(3)}}$.

For any $u \in C_L$, such that: $L(u) = 0$ in A , $a^{hk} u_{x_h} n_k = 0$ a.e. on $\overline{\Sigma^{(3)}} - \overline{\Sigma_D^{(3)}}$, the inequality holds

(3.9)
$$\left(\int_A |u|^p dx\right)^{\frac{1}{p}} \leq \left\{\frac{\underset{\Sigma^{(2)}}{\ell.u.b.}\,|bw|}{\underset{A\cup\Sigma}{\min}\,[L^*(w) + (p-1)cw]}\right\}^{\frac{1}{p}} \left(\int_{\Sigma^{(2)}} |u|^p d\sigma\right)^{\frac{1}{p}} + \left\{\frac{\underset{\Sigma_D^{(3)}}{\ell.u.b.}\,|a^{hk} w_{x_h} n_k|}{\underset{A\cup\Sigma}{\min}\,[L^*(w) + (p-1)cw]}\right\}^{\frac{1}{p}} \left(\int_{\overline{\Sigma_D^{(3)}}} |u|^p d\sigma\right)^{\frac{1}{p}} .$$

From (3. 3) and the hypotheses for u and w , it follows that

$$\int_A \{(u^2 + \delta)^{\frac{p}{2}} L^*(w) - cw(u^2 + \delta)^{\frac{p}{2}-1} [(1-p)u^2 + \delta]\}\, dx$$

$$\leq \int_{\Sigma^{(2)}} bw(u^2 + \delta)^{\frac{p}{2}} d\sigma - \int_{\overline{\Sigma_D^{(3)}}} (u^2 + \delta)^{\frac{p}{2}} a^{hk} w_{x_h} n_k \, d\sigma .$$

For $\delta \to 0$

$$\int_A (u^2)^{\frac{p}{2}} [L^*(w) + (p-1)cw]dx \leq \int_{\Sigma^{(2)}} w(u^2)^{\frac{p}{2}} b\, d\sigma - \int_{\overline{\Sigma_D^{(3)}}} (u^2)^{\frac{p}{2}} a^{hk} w_{x_h} n_k d\sigma ;$$

(3.9) follows easily from this inequality.

XII. Let c be negative in $A \cup \Sigma$ and a function $w \in C^2(A \cup \Sigma)$ exist satisfying the conditions:

$$w < 0 \ \underline{\text{in}}\ A \cup \Sigma\ , \quad a^{hk} w_{x_h} n_k - bw \geq 0 \quad \underline{\text{on}} \quad \Sigma^{(3)} - \overline{\Sigma_D^{(3)}}\ .$$

For any $u \in C_L$ satisfying the conditions of theorem XI the following maximum principle holds:

$$\boxed{\max_{A \cup \Sigma} |u| = \max_{\overline{\Sigma^{(2)} \cup \Sigma_D^{(3)}}} |u|} \ . \tag{3.10}$$

If p is an arbitrary even integer, we can use (3.3) with $\delta = 0$. Under the assumed hypotheses for w and u we then obtain

$$\begin{aligned} &\min_{A \cup \Sigma} [L^*(w) + (p-1)cw] \int_A u^p dx \leq \ell.\text{u.b.}_{\Sigma^{(2)}} |bw| \int_{\Sigma^{(2)}} u^p d\sigma + \\ (3.11)\quad & + p \max_{\overline{\Sigma_D^{(3)}}} |w| \int_{\overline{\Sigma_D^{(3)}}} |u|^{p-1} |a^{hk} u_{x_h} n_k| d\sigma + \ell.\text{u.b.}_{\overline{\Sigma_D^{(3)}}} |a^{hk} w_{x_h} n_k - bw| \int_{\overline{\Sigma_D^{(3)}}} u^p d\sigma . \end{aligned}$$

Let us first suppose $u = 0$ a.e. on $\overline{\Sigma_D^{(3)}}$. Since two positive numbers P_1 and P_2 exist such that for p large enough, $P_1 \leq \min_{A \cup \Sigma} [L^*(w) + (p-1)cw] \leq P_2 p$, it follows that $\lim_{p \to \infty} \left\{ \min_{A \cup \Sigma} [L^*(w) + (p-1)cw] \right\}^{\frac{1}{p}} = 1$. From (3.11) the inequality (3.10) follows easily.

Let us now consider the case that u does not vanish a.e. on $\overline{\Sigma_D^{(3)}}$. By considering the Schwarz-Hölder inequality,

$$\int_{\overline{\Sigma_D^{(3)}}} |u|^{p-1} |a^{hk} u_{x_h} n_k| d\sigma \leq \left(\int_{\overline{\Sigma_D^{(3)}}} u^p d\sigma \right)^{\frac{p-1}{p}} \left(\int_{\overline{\Sigma_D^{(3)}}} |a^{hk} u_{x_h} n_k|^p d\sigma \right)^{\frac{1}{p}},$$

from (3.11) we get

$$\min_{A \cup \Sigma} [L^*(w) + (p-1)cw] \int_A u^p d\sigma \leq K_p \int_{\Sigma^{(2)} \cup \overline{\Sigma_D^{(3)}}} u^p d\sigma \tag{3.12}$$

where

$$K_p = \underset{\Sigma^{(2)}}{\ell.u.b.}\ |bw| + p \max_{\Sigma_D^{(3)}} |w| \left(\int_{\Sigma_D^{(3)}} u^p d\sigma\right)^{-\frac{1}{p}} .$$

$$\cdot \left(\int_{\Sigma_D^{(3)}} |a^{hk} u_{x_h} n_k|^p d\sigma\right)^{\frac{1}{p}} + \underset{\Sigma_D^{(3)}}{\ell.u.b.}\ |a^{hk} w_{x_h} n_k - bw| .$$

Let M be a positive number such that, for any even integer p ,

$$\left(\int_{\Sigma_D^{(3)}} u^p d\sigma\right)^{-\frac{1}{p}} \left(\int_{\Sigma_D^{(3)}} |a^{hk} u_{x_h} n_k|^p d\sigma\right)^{\frac{1}{p}} \leq M .$$

We get

$$K_p^{\frac{1}{p}} \leq [\underset{\Sigma^{(2)}}{\ell.u.b.}\ |bw| + p \max_{\Sigma_D^{(3)}} |w| M + \underset{\Sigma_D^{(3)}}{\ell.u.b.}\ |a^{hk} w_{x_h} n_k - bw|^{\frac{1}{p}} \leq$$

$$\leq p^{\frac{1}{p}} [\underset{\Sigma^{(2)}}{\ell.u.b.}\ |bw| + M \max_{\Sigma_D^{(3)}} |w| + \underset{\Sigma_D^{(3)}}{\ell.u.b.}\ |a^{hk} w_{x_h} n_k - bw|]^{\frac{1}{p}}$$

and

$$\max \lim_{p \to +\infty} K_p^{\frac{1}{p}} \leq 1 .$$

Let p_0 be such that $\min_{A \cup \Sigma} [L^*(w) + (p-1)cw] \geq 0$ for $p > p_0$.

For $p > p_0$, from (3.12) we obtain

$$\left(\min_{A \cup \Sigma} [L^*(w) + (p-1)cw]\right)^{\frac{1}{p}} \left(\int_A u^p d\sigma\right)^{\frac{1}{p}} \leq K_p^{\frac{1}{p}} \left(\int_{\Sigma^{(2)} \cup \Sigma_D^{(3)}} u^p d\sigma\right)^{\frac{1}{p}}$$

and for $p \to \infty$ we obtain (3.10).

XIII. <u>Let c be negative in $A \cup \Sigma$. For any solution u of $L(u)$ of the class C_L not identically vanishing in A , the following maximum principle holds</u>:

$$|u(x)| < \max_{\overline{\Sigma^{(2)}} \cup \overline{\Sigma^{(3)}}} |u(x)| \quad , \quad x \in A \,.$$

Let us assume $\Sigma_D^{(3)} = \Sigma^{(3)}$. Then as a function w satisfying the hypotheses of the previous theorem we can select $w \equiv -1$. In this case the inequality (3.10) is the following:

$$\max_{A \cup \Sigma} |u(x)| = \max_{\Sigma^{(2)} \cup \Sigma^{(3)}} |u| \,.$$

Since $\max_{A \cup \Sigma} |u| = \max_{A \cup \Sigma} u$ or $\max_{A \cup \Sigma} |u| = -\min_{A \cup \Sigma} u$, it follows that u has in $A \cup \Sigma$ a positive maximum or a negative minimum.

From the condition $c < 0$, by a well known argument, it follows that such a positive maximum or negative minimum cannot be attained in a point of A [(6)]. Therefore

$$|u(x)| < \max_{A \cup \Sigma} |u(x)| \quad \text{for } x \in A \,.$$

It is evident that the same argument could be given to establish the maximum principle (as in XIII) in the general case $\Sigma_N^{(3)} \neq \emptyset$.

§4. An abstract existence principle

In order to establish the necessary and sufficient condition for the existence of a weak solution of the problem (1.1), we shall make use of an abstract existence principle in Banach spaces.

Let $\mathscr{V}$ be an abstract manifold linear with respect to the real field and B_1 and B_2 real Banach spaces. Let M_i $(i = 1, 2)$ be a linear homomorphism of $\mathscr{V}$ into B_i ; ϕ and ψ denote vectors of the adjoint spaces B_1^* and B_2^* , respectively. We consider for any $v \in \mathscr{V}$ the following functional equation:

$$\langle \phi, M_1(v) \rangle = \langle \psi, M_2(v) \rangle \,, \tag{4.1}$$

where ϕ is a given vector and ψ is the unknown. Let $\mathscr{V}_2$ be the kernel of the homomorphism M_2 . The given vector ϕ must satisfy the following necessary conditions:

$$\langle \phi, M_1(v_2) \rangle = 0 \quad \text{for any } v_2 \in \mathscr{V}_2 \,. \tag{4.2}$$

Let $M_1(\mathscr{V}_2)$ denote the image of $\mathscr{V}_2$ on B_1 , for M_1 and $\overline{M_1(\mathscr{V}_2)}$ its closure. Let us consider the Banach factor-space:

$Q = B_1 / \overline{M_1(\mathscr{V}_2)}$. Let $\mathscr{M}_1$ be the homomorphism that maps $v \in \mathscr{V}$ in the equivalence class $[M_1(v)]$ of Q .

The following existence principle holds:

XIV. A solution ψ of the functional equation (4.1) exists for any fixed ϕ satisfying (4.2), when and only when a constant K exists such that for any $v \in \mathscr{V}$ the inequality holds

$$(4.3) \qquad \| \mathscr{M}_1(v) \|_Q \leq K \, \| M_2(v) \|_{B_2} \, . \quad (7)$$

Let $\mathscr{A}$ be the (closed) subspace of $B_2{}^*$, consisting of the vectors ψ, solutions of the "homogeneous" problem,

$$\langle \psi, \; M_2(v) \rangle = 0 \, , \text{ for any } v \in \mathscr{V} \, .$$

We denote by $\mathscr{F}$ the Banach factor-space: $\mathscr{F} = B_2{}^*/\mathscr{A}$. For any $\phi \in B_1{}^*$ satisfying the compatibility condition (4.2) (that is to say for any element of the adjoint space Q^*) an element Ψ of $\mathscr{F}$ is uniquely determined such that if ψ is any element in the equivalence class Ψ , then ψ is a solution of (4.1).

XV. The element Ψ of $\mathscr{F}$ corresponding to $\phi \in B_1{}^*$ (satisfying the compatibility conditions (4.2)) satisfies the inequality

$$(4.4) \qquad \| \Psi \|_{\mathscr{F}} \leq K \, \| \phi \|_{B_1{}^*} \, . \quad (8)$$

Inequality (4.4) is said to be the dual inequality of (4.3).

§5. Existence of weak solutions for problem (1.1)

Let $u \in C_L$ and $v \in C_{L^*}$. Then the Green's identity holds

$$(5.1) \qquad \int_A (vL(u) - uL^*(v))dx = \int_{\Sigma^{(3)}} [u a^{hk} v_{x_h} n_k - v a^{hk} u_{x_h} n_k] d\sigma - \int_{\Sigma^{(1)} \cup \Sigma^{(2)}} u v b \, d\sigma .$$

Let us suppose that u satisfy the boundary conditions,

$$(5.2) \qquad u = 0 \text{ a.e. on } \Sigma^{(2)} \cup \Sigma^{(3)}_D , \quad a^{hk} u_{x_h} n_k = 0 \text{ a.e. on } \Sigma^{(3)}_N \, .$$

From (5.1) it follows easily that

$$\int_A [uL^*(v) - vL(u)]dx = \int_{\Sigma^{(1)}} uvb d\sigma + \int_{\overline{\Sigma^{(3)}_D}} v a^{hk} u_{x_h} n_k d\sigma - \int_{\Sigma^{(3)} - \overline{\Sigma^{(3)}_D}} u(a^{hk} v_{x_h} n_k - bv) d\sigma \, .$$

Let $\mathscr{V}$ be the linear manifold of the functions of C_L^* such that for any $u \in C_L$ satisfying (5.2)

$$\int_{\Sigma^{(1)}} uvb\,d\sigma + \int_{\Sigma_D^{(3)}} va^{hk} u_{x_h} n_k\,d\sigma - \int_{\Sigma^{(3)} - \Sigma_D^{(3)}} u(a^{hk} v_{x_h} n_k - bv)\,d\sigma = 0 \; .$$

Let us set: $L(u) = f$. It follows that

$$\int_A vf\,dx = \int_A u\,L^*(v)\,dx \tag{5.3}$$

for any $v \in \mathscr{V}$.

We shall say that the problem (1.1) [with homogeneous boundary conditions $(g \equiv 0 \;,\; h \equiv 0)$] admits an $\mathscr{L}^p$-weak solution if for $f \in \mathscr{L}^{(p)}(A)$ $(p > 1)$, a function $u \in \mathscr{L}^{(p)}(A)$ exists satisfying (5.3) for any $v \in \mathscr{V}$.

From theorems XIV, XV and by the representation theorems of linear bounded functionals in the $\mathscr{L}^{(p)}$-spaces this general condition follows:

XVI. An $\mathscr{L}^{(p)}$-weak solution of problem (1.1) exists for any $f \in \mathscr{L}^{(p)}(A)$ such that

$$\int_A v_0\, f\,dx = 0 \qquad (v_0 \in \mathscr{V} \;,\; L^*(v_0) = 0\,)$$

when and only when a constant K exists such that:

$$\underset{v_0 \in \mathscr{V}_0}{\text{g.l.b.}} \left(\int_A |v + v_0|^{\frac{p}{p-1}} dx \right)^{\frac{p-1}{p}} \leq K \left(\int_A |L^*(v)|^{\frac{p}{p-1}} dx \right)^{\frac{p-1}{p}} \tag{5.4}$$

where $\mathscr{V}_0$ is the subset of $\mathscr{V}$ of all the functions which are solutions of the adjoint equation $L^*(v) = 0$.

When (5.4) holds, any $\mathscr{L}^{(p)}$-weak solution satisfies the inequality,

$$\underset{u_0 \in \mathscr{U}_0}{\text{g.l.b.}} \left(\int_A |u + u_0)^p dx \right)^{\frac{1}{p}} \leq K \left(\int_A |f|^p dx \right)^{\frac{1}{p}} \tag{5.5}$$

where $\mathscr{U}_0$ is the class of the $\mathscr{L}^{(p)}$-functions satisfying the conditions,

$$\int_A u_0 L^*(v)\,dx = 0$$

for any $v \in \mathscr{V}$.

Inequality (5.5) shows that the solution u of problem (1.1) depends continuously--in the $\mathscr{L}^{(p)}$-norm--on the datum f , modulo the eigen-solutions of the problem.

Therefore, when (5.4) has been proved, it seems reasonable from the last observation to consider problem (1.1) as a well posed boundary value problem.

The a priori estimates proved in section 3 combined with theorem XV permit us to state that,

XVII. Inequality (5.4) holds when the hypotheses of theorem VII are satisfied.

The inequality (5.4) is deduced from the dual inequality of (3.2).

Other conditions for the validity of (5.4) can be obtained when it is possible to apply to the functions of $\mathscr{V}$ the results of section 3 considered with respect to the operator L^* . For simplicity let us consider the particular case $\Sigma^{(3)} \equiv \Sigma^{(3)}_D$ and suppose that $\mathscr{V}$ coincides with the class of functions of $C_L{}^*$ satisfying a.e. the boundary condition $v = 0$ on $\Sigma^{*(2)} \cup \Sigma^{(3)}$, where $\Sigma^{*(i)}$ $(i = 1, 2)$ is defined with respect to L^* as $\Sigma^{(i)}$ was defined with respect to L.

This hypothesis on $\mathscr{V}$ will be denoted as hypothesis $\alpha)$. We denote by $\Sigma_0^{(1)}$ the subset of $\Sigma^{(1)}$ where $b = 0$. The hypothesis $\alpha)$ is satisfied when the space spanned by the function η defined by,

$$\eta \begin{cases} = u & \text{on } \Sigma^{(1)} - \Sigma_0^{(1)} \\ = a^{hk} u_{x_h} n_k & \text{on } \Sigma^{(3)} \end{cases}$$

(for any $u \in C_L$ and satisfying (5.2)) is dense in $\mathscr{L}^{(1)}([\Sigma^{(1)} - \Sigma_0^{(1)}] \cup \Sigma^{(3)})$.

From theorem I we deduce that

XVIII. If hypothesis $\alpha)$ is satisfied and a function w exists satisfying the conditions

$$w \leq 0 \ , \quad L(w) + \frac{1}{p-1} c^* w > 0 \qquad \text{in } A \cup \Sigma \quad (p > 1) \ ,$$

then for any $v \in \mathscr{V}$ the inequality holds

$$\left(\int_A |v|^{\frac{p}{p-1}} dx \right)^{\frac{p-1}{p}} \leq K \left(\int_A |L^* w|^{\frac{p}{p-1}} dx \right)^{\frac{p-1}{p}}$$

where

$$K = \frac{p}{p-1} \frac{\max\limits_{A \cup \Sigma} |u|}{\min\limits_{A \cup \Sigma} [L(w) + \frac{1}{p-1} c^* w]} .$$

In this case the $\mathscr{L}^{(p)}$-weak solution of problem (1. 1) exists for any fixed $f \in \mathscr{L}^{(p)}(A)$.

Let us now suppose that a sequence of functions u_n exist, satisfying (5. 2) and belonging to C_L , such that

(5. 6) $$\lim_{n\to\infty} \int_A |u-u_n|^p dx = \lim_{n\to\infty} \int_A |L(u)-f|^p dx = 0 .$$

Then u is said to be (according to Friedrichs) an $\mathscr{L}^{(p)}$-strong solution of problem (1. 1) (with homogeneous boundary condition). It is obvious that any $\mathscr{L}^{(p)}$-strong solution is a $\mathscr{L}^{(p)}$-weak solution.

We shall denote as problem (1. 1)* the following one $(\Sigma^{(3)} = \Sigma_D^{(3)})$:

(1. 1)* $L^*(v) = f$ in A , $v = 0$ on $\Sigma^{*(2)} \cup \Sigma^{*(3)}$.

XIX. Let the hypothesis a) hold. If the $\mathscr{L}^{(p)}$-weak solution $(p > 1)$ of (5. 3) exists for any $f \in \mathscr{L}^{(p)}$ and is unique, and if the $\mathscr{L}^{\frac{p}{p-1}}$-weak solution of problem (1. 1)* is unique, then any $\mathscr{L}^{(p)}$-weak solution of (5. 3) is an $\mathscr{L}^{(p)}$-strong solution.

For the existence and uniqueness of the $\mathscr{L}^{(p)}$-weak solution of (5.3) it follows that the inequality holds

(5. 7) $$\int_A |u|^p dx \leq K \int_A |f|^p dx .$$

Since only the zero function of $\mathscr{L}^{(\frac{p}{p-1})}(A)$ is orthogonal to every $L(u)$ ($u \in C_L$ and satisfying (5. 2)) a sequence u_n of such functions can be chosen in such a way that $L(u_n)$ converge to f ; (5. 6) then follows from (5. 7).

§6. The $\mathscr{H}$-weak solutions

We want now to consider a different approach to problem (1. 1) that appears as a natural extension to our elliptic-parabolic problems of the well known method for elliptic equations founded on energy integral.

We shall only consider, for the sake of simplicity, the case

$\Sigma^{(3)} \equiv \Sigma^{(3)}_{D}$ with homogeneous boundary conditions

$$(1.1)_0 \qquad L(u) = f \text{ in } A \;, \quad u = 0 \text{ on } \Sigma^{(2)} \cup \Sigma^{(3)} \;.$$

For a function $u \in C_L$ and a function $v \in C^1(A \cup \Sigma)$ the integral identity holds

$$\int_A vL(u)dx = -\int_A [a^{hk} v_{x_h} u_{x_k} + u(b^h - a^{hk}_{x_h}) v_{x_k} + (b^h_{x_h} - a^{hk}_{x_h x_k} - c)uv]dx -$$

$$-\int_{\Sigma^{(3)}} v a^{hk} u_{x_h} n_k d\sigma - \int_{\Sigma} u v b d\sigma \;.$$

Let $\mathscr{W}$ be the class of functions belonging to $C^1(A \cup \Sigma)$ and vanishing on $\Sigma^{(3)}$ (when not empty). If $u \in C_L$ and vanishes a.e. on $\Sigma^{(2)} \cup \Sigma^{(3)}$, then for any $v \in \mathscr{W}$ the identity is satisfied

$$\int_A vL(u)dx = -\int_A [a^{hk} v_{x_h} u_{x_k} + u(b^h - a^{hk}_{x_h}) v_{x_k} + (b^h_{x_h} - a^{hk}_{x_h x_k} - c)uv]dx -$$

$$-\int_{\Sigma^{(1)}} u v b d\sigma \;.$$

Let us introduce a scalar product in $\mathscr{W}$ in the following way:

$$(u, v) = \int_A (a^{hk} u_{x_h} v_{x_k} + uv)dx + \int_{\Sigma^{(1)} \cup \Sigma^{(2)}} u v \, |b| \, d\sigma \;.$$

The space $\mathscr{H}$ is the Hilbert space obtained by functional completion from $\mathscr{W}$ with the introduced scalar product.

Let us consider for $u, v \in \mathscr{W}$ the bilinear form

$$B(u, v) = -\int_A [a^{hk} v_{x_h} u_{x_k} + u(b^h - a^{hk}_{x_k}) v_{x_h} + (b^h_{x_h} - a^{hk}_{x_h x_k} - c)uv]dx -$$

$$-\int_{\Sigma^{(1)}} u v b d\sigma \;.$$

It is easily seen that:

$$|B(u,v)| \le M\Big(\int_A (|\mathrm{grad}\, v| + v^2)dx + \int_{\Sigma^{(1)}} |v|^2 d\sigma\Big)^{\frac{1}{2}} \|u\|$$

where M is a constant depending on the coefficients of L. For any fixed $v \in \mathscr{W}$, $B(u,v)$ can be considered as a linear bounded functional of u defined on $\mathscr{H}$.

Given $f \in \mathscr{L}^{(2)}(A)$, we define as an $\mathscr{H}$-weak solution of the problem $(1.1)_0$ a function u in $\mathscr{H}$ satisfying the equation

$$\int_A v f\, dx = B(u,v) ,$$

for any $v \in \mathscr{W}$.

Assuming hypothesis α) it is evident that any $\mathscr{H}$-weak solution is an $\mathscr{L}^{(2)}$-weak solution.

For the representation theorem of linear functionals in Hilbert space, we have for $u \in \mathscr{H}$, $v \in \mathscr{W}$:

$$B(u,v) = (u,\ T(v)) .$$

$T(v)$ is a linear transformation defined in $\mathscr{W}$ and with range in $\mathscr{H}$.

For $u \in \mathscr{W}$, and $v \in \mathscr{W}$, we have

$$\begin{aligned}(6.1)\qquad B(u,v) = &-\int_A [a^{hk} v_{x_h} u_{x_k} + \tfrac{1}{2} u(b^h - a^{hk}_{x_k}) v_{x_h} - \tfrac{1}{2} v(b^h - a^{hk}_{x_k}) u_{x_h} + \\ &+ (\tfrac{1}{2} b^h_{x_h} - \tfrac{1}{2} a^{hk}_{x_h x_k} - c) uv] dx - \tfrac{1}{2}\int_{\Sigma^{(1)}} uvb\, d\sigma + \tfrac{1}{2}\int_{\Sigma^{(2)}} uvb\, d\sigma .\end{aligned}$$

Let us suppose that:

$$(6.2)\qquad \tfrac{1}{2} b^h_{x_h} - \tfrac{1}{2} a^{hk}_{x_h x_k} - c > m_0 > 0 \quad \text{in } A \cup \Sigma .$$

This condition is satisfied if we assume c negative and $|c|$ large enough. If (6.2) is satisfied we easily get from (6.1) for $v \in \mathscr{W}$:

$$\begin{aligned}|B(v,v)| = &\int_A [a^{hk} v_{x_h} v_{x_k} + (\tfrac{1}{2} b^h_{x_h} - \tfrac{1}{2} a^{hk}_{x_h x_k} - c) v^2] dx + \\ &+ \tfrac{1}{2}\int_{\Sigma^{(1)}} v^2 b\, d\sigma - \tfrac{1}{2}\int_{\Sigma^{(2)}} v^2 b\, d\sigma \ge \lambda_0 \|v\|^2 \qquad (\lambda_0 > 0) .\end{aligned}$$

It follows that

$$\|v\|^2 \leq \frac{1}{\lambda_0} |B(v,v)| \leq |(v, T(v)| \leq \|v\| \, \|T(v)\|$$

(6.3)

$$\left(\int_A v^2 dx\right)^{\frac{1}{2}} \leq \frac{1}{\lambda_0} \|T(v)\| \ .$$

From theorem XIV we deduce:

XX. If condition (6.2) is satisfied, for any $f \in \mathscr{L}^{(2)}(A)$ a $\mathscr{H}$-weak solution of problem $(1.1)_0$ exists.

The unicity of the $\mathscr{H}$-weak solution is an open question. It is connected with the continuity of the bilinear form $B(u,v)$ with respect to the pair (u,v). When this is the case then, since $B(u,v)$ can be extended by continuity in $\mathscr{H} \times \mathscr{H}$, from (6.3) uniquess of the $\mathscr{H}$-weak solution follows easily.

$B(u,v)$ is continuous with respect to the pair (u,v) in the case that L be self-adjoint, i.e., $b^h \equiv a^{hk}_{x_k}$. This is easily seen from (6.1). In this case, if c is negative in $A \cup \Sigma$, a $\mathscr{H}$-weak solution exists for any given $f \in \mathscr{L}^{(2)}(A)$ and is unique.

NOTES

1. The summation convention is assumed throughout this paper.
2. Extensions of $b(x)$ for different h's generally do not agree at the common points of the borders or two different Σ_h's.
3. C. Pucci (Rend. Acc. Nax. Lincei, 1957) proved (3.8), by a different method, under the hypothesis $u = 0$ on the whole of Σ. It must be observed that the set $\Sigma^{(2)} \cup \Sigma^{(3)}$, where u is required to vanish a.e. in order to establish (3.8), may be empty as some of the examples given in section 2 prove.
4. $\overline{\Sigma^{(3)}_D}$ denotes the closure of $\Sigma^{(3)}_D$.
5. For details see [5].
6. Let x_0 be a point of minimum for u in A. Then $[L(w)-cu]_{x=x_0} = a^{hk}(x_0)u_{x_h x_k}(x_0)$. We have $\sum_{h,k}^{1,r} u_{x_h x_k}(x_0)\lambda_h\lambda_k \geq 0$ and $a^{hk}\lambda_h\lambda_k = \sum_{m=1}^{r}(g^h_m \lambda_h)^2$. We get $a^{hk}u_{x_h x_k} = \sum_{m=1}^{r} g^h_m g^k_m u_{x_h x_k} \geq 0$ for $x = x_0$. It follows from $c < 0$ that $u(x_0) \geq 0$. Analogously it is proved that $u(x_0) \leq 0$ if x_0 is a point of maximum for u in A.

7. For the proof of this theorem, see [3], [5].

8. See [3], [5].

BIBLIOGRAPHY

1. Ascoli, G., Burgatti, P., and Giraud, G., Equazioni alle derivate parziali di tipo ellittico e parabolico, G. C. Sansoni Edit. Firenze 1936.

2. Cimmino, G., Su un problema di valori al contorno per le equazioni a derivate parziali di tipo parabolico, indipendente dalla natura delle caratteristiche, Atti Acc. Sci. Torino, 1930.

3. Fichera, G., Alcuni recenti sviluppi della teoria dei problemi al contorno per le equazioni alle derivate parziali, Atti del Convegno Internaz. di Trieste, 1954.

4. Fichera, G., Sulle equazioni differenziali lineari ellittico-paraboliche del secondo ordine, Atti Acc. Naz. Lincei, 1956.

5. Fichera, G., Premesse ad una teoria generale dei problemi al contorno per le equazioni differenziali, Corsi Istituto Naz. Alta Matem. 1958, Libreria Veschi, Roma.

6. Friedrichs, K. O., The identity of weak and strong extensions of differential operators, Trans. Amer. Math. Soc, 1944.

7. Friedrichs, K. O., Symmetric positive linear differential equations, Comm. Pure Appl. Math., 1958.

8. Gevrey, M., Sur les equations aux derivées partielles du type parabolique, Journ. de Matem., 1913 e 1914.

9. Lax, P., and Milgram, A., Parabolic equations, Contribution to the Theory of Partial Differential Equations, Princeton, 1954.

10. Lions, J. L., Problems aux limites en théorie des distributions, Acta Math., 1955.

11. Lions, J. L., Sur les problemes mixtes pour certaines systèmes paraboliques dans les ouvertes non cylindriques, Ann. Inst. Fourier, 1957.

12. Magenes, E., Il problema della derivata obliqua regolare per le equazioni lineari ellittico-paraboliche del secondo ordine in m variabili, Rend. di Matem., 1957.

13. Picone, M., Appunti di Analisi Superiore, Rondinella, Napoli, 1940.

14. Picone, M., Maggiorazione degli integrali delle equazioni totalmente paraboliche alle derivate parziali del secondo ordine, Ann. di Mat. pura e appl., 1929.

RICHARD S. VARGA

Factorization and Normalized Iterative Methods

§1. Introduction

In studying the literature on iterative methods for solving elliptic difference equations, one finds that these iterative methods can be phrased so that they all depend upon the ability to directly solve appropriate matrix equations in few unknowns. In some cases, such as the Young-Frankel successive overrelaxation iterative method [38, 10] and the Richardson iterative method [24, 39], the matrix equations to be directly solved involve only one linear equation in one unknown. In the other cases, such as the Peaceman-Rachford iterative method [21], and the Douglas-Rachford iterative method [8], tridiagonal matrix equations are directly solved. While the idea of group relaxation [19, 13, 4], the direct solution of matrix equations in few unknowns, has for some time been recognized to be advantageous, it appears that only the systematic direct solution of tridiagonal matrix equations has gained popularity in practical machine codes for solving elliptic difference equations.

The main purpose of this article is to introduce a class of iterative methods which depend upon the direct solution of matrix equations involving matrices more general than tridiagonal matrices. We shall show how these appropriate matrix equations can be directly and efficiently solved, and we shall show in addition how standard methods for accelerating convergence can be applied.

§§2. Regular Splittings

We seek to solve the matrix equation

$$A\underline{x} = \underline{k} \quad , \tag{2.1}$$

where $A = (a_{i,j})$ is a given $n \times n$ non-singular matrix, and $\underline{k}$ is a given column vector with n components. As in [17], we split the matrix A into

$$A = B - C \quad , \tag{2.2}$$

where B and C are $n \times n$ matrices. If, for an arbitrary $n \times n$

matrix M , M has nonnegative entries, we write $M \geq 0$. If M has only positive entries, we write $M > 0$. Similarly, if the matrix $M_1 - M_2$ has nonnegative entries, we write $M_1 \geq M_2$.

Definition 1. $A = B - C$ is a regular splitting of A if and only if $B^{-1} \geq 0$ and $C \geq 0$.

In what is to follow, we assume that matrix equations of the form

$$(2.3) \qquad B\underline{x} = \underline{g} ,$$

where $\underline{g}$ is a given column vector, can be directly solved for the vector $\underline{x}$. If (2.2) represents a regular splitting of A , then the iterative method

$$(2.4) \qquad B\underline{x}^{(m+1)} = C\underline{x}^{(m)} + \underline{k} , \quad m = 0, 1, 2, \ldots ,$$

where $\underline{x}^{(0)}$ is an arbitrary vector, can be carried out. Equivalently, we write (2.4) in the form

$$(2.4') \qquad \underline{x}^{(m+1)} = B^{-1} C\underline{x}^{(m)} + B^{-1} \underline{k} , \quad m = 0, 1, 2, \ldots .$$

The matrix $D \equiv B^{-1}C$ has non-negative entries if (2.2) represents a regular splitting of A . Using (2.2), we express the matrix D as

$$(2.5) \qquad D = (A + C)^{-1} C = (I + A^{-1}C)^{-1} A^{-1} C .$$

If $E \equiv A^{-1}C$, then

$$(2.5') \qquad D = (I + E)^{-1} E .$$

If $A^{-1} > 0$, and $A = B - C$ is a regular splitting of A , then the matrix E has only non-negative entries. If, for an arbitrary square matrix M , $\bar{\mu}[M]$ denotes the spectral radius of M ,i.e. $\bar{\mu}[M] = \max_k |\lambda_k|$, where λ_k is an eigenvalue of M , then we say M is convergent if and only if $\bar{\mu}[M] < 1$.

Lemma 1. If $A = B - C$ is a regular splitting of A and $A^{-1} > 0$, then

$$(2.6) \qquad \bar{\mu}[D] = \frac{\bar{\mu}[E]}{1 + \bar{\mu}[E]} ,$$

and the matrix D is convergent.

Proof. It is clear from (2.5') that eigenvectors of E are also eigenvectors of D . Thus, if $E\underline{a}_j = \lambda_j \underline{a}_j$, then $D\underline{a}_j = \frac{\lambda_j}{1 + \lambda_j} \underline{a}_j$.

Since both D and E are non-negative matrices, the result of (2.6) is an immediate consequence of the Perron-Frobenius theory of nonnegative matrices [22, 12, 7]. From (2.6) it follows that $\overline{\mu}[D] < 1$ and thus D is convergent.

As a consequence of this lemma, the iterative method of (2.4) is necessarily convergent.

We now assume that $A = B_1 - C_1 = B_2 - C_2$ are two regular splittings of A. With $D_i \equiv B_i^{-1} C_i$, we now compare the spectral radii of the matrices D_1 and D_2.

Theorem 1. Let $A = B_1 - C_1 = B_2 - C_2$ be two regular splittings of A, where $A^{-1} > 0$. If $C_2 \geq C_1 \geq 0$, equality excluded*, then

$$1 > \overline{\mu}[D_2] > \overline{\mu}[D_1] > 0 . \tag{2.7}$$

Proof. From (2.6), $\overline{\mu}[D]$ is monotone with respect to $\overline{\mu}[E]$, and it thus suffices to prove that $\overline{\mu}[E_2] > \overline{\mu}[E_1] > 0$. Since $C_2 \geq C_1 \geq 0$, equality excluded. and $A^{-1} > 0$, it follows that $E_2 \geq E_1 \geq 0$, equality excluded. We first assume that the matrix E_1 is irreducible, i.e. there exists no $n \times n$ permutation matrix Λ such that

$$\Lambda E_1 \Lambda^{-1} = \begin{bmatrix} E^{(1)}_{1,1} & E^{(1)}_{1,2} \\ 0 & E^{(1)}_{2,2} \end{bmatrix}, \tag{2.8}$$

where $E^{(1)}_{1,1}$ and $E^{(1)}_{2,2}$ are square submatrices. With E_1 irreducible, and $E_2 \geq E_1 \geq 0$, equality excluded, it follows [7, p. 598] that $\overline{\mu}[E_2] > \overline{\mu}[E_1] > 0$. If E_1 is reducible, let Λ be $n \times n$ permutation matrix for which (2.8) is valid. With

$$\Lambda A^{-1} \Lambda^{-1} \equiv \begin{bmatrix} M_{1,1} & M_{1,2} \\ M_{2,1} & M_{2,2} \end{bmatrix} ; \Lambda C_1 \Lambda^{-1} \equiv \begin{bmatrix} C^{(1)}_{1,1} & C^{(1)}_{1,2} \\ C^{(1)}_{2,1} & C^{(1)}_{2,2} \end{bmatrix}, \tag{2.9}$$

then since $A^{-1} > 0$ and $E_1 = A^{-1} C_1$, it follows from (2.8) that both $C^{(1)}_{1,1}$ and $C^{(1)}_{2,1}$ are null, and thus $E^{(1)}_{1,1}$ is also null. Thus, if E_1 is reducible, we may assume in (2.8) that $E^{(1)}_{1,1}$ is null, and that $E^{(1)}_{2,2}$ is irreducible since $E_1 \geq 0$, equality excluded. The non-zero eigenvalues of the matrix E_1 are just the non-zero eigenvalues of the irreducible nonnegative submatrix $E^{(1)}_{2,2}$, and $\overline{\mu}[E_1] = \overline{\mu}[E^{(1)}_{2,2}] > 0$. Actually, the irreducibility of $E^{(1)}_{2,2}$ and

$A^{-1} > 0$ imply that $E^{(1)}_{2,2} > 0$ and $E^{(1)}_{1,2} > 0$. Since $C_2 \geq C_1$, equality excluded, then either $E^{(2)}_{2,2} \geq E^{(1)}_{2,2}$, equality excluded, or else $E^{(1)}_{2,2} = E^{(2)}_{2,2}$ is a principal minor of a larger irreducible square submatrix of E_2, and thus [7], $\overline{\mu}[E_2] > \overline{\mu}[E_1]$, which completes the proof.

The result of Theorem 1 is a generalization of recent results of Householder [16, Theorems 4.12 and 4.13], which generalize results of Fiedler and Pták [9]. The basic idea for this result, however, goes back to the work of Stein and Rosenberg [26]. The particular setting of Theorem 1 will be convenient, as we shall see, for applications to the numerical solution of elliptic difference equations.

It is not difficult to find matrices A which admit regular splittings, and have $A^{-1} > 0$. In fact, consider any $n \times n$ matrix $A = (a_{i,j})$ having the following properties:

(2.10)
1. $a_{i,j} \leq 0$ for all $i \neq j$, $1 \leq i, j \leq n$.
2. A is irreducible.
3. $\Sigma_{j=1}^{n} a_{i,j} \geq 0$ for all $1 \leq i \leq n$, with strict inequality for some i.

It follows [7] that A^{-1} has positive entries. From the conditions of (2.10), the diagonal entries of A are positive. Thus, if B is the positive diagonal matrix derived from the diagonal entries of A, then $B^{-1} \geq 0$, and defining $C \equiv B - A$, it follows that $C \geq 0$. Thus $A = B - C$ is a regular splitting of A. Generalizing, if B is any matrix derived from the matrix A satisfying (2.10) by setting certain off-diagonal entries of A to zero, then $B^{-1} \geq 0$ [7, 37], and $A = B - C$ represents a regular splitting of A. Of considerable practical interest is the fact that five-point discrete approximations on a rectangular mesh to the self-adjoint elliptic partial differential equation

$$(2.11) \quad -\nabla\cdot(D\nabla u) + \Sigma u = S, \quad \Sigma(\underline{x}) \geq 0, \quad D(\underline{x}) > 0, \quad S = S(\underline{x})$$

for general bounded regions in the plane with suitable boundary conditions, can be derived [31] so that the resulting matrix A, determined by the associated system of linear equations, satisfies (2.10). If a matrix A satisfying (2.10) is symmetric, then it is positive definite [29]. Irreducible symmetric and positive definite matrices A with non-positive off-diagonal entries are called <u>Stieltjes matrices</u> [3] and for these matrices, it is also known that $A^{-1} > 0$. The original idea for this goes back to an early result of Stieltjes [28].

<u>Lemma 2.</u> Let A be a Stieltjes matrix, and let $A = B - C$ be a regular splitting of the matrix A, where C is symmetric. Then

$$(2.12) \qquad \bar{\mu}[D] \le \frac{\bar{\mu}[C]\,\bar{\mu}[A^{-1}]}{1+\bar{\mu}[C]\,\bar{\mu}[A^{-1}]} ,$$

with equality if the matrices A and C commute.

Proof. It suffices to show that $\bar{\mu}[A^{-1}C] \le \bar{\mu}[A^{-1}]\cdot\bar{\mu}[C]$. For symmetric matrices, it is known [16, p. 219] that the value of the spectral norm is that of the spectral radius. Hence, since A^{-1} and C are symmetric, $\bar{\mu}[A^{-1}C] \le \|A^{-1}C\| \le \|A^{-1}\|\cdot\|C\| = \bar{\mu}[A^{-1}]\cdot\bar{\mu}[C]$, from which the inequality of (2.12) follows.

If M is an arbitrary convergent matrix, the rate of convergence [38] of the matrix M is defined by the positive quantity

$$(2.13) \qquad R(M) = -\ln \bar{\mu}[M] .$$

Theorem 2. Let A be a Stieltjes matrix, and let $A = B_1 - C_1 = B_2 - C_2$ be two regular splittings of A , with $0 \le C_1 \le C_2$, equality excluded. If C_1 and C_1 are symmetric and $\bar{\mu}[E_1] \to +\infty$, then

$$(2.14) \qquad \frac{R(D_1)}{R(D_2)} \sim \frac{\bar{\mu}[E_2]}{\bar{\mu}[E_1]} .$$

Moreover, if C_2 commutes with A , then

$$(2.15) \qquad \frac{\bar{\mu}[E_2]}{\bar{\mu}[E_1]} \ge \frac{\bar{\mu}[C_2]}{\bar{\mu}[C_1]} > 1 .$$

Proof. From the proof of Theorem 1, $\bar{\mu}[E_2] > \bar{\mu}[E_1]$, and from (2.6) we have that

$$R(D_i) = +\ln\left(1 + \frac{1}{\bar{\mu}[E_i]}\right) = \frac{1}{\bar{\mu}[E_i]} + 0\left(\frac{1}{\bar{\mu}^{-2}[E_i]}\right), \text{ as } \bar{\mu}[E_i] \to +\infty ,$$

and (2.14) follows. If C_2 commutes with A , the inequalities of (2.15) follow respectively from the proof of Theorem 1, Lemma 2, and the assumption that $C_2 \ge C_1 \ge 0$.

We shall later find it convenient to compare the rates of convergence of two iterative methods by means of the (2.14) and (2.15).

§3. Acceleration Methods

We shall henceforth assume that A is a Stieltjes matrix, and (2.2) represents a regular splitting of A , where B is symmetric and positive definite. It follows that C is symmetric and has nonnegative entries. Again we assume that matrix equations of the form (2.3) can be directly solved.

The first acceleration method which we consider is the Young-Frankel successive overrelaxation iterative method [38, 10], and its generalization by Arms, Gates, and Zondek [1]. If the matrix A and the column vectors $\underline{x}$ and $\underline{k}$ are partitioned into the form

(3.1)
$$A = \begin{bmatrix} A_{1,1} & A_{1,2} \cdots A_{1,N} \\ A_{2,1} & A_{2,2} \cdots A_{2,N} \\ \vdots & \vdots \\ A_{N,1} & A_{N,2} \cdots A_{N,N} \end{bmatrix}, \quad \underline{x} = \begin{bmatrix} X_1 \\ X_2 \\ \vdots \\ X_N \end{bmatrix}, \quad \underline{k} = \begin{bmatrix} K_1 \\ K_2 \\ \vdots \\ K_N \end{bmatrix},$$

where the diagonal submatrices $A_{j,j}$ are square, we can write (2.1) equivalently as

(3.2)
$$\sum_{j=1}^{N} A_{i,j} X_j = K_i \ , \ i = 1, 2, \ldots, N \ .$$

Let B be the diagonal block matrix

(3.3)
$$B = \begin{bmatrix} A_{1,1} & 0 & \ldots & 0 \\ 0 & A_{2,2} & \ldots & 0 \\ \vdots & & & \vdots \\ 0 & 0 & \ldots & A_{N,N} \end{bmatrix},$$

and let the matrix C be defined by $A = B - C$. Since A is a Stieltjes matrix, then B and C are both symmetric, and $C \geq 0$. Since B is the direct sum of principal minors of A , then B is positive definite, with non-positive off-diagonal entries. It follows [2] that $B^{-1} \geq 0$, and hence, for this definition of the matrices B and C , we have a regular splitting of A . The successive over-relaxation iterative method, applied to (3.2), is defined by

(3.4)
$$X_i^{(m+1)} = X_i^{(m)} + \omega \left\{ A_{i,i}^{-1} \left(-\sum_{j<i} A_{i,j} X_j^{(m+1)} - \sum_{j>i} A_{i,j} X_j^{(m)} + K_i \right) - X_i^{(m)} \right\},$$

$m = 0, 1, 2, \ldots, i = 1, 2, \ldots, N$, where $\underline{x}^{(0)}$ is an arbitrary vector. The quantity ω is the relaxation factor. In actual computations, the equivalent form of (3.4)

(3.5)
$$A_{i,i} \overset{*}{X}_i^{(m+1)} = -\sum_{j<i} A_{i,j} X_j^{(m+1)} - \sum_{j>i} A_{i,j} X_j^{(m)} + K_i, \ i=1,2,\ldots,N ,$$

and

(3.5') $$x_i^{(m+1)} \equiv x_i^{(m)} + \omega \left\{ \overset{*}{X}_i^{(m+1)} - x_i^{(m)} \right\}, \quad i = 1, 2, \ldots, N,$$

may be more useful. We now assume that the matrix A satisfies property A^{π}, and is (consistently) ordered [1]. We write (3.4) in the form

(3.6) $$\underline{x}^{(m+1)} = \mathscr{L}_{\omega}\underline{x}^{(m)} + \underline{g}, \quad m = 0, 1, 2, \ldots,$$

where $\mathscr{L}_{\omega}$ denotes the successive overrelaxation iteration matrix. Since A is by assumption a Stieltjes matrix, and B is, by construction, symmetric and positive definite, we can apply directly the results of Arms, Gates, and Zondek [1], which generalized Young's original results [38], and we obtain

Theorem 3. Let the partitioned Stieltjes matrix A of (3.1) satisfy property A^{π} and be (consistently) ordered. Then, the optimum value of ω, ω_b, which minimizes $\bar{\mu}[\mathscr{L}_{\omega}]$ as a function of the real variable ω, is given by

(3.7) $$\omega_b = \frac{2}{1 + \sqrt{1 - \bar{\mu}^2[D]}},$$

and

(3.8) $$\bar{\mu}[\mathscr{L}_{\omega_b}] = \omega_b - 1.$$

Moreover, as $\bar{\mu}[D] \to 1-$, then

(3.9) $$R(\mathscr{L}_{\omega_b}) \sim 2\sqrt{2}\,[R(D)]^{\frac{1}{2}}.$$

Since ω_b of (3.7) increases monotonically with $\bar{\mu}[D]$, we obtain from Theorems 2 and 3 the following

Corollary 1. Let $A = B_1 - C_1 = B_2 - C_2$ be two regular splittings of the Stieltjes matrix A, where $0 \leq C_1 \leq C_2$, equality excluded. Let B_1 and B_2 be diagonal block matrices, as in (3.3), derived from different partitionings of A, where each partitioning of A satisfies property A^{π} and is consistently ordered. Then,

(3.10) $$\frac{R(\mathscr{L}_{\omega_b}^{(1)})}{R(\mathscr{L}_{\omega_b}^{(2)})} > 1.$$

Moreover, if both C_1 and C_2 commute with A, and $\bar{\mu}[E_1] \to +\infty$, then

$$(3.11)\qquad \frac{R(\mathscr{L}^{(1)}_{\omega_b})}{R(\mathscr{L}^{(2)}_{\omega_b})} \sim \left(\frac{\bar{\mu}[C_2]}{\bar{\mu}[C_1]}\right)^{1/2} .$$

Of practical importance is the fact that the matrix $D = B^{-1}C \equiv (d_{i,j})$, derived from a regular splitting of A, has nonnegative entries, and thus [7] if $\underline{u}$ is any vector with positive components u_i, then nontrivial upper and lower bounds for the spectral radius of D are given by

$$(3.12)\qquad \min_i \left(\frac{\sum_j d_{i,j}\, u_j}{u_i}\right) \le \bar{\mu}[D] \le \max_i \left(\frac{\sum_j d_{i,j}\, u_j}{u_i}\right) .$$

If D is, moreover, irreducible, then $\bar{\mu}[D]$ can be expressed [35] as a minimax

$$(3.12')\qquad \max_{\underline{u}\in P}\left\{\min_i \left(\frac{\sum_j d_{i,j}\, u_j}{u_i}\right)\right\} = \bar{\mu}[D] = \min_{\underline{u}\in P}\left\{\max_i \left(\frac{\sum_j d_{i,j}\, u_j}{u_i}\right)\right\}$$

where P is the set of all column vectors $\underline{u}$ with positive components. Upper and lower bounds for $\bar{\mu}[D]$ give, respectively, upper and lower bounds[§] for ω_b, defined in (3.7).

Our next acceleration method is what we call the Chebyshev semi-iterative method with respect to the matrix D, and has been widely discussed in various forms in the literature [18, 27, 33, 39].

Here we need only our previous assumptions, A a Stieltjes matrix, B and C defining a regular splitting of A, and B symmetric and positive definite, to enable us to rigorously apply this method. The matrix $D = B^{-1}C$ is nonnegative, and has real eigenvalues, since D is similar to a symmetric matrix. It follows, from the Perron-Frobenius theory of nonnegative matrices and Lemma 1, that the eigenvalues μ of D at least satisfy

$$(3.13)\qquad -\bar{\mu}[D] \le \mu \le \bar{\mu}[D] < 1 .$$

If $C_m(x)$ is the Chebyshev polynomial of degree m, defined by

$$(3.14)\qquad C_m(x) = \cos\,[m \cos^{-1} x]\,, \quad |x| \le 1\,, \quad m = 0, 1, 2, \ldots ,$$

then by using the following well known three term recurrence relation for Chebyshev polynomials

$$(3.15)\quad \begin{cases} C_0(x) = 1\ ;\ C_1(x) = x\ , \\ C_{m+1}(x) = 2x\, C_m(x) - C_{m-1}(x)\ ,\ m = 1,\ 2,\ \dots\ , \end{cases}$$

the Chebyshev semi-iterative method with respect to the matrix D, applied to (2.4), is defined# by

$$(3.16)\quad \underline{x}^{(m+1)} = \alpha_{m+1}\{D\underline{x}^{(m)} + B^{-1}\underline{k} - \underline{x}^{(m-1)}\} + \underline{x}^{(m-1)},\ m=0,1,2,\dots,$$

where

$$(3.17)\quad \alpha_1 = 1\ ,\ \alpha_{m+1} = \frac{2\, C_m(1/\bar{\mu})}{\bar{\mu}\, C_{m+1}(1/\bar{\mu})},\ m = 1,2,\dots,$$

and $\bar{\mu} \equiv \bar{\mu}[D]$. Again, in actual computations, the equivalent form of (3.16),

$$(3.18)\quad B\underline{\overset{*}{x}}^{(m+1)} = C\underline{x}^{(m)} + \underline{k}\ ,$$

and

$$(3.18')\quad \underline{x}^{(m+1)} = \alpha_{m+1}\{\underline{\overset{*}{x}}^{(m+1)} - \underline{x}^{(m-1)}\} + \underline{x}^{(m-1)}\ ,$$

may be more useful. If the interval $-\bar{\mu} \le t \le +\bar{\mu}$ is the smallest interval containing all the eigenvalues of D, it is known [33, 39] that the Chebyshev semi-iterative method with respect to the matrix D has the fastest average rate of convergence among all semi-iterative methods, in a certain norm, with respect to the matrix D.

We thus far have considered two acceleration methods applied to the basic iterative method of (2.4). The latter method has the advantage that it requires no further assumptions, such as property A^{π} or a (consistent) ordering to be rigorously applied. The former method on the other hand is, if applicable, faster in rate of convergence [33, 40] and requires in actual computations less vector storage than the Chebyshev semi-iterative method defined in (3.16).

We now consider a new type of splitting of the matrix A, where A is a Stieltjes matrix, B is symmetric and positive definite, but C is now symmetric and non-positive definite. Defining $C \equiv -F$, then F is symmetric and non-negative definite. We furthermore assume that matrix equations of the form

$$(3.19)\quad (B + \rho I)\,\underline{x} = \underline{g}\ ,$$

and

$$(3.19')\quad (F + \rho I)\,\underline{x} = \underline{g}\ ,$$

can be directly solved for the vector $\underline{x}$ for all vectors $\underline{g}$ and all positive scalars ρ. With

$$(3.20) \qquad A = B + F \ ,$$

the Peaceman-Rachford iterative method [21], applied to (2.1), is defined by

$$(3.21) \qquad (B + \rho_m) \underline{x}^{*(m)} = (\rho_m I - F) \underline{x}^{(m)} + \underline{k} \ ,$$

and

$$(3.21') \qquad (F + \rho_m I) \underline{x}^{(m+1)} = (\rho_m I - B) \underline{x}^{*(m)} + \underline{k} \ ,$$

where the ρ_m are positive scalars. The process can be carried out because of our assumptions concerning (3.19) and (3.19'). Similarly, the Douglas-Rachford iterative method [8], applied to (2.1), is defined by (3.21) and

$$(3.21^*) \qquad (F + \rho_m I) \underline{x}^{(m+1)} = F \underline{x}^{(m)} + \rho_m \underline{x}^{*(m)} \ .$$

Combining (3.21) and (3.21'), we obtain

$$(3.22) \qquad \underline{x}^{(m+1)} = T_{\rho_m} \underline{x}^{(m)} + \underline{g}(\rho_m) \ ,$$

where

$$(3.23) \qquad T_\rho \equiv (F + \rho I)^{-1} (\rho I - B)(B + \rho I)^{-1} (\rho I - F) \ .$$

Similarly, combining (3.21) and (3.21*), we obtain

$$(3.24) \qquad \underline{x}^{(m+1)} = U_{\rho_m} \underline{x}^{(m)} + \underline{h}(\rho_m) \ ,$$

where

$$(3.25) \qquad U_\rho \equiv (F + \rho I)^{-1} (B + \rho I)^{-1} \{\rho^2 I + B \cdot F\} \ .$$

We call the matrices T_ρ and U_ρ respectively the Peaceman-Rachford and Douglas-Rachford iteration matrices. If the matrices B and F commute, then the positive scalars ρ_m can be suitably chosen so as to make these iterative methods rapidly convergent [3, 8, 21, 34]. In the case that B and F do not commute, both of these iterative methods are convergent for fixed $\rho > 0$ [3].

Having considered several iterative methods for solving the matrix equation of (2.1), we turn now to the practical question of how these ideas can be actually utilized.

§4. Factorization and Normalized Iterative Techniques

We again assume that A is a Stieltjes matrix, that (2.2) represents a regular splitting of A, and that B is symmetric and positive-definite. It is well known [20] that there exists a real unique upper triangular matrix T with positive diagonal entries such that B can be factored into

$$B \equiv T' T \quad . \tag{4.1}$$

If the matrix T is known, then the matrix equation (2.3) can be directly solved by the writing (2.3) in the form

$$T' \underline{s} = \underline{g} \quad , \tag{4.2}$$

where

$$T \underline{x} = \underline{s} \quad . \tag{4.2'}$$

Both matrix equations of (4.2) and (4.2') can be directly solved by backward substitution.

Now let

$$T \equiv \widetilde{T} R \quad , \tag{4.3}$$

where $\widetilde{T}$ is an upper triangular matrix with unit diagonal entries, and R is a positive diagonal matrix, so that the matrices T, $\widetilde{T}$, and R are all uniquely determined from B. If $R\underline{x} \equiv \underline{y}$, then (2.1) can be written equivalently as

$$\widetilde{T}'\widetilde{T}\underline{y} = \widetilde{C}\underline{y} + R^{-1}\underline{k} \quad , \tag{4.4}$$

where

$$\widetilde{C} \equiv R^{-1} C R^{-1} \quad . \tag{4.5}$$

In analogy to the iterative method of (2.4), we consider the iterative method

$$\widetilde{T}' \widetilde{T} \underline{y}^{(m+1)} = \widetilde{C}\underline{y}^{(m)} + R^{-1}\underline{k} \quad , \quad m = 0, 1, 2, \ldots \quad , \tag{4.6}$$

where $\underline{y}^{(0)}$ is an arbitrary vector. From the definition of the matrices $\widetilde{T}$, $\widetilde{R}$, and $\widetilde{C}$, it follows that $R^{-1}A R^{-1} = \widetilde{T}' \widetilde{T} - \widetilde{C}$ is a regular splitting of $R^{-1}A R^{-1}$. In the case where the matrix $\widetilde{B}$ is symmetric and positive definite and $\widetilde{C}$ is symmetric, we say that $\widetilde{A} = \widetilde{B} - \widetilde{C}$ is a <u>normalized</u> regular splitting of A if $\widetilde{A} = \widetilde{B} - \widetilde{C}$ is a regular splitting of $\widetilde{A}$ and $\widetilde{B} = \widetilde{T}' \widetilde{T}$, where $\widetilde{T}$ is upper triangular with unit diagonal entries. In analogy to §2, if we define

$$\widetilde{D} = (\widetilde{T}' \widetilde{T})^{-1} \widetilde{C} \quad , \tag{4.7}$$

then

$$\widetilde{D} = R D R^{-1} \quad . \tag{4.8}$$

Thus, the matrices D and $\widetilde{D}$ are similar, and evidently have the same spectral radius, proving that the normalization of the basic iterative method of (2.4) does not affect the rate of convergence of the basic iterative method.

The reason for normalizing$^{\pm}$ is purely one of increased efficiency on a digital computing machine, since solving $T'T\underline{x} = \underline{g}$ for the vector $\underline{x}$ requires in general two more multiplications per component than does solving $\widetilde{T}'\widetilde{T}\underline{y} = \underline{h}$ for the vector $\underline{y}$. Thus, if many iterations of (2.4) or (4.6) are anticipated, iterating by means of (4.6) is preferable, since passing finally from the vector $\underline{y}$ to the vector $\underline{x}$ requires but one multiplication per component.

§5. Cyclic Methods

We now consider several practical iterative methods, which can be accelerated by means of the Young-Frankel successive overrelaxation method. We call these methods cyclic iterative methods (as opposed to the primitive methods of §6) since if the partitioned matrix A of (3.1) satisfies property A^{π}, it can be shown [32] that the matrix $D = B^{-1}C$ is cyclic of index 2 in the sense of Romanovsky [25], i.e. there exists a $n \times n$ permutation matrix Λ such that

$$\Lambda D \Lambda^{-1} = \begin{bmatrix} 0 & D_{1,2} \\ D_{2,1} & 0 \end{bmatrix}, \tag{5.1}$$

where the diagonal submatrices are square.

We now consider three iterative techniques simultaneously. Let A be a Stieltjes matrix arising from a five-point approximation on a rectangular mesh in the plane to the self-adjoint elliptic partial differential equation of (2.11), with Dirichlet type boundary conditions. First, let B_3 be the positive diagonal matrix composed of the diagonal entries of A, i.e. B_3 is the matrix of (3.3), corresponding to the partitioning of the matrix A in which the diagonal blocks $A_{j,j}$ of A in (3.1) are all 1×1 matrices. Next, for our rectangular mesh, we number our mesh points along successive horizontal mesh lines, as in Figure 1.

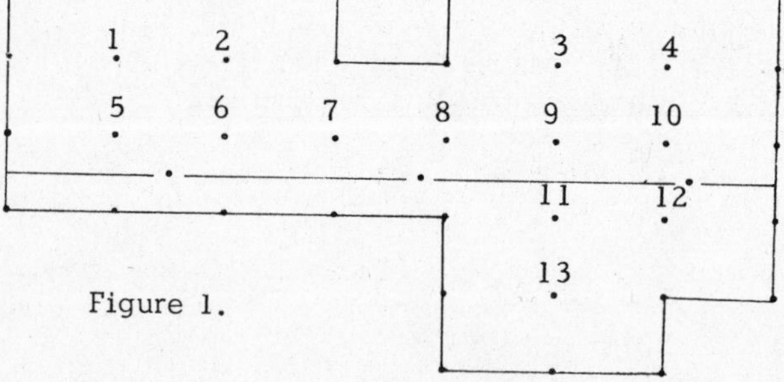

Figure 1.

Since each mesh point is coupled only to its four adjacent mesh points, then let B_2 be the diagonal block matrix of (3.3), corresponding to the partitioning of A into successive blocks consisting of mesh points on a single horizontal mesh line. Finally, let B_1 be the diagonal block matrix corresponding to the partitioning of the matrix A into blocks consisting of mesh points on successive pairs of horizontal mesh lines. Specifically, referring to Figure 1, the matrix B_1 can be expressed as

$$B_1 = \begin{bmatrix} A^{(1)}_{1,1} & 0 \\ 0 & A^{(1)}_{2,2} \end{bmatrix}, \tag{5.2}$$

where $A^{(1)}_{1,1}$ is the 10×10 submatrix coupling the unknowns $x_1, \ldots, x_{10}$, and $A^{(1)}_{2,2}$ is the 3×3 submatrix coupling the unknowns x_{11}, x_{12}, and x_{13}. Defining the matrices C_i by

$$A = B_i - C_i, \quad i = 1, 2, 3, \tag{5.3}$$

it follows that all three different partitionings of the matrix A correspond to regular splittings of A, and in each case the partitioned matrix A satisfies property A^{π}, and can be (consistently) ordered. Moreover,

$$0 \le C_1 \le C_2 \le C_3, \tag{5.4}$$

equality excluded if, as in Figure 1, there are three or more horizontal mesh lines. By means of Corollary 1, it follows that the successive overrelaxation iterative method, with optimum ω, applied to the regular splitting $A = B_1 - C_1$ is faster in rate of convergence than the successive overrelaxation iterative method, with optimum ω's, applied to the remaining cases. The application of the successive overrelaxation iterative method to the regular splitting $A = B_3 - C_3$, which we denote by SOR, is due originally to Young [38] and Frankel [10]. While the theory of [1] applies to both the regular splittings $A = B_1 - C_1 = B_2 - C_2$, only in the latter case has the successive overrelaxation iterative method, denoted by SLOR, been actually considered in solving two-dimensional elliptic difference equations [1, 6, 11, 17]. Since the matrix B_1 couples together adjacent lines of mesh points, we denote the successive overrelaxation iterative method applied to the regular splitting $A = B_1 - C_1$ by S2LOR.

We now show how the iterative method S2LOR can be carried out numerically. Because the matrix A is derived from a five-point formula, the matrix B_1, after a suitable permutation of indices of the mesh points, is a symmetric, positive definite, and five-diagonal matrix. Thus, $B_1 = T'_1 T_1$, where T_1 is an upper tridiagonal matrix with positive diagonal entries. To illustrate this, we have relabled the mesh points of $A^{(1)}_{1,1}$ of (5.2) in Figure 2, which shows that the corresponding matrix coupling the unknowns $x_1, x_2, \ldots, x_{10}$

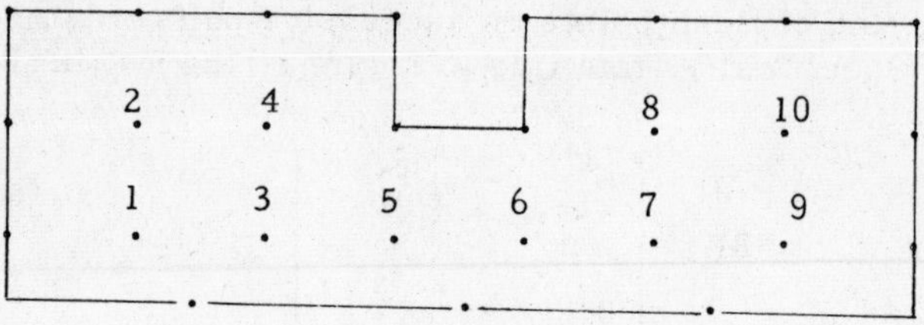

Figure 2.

is a five-diagonal matrix. While matrix equations of the form (2.3), where B is a five-diagonal matrix, can be directly solved by the Gauss elimination method, it is more efficient if one has the upper tridiagonal matrix T_1, where $B = T_1' T_1$, to solve equation (2.3) in the manner of (4.2) - (4.2'). Given the five-diagonal positive definite symmetric matrix B, we can generate the entries of the upper tridiagonal matrix T_1 as follows. Let

(5.5)
$$B = \begin{bmatrix} b_{1,1} & b_{1,2} & b_{1,3} & 0 & 0 & \ldots & 0 \\ b_{1,2} & b_{2,2} & b_{2,3} & b_{2,4} & 0 & \ldots & 0 \\ b_{1,3} & b_{2,3} & b_{3,3} & b_{3,4} & b_{3,5} & \ldots & 0 \\ \vdots & & & & & & \vdots \\ 0 & 0 & 0 & 0 & 0 & \ldots & b_{n,n} \end{bmatrix},$$

(5.5')
$$T = \begin{bmatrix} t_{1,1} & t_{1,2} & t_{1,3} & 0 & 0 & \ldots & 0 \\ 0 & t_{2,2} & t_{2,3} & t_{2,4} & 0 & \ldots & 0 \\ 0 & 0 & t_{3,3} & t_{3,4} & t_{3,5} & \ldots & 0 \\ \vdots & & & & & & \vdots \\ 0 & 0 & 0 & 0 & 0 & \ldots & t_{n,n} \end{bmatrix}$$

If $t_{-1,m} = t_{0,m} \equiv 0$ for $m = 1, 2$, then

$$
(5.6)\quad \begin{cases} t^2_{j-2,j} + t^2_{j-1,j} + t^2_{j,j} = b_{j,j} & , j = 1, 2, \ldots, n , \\ t_{j-1,j}\, t_{j-1,j+1} + t_{j,j}\, t_{j,j+1} = b_{j,j+1} & , j = 1, 2, \ldots, n-1 , \\ t_{j,j}\, t_{j,j+2} = b_{j,j+2} & , j = 1, 2, \ldots, n-2 , \end{cases}
$$

With (5.6), it is clear how a normalized $\tilde{T}_1$, with unit diagonal entries, can be similarly generated.

It is convenient now to consider the P-condition numbers of the matrices B_i, $i = 1, 2, 3$. Following Todd [30], we define the P-condition number $P(M)$ of an arbitrary non-singular matrix M as

$$
(5.7)\qquad P(M) = \frac{\max\limits_k |\lambda_k|}{\min\limits_k |\lambda_k|} ,
$$

where the λ_k are eigenvalues of M. Since the matrices B_i are all symmetric and positive definite, the eigenvalues $\lambda_k(i)$ of the matrices B_i are positive real numbers, and thus

$$
(5.7')\qquad P(B_i) = \frac{\max\limits_k \lambda_k(i)}{\min\limits_k \lambda_k(i)} , \qquad i = 1, 2, 3 .
$$

The following table** gives information about the application of the normalized iterative methods SOR, SLOR, and S2LOR, to the numerical solution of matrix problems arising from a five-point approximation, on a rectangular mesh in the plane, to the partial differential equation of (2.11), with Dirichlet-type boundary conditions. For the second

Method	Operations per Mesh Point		Estimate of $\overline{\mu}[C]$	P(B)
SOR	5m	6a	4	1
SLOR	5m	6a	2	3
S2LOR	6m	7a	1	7

TABLE I. Five-Point Formula in Two Dimensions

and third columns, only Laplace's equation on a uniform mesh is considered. The second column gives upper bounds, by Gerschgorin's lemma [14], for the spectral radii of the corresponding matrices C_i. The third column gives upper bounds for the P-condition numbers of the unnormalized matrices B_i.

It is interesting to note that the numbers in Table I are independent of the actual numbers of mesh points considered. From Table I, we can conclude that, for the matrices B_i, directly solving matrix equations of the form (2. 3) does not give rise to serious round-off error difficulties. To illustrate the usefulness of the second column of numbers, we consider the numerical solution of the Dirichlet problem in a unit square on a uniform mesh of side h. For this specific problem, it is known [1, 17] that the matrices C_2, C_3, and A commute, and that

$$(5.8) \qquad \lim_{h \to 0} \frac{R(\mathscr{L}^{(2)}_{\omega_b})}{R(\mathscr{L}^{(3)}_{\omega_b})} = \sqrt{2} .$$

However, since $\bar{\mu}[C_3] \to 4$, $\bar{\mu}[C_2] \to 2$; $\bar{\mu}[C_1] \to 1$, and $\bar{\mu}[A^{-1}] \to +\infty$ as $h \to 0$, we can obtain the above result as a consequence of Theorem 2 and Corollary 1, as well as the fact that

$$(5.8') \qquad \lim_{h \to 0} \frac{R(\mathscr{L}^{(1)}_{\omega_b})}{R(\mathscr{L}^{(2)}_{\omega_b})} \geq \sqrt{2} .$$

Thus, the rate of convergence of the iterative method S2LOR with optimum ω, is, for small mesh spacings h, considerably greater than the rates of convergence of the iterative methods SLOR and SOR, with optimum ω's.

As pointed out in [1], the iterative method SLOR can be rigorously applied to the iterative solution of matrix problems arising from a nine-point approximation to (2. 11) in two dimensions. While it is easy to see that the iterative method S2LOR can also be applied to this problem, the surprising result, as indicated in Table II, is that the normalized iterative method S2LOR requires in general the <u>same</u> number of operations per mesh point as does either the normalized iterative method SLOR or the normalized iterative method SOR. As in Table I, the information in Table II concerns the normalized iterative methods SOR, SLOR,

Method	Operations per Mesh Point		Estimate of $\bar{\mu}[C]$	$P(B)$
SOR	9m	10a	20	1
SLOR	9m	10a	12	7/3
S2LOR	9m	10a	6	17/3

TABLE II. Nine-Point Formula in Two Dimensions

S2LOR, and the last two columns refer to the numerical solution of Laplace's equation on a uniform mesh in the plane. The arguments extend to three dimensions, and we include, for completeness, the seven point approximation in three dimensions to the partial differential equation of (2.11), with given Dirichlet-type boundary conditions.

Method	Operations per Mesh Point		Estimate of $\overline{\mu}[C]$	P(B)
SOR	7m	8a	6	1
SLOR	7m	8a	4	2
S2LOR	8m	9a	3	3

TABLE III. Seven-Point Formula in Three Dimensions

The range of application of iterative method S2LOR is not restricted to rectangular meshes in two and three dimensions. As another application, we consider solving Laplace's equation on a uniform triangular mesh in the plane, and we couple together mesh points on successive pairs of horizontal mesh lines. If we use a seven-point approximation to Laplace's equation in the plane, then, as illustrated in Figure 3, the matrix coupling the unknowns $x_1, \ldots, x_9$ is again a five-diagonal symmetric and positive definite matrix, which can be factored into $T'T$, where T is upper tridiagonal. It is easy to verify that the Stieltjes matrix A, so partitioned, is a tridiagonal block matrix, and therefore [1] satisfies property A^{π} is and (consistently) ordered. Thus, the successive overrelaxation iterative method can be rigorously applied in this case, and the rate of convergence of the iterative method S2LOR is again faster than the rates of convergence of the iterative methods SLOR and SOR.

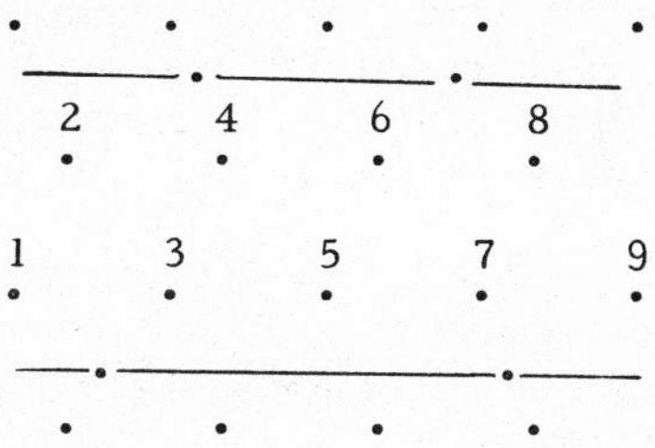

Figure 3.

A far more interesting application of the iterative method S2LOR is to the numerical solution of the biharmonic equation in the plane, over a thirteen-point mesh [5, p. 506]. As pointed out by Heller [15], coupling the mesh points along two neighboring horizontal mesh lines partitions matrix A into a tridiagonal block matrix, which satisfies property A^{π}, and is (consistently) ordered. With suitable boundary conditions, the matrix A can be derived in such a way so that A is symmetric and positive definite, and the diagonal blocks of the partitioned matrix A, corresponding

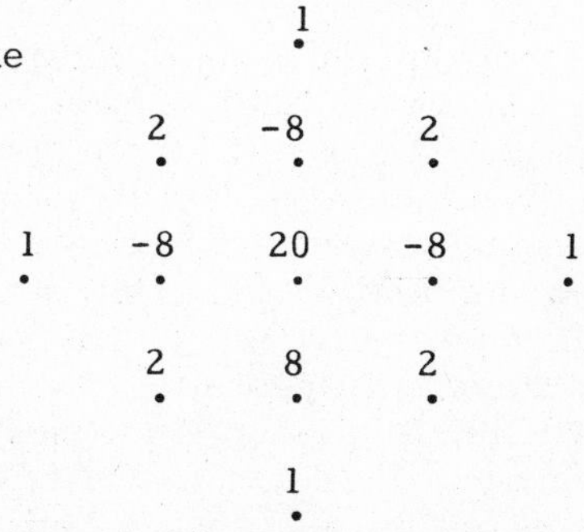

Fig. 4. Thirteen-Point Star

to the coupling of mesh points on two adjacent horizontal mesh lines, are also symmetric and positive definite. Thus, based on a generalization of Reich's Theorem [23], the iterative method S2LOR with $\omega = 1$ (Gauss-Seidel or single step method) is convergent. Since the matrix A satisfies property A^{π} and is (consistently) ordered, it follows [1] that the Richardson iterative method (total step method) is also convergent. The same is not always true for the iterative method SLOR [15, 36]. It is significant, however, that by means of normalization, both the normalized iterative method S2LOR and the normalized iterative method SLOR require 13 multiplications and 14 additions per mesh point. For this application, the matrix B of (3.3) is the direct sum of eight-diagonal symmetric and positive definite matrices, each of which factors into $T'T$ where T is an upper five-diagonal matrix.

§6. Primitive Iterative Methods

In the previous section, the basic idea presented involved partitioning the matrix A into a form for which matrix equations, involving only the diagonal blocks of the partitioned matrix A, could be directly solved. It is natural to consider the problem of factoring the entire Stieltjes matrix A into

$$A = T'T, \tag{6.1}$$

where T is an upper triangular matrix with positive diagonal entries. §§ Unfortunately, for large practical problems the resulting matrix T is seldom sparse, and the growth of round-off errors is now more serious. The same is true of directly applying the Gauss elimination method to (2.1). Instead, we now attempt to approximately factor the matrix A into the form of (6.1), where the matrix T is sparse. Allowing for an error matrix C, we write

$$A = T'T - C. \tag{6.2}$$

In particular, if A is a Stieltjes matrix arising from a five-point approximation to (2.11) on a rectangular mesh in a plane region with given Dirichlet-type boundary conditions, let the directed graph of the upper triangular matrix T be as in Figure 5, where arrows connecting mesh points are interpreted as non-zero coefficients in the matrix T. Specifically, if in Figure 5 the mesh points (k,m), $(k+1,m)$, and $(k,m+1)$ are called the i-th, i+1-st, and j-th mesh points respectively, then the only entries in the i-th row of the matrix $T = (t_{i,j})$ permitted to be non-zero are $t_{i,i}$, $t_{i,i+1}$, and $t_{i,j}$.

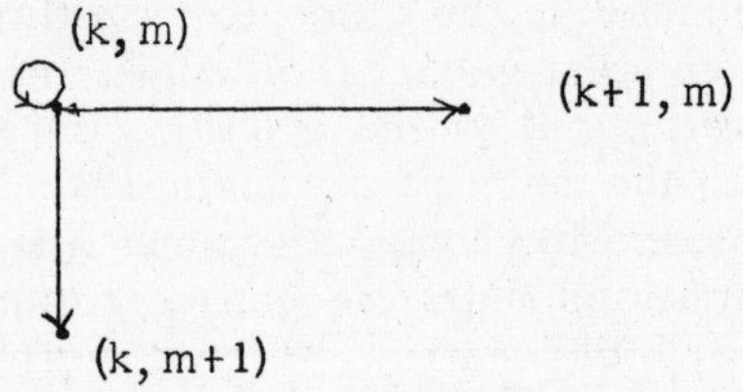

Figure 5. Five-Point Star

While the matrix T so generated is evidently upper triangular and sparse, the matrix C of (6.2) is not in general null. In fact, if $C = (c_{i,j})$, then C is symmetric, and

$$c_{i+1,j} = t_{i,i+1} t_{i,j} \tag{6.3}$$

can be different from zero. The matrix T can be derived so that the only non-zero entries of the error matrix C are of the form (6.3). Moreover, with A a Stieltjes matrix, it can be verified that $A = T'T - C$ is a regular splitting of A, so that $(T'T)^{-1} \geq 0$. We include, for completeness, the following

<u>Theorem 4.</u> The matrix $(T'T)^{-1}$ is nonnegative and primitive. If the finite mesh region is convex, then $(T'T)^{-1} > 0$.

<u>Proof.</u> By a classic theorem of Frobenius [12], a primitive matrix is a matrix M such that $M \geq 0$, and such that $M^m > 0$ for some positive integer m. Since (6.2) represents a regular splitting of A, then $(T'T)^{-1} \geq 0$. Moreover, it can be verified that the diagonal entries of $(T'T)^{-1}$ are positive, and, since A is irreducible, the matrix $(T'T)^{-1}$ is also irreducible. Thus [35], $(T'T)^{-1}$ is primitive. If the finite mesh region is convex, then it can be verified that the upper triangular matrix T^{-1} has every entry on or above the main diagonal positive. Thus, $(T'T)^{-1} > 0$.

As consequences of this theorem, we observe, for convex mesh regions, that the matrix $B = T'T$ of (6.2) and the Stieltjes matrix A which B approximates have the common feature that their inverses have only positive entries. Opposed to this, we find that for cyclic iterative methods, the matrix B of (3.3) is such that $B^{-1} \geq 0$, but B^{-1} does not have only positive entries unless C is the null matrix. Next, it follows, for convex mesh regions, that if the matrix C of (6.2) is not null, then the matrix $D \equiv (T'T)^{-1}C$ is <u>not</u> cyclic of index 2. While the successive overrelaxation iterative method cannot directly be used to accelerate the convergence of the basic iterative method of (2.3), the Chebyshev semi-iterative method nevertheless can be applied.##

The use of primitive iterative methods is obviously not restricted to five-point approximations of (2.11). If nine-point approximations of (2.11) in the plane are considered, then the analogous directed graph of the upper triangular matrix T is given in Figure 6. Other extensions are easily obtained.

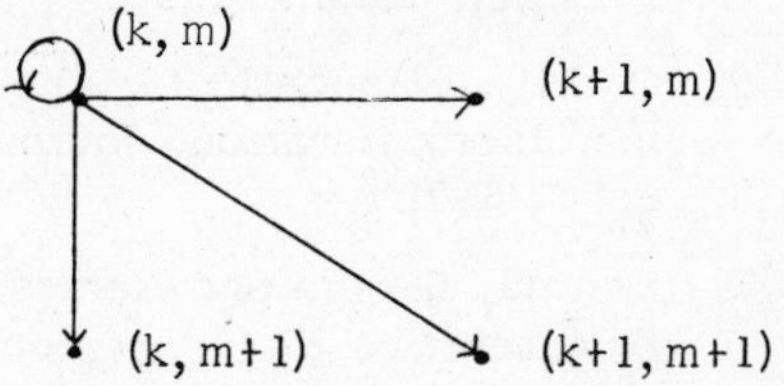

Figure 6. Nine-Point Star

NOTES

*By this, we mean that neither C_1 or $C_2 - C_1$ is the null matrix.

§For special applications of this result, see [6, 31].

#This particular application of Chebyshev polynomials can be derived from (17) of [27], upon making proper identifications.

± An example of a normalized iterative technique is given in [6].

**The quantities m and a refer respectively to multiplications and additions.

§§A similar approach has been considered by T. A. Oliphant in "A direct implicit scheme for solving two dimensional steady-state diffusion problems", The Rice Institute (1958).

##At the present time, Mr. William R. Cadwell, a graduate student at the University of Pittsburgh, is experimenting with this iterative method as well as the iterative method S2LOR on the IBM-704. The numerical results are to be included in his M.A. Thesis.

BIBLIOGRAPHY

1. Arms, R.J., Gates, L.D., Zondek, B., A method of block iteration, Journal Soc. Indust. Appl. Math. 4 (1956), pp. 220-229.

2. Birkhoff, Garrett, and Varga, Richard S., Reactor criticality and nonnegative matrices, Journal Soc. Indust. Appl. Math. 6 (1958), pp. 354-377.

3. Birkhoff, Garrett, and Varga, Richard S., Implicit alternating direction methods, Trans. Amer. Math. Soc., 92(1959), pp. 13-24.

4. Bodewig, Matrix Calculus, Interscience Publishers, Inc., New York, 1956.

5. Collatz, L., Numerische Behandlung von Differentialgleichungen, Springer, Berlin, 1955.

6. Cuthill, Elizabeth H., and Varga, Richard S., A method of normalized block iteration, Journal Assoc. Computing Mach. 6 (1959), pp. 236-244.

7. Debreu, Gerard and Herstein, I. N., Nonnegative square matrices, Econometrica 21 (1953), pp. 597-607.

8. Douglas, Jim, Jr. and Rachford, H. H., Jr., On the numerical solution of heat conduction problems in two and three space variables, Trans. Amer. Math. Soc. 82 (1956), pp. 421-439.

9. Fiedler, Miroslav and Pták, Vlastimil, Über die Konvergenz des verallgemeinerten Seidelschen Verfahren zur Lösung von Systemen linearer Gleichungen, Math. Nachrichten 15 (1956), pp. 31-38.

10. Frankel, Stanley P., Convergence rates of iterative treatments of partial differential equations, Math. Tables Aids Comput. 4 (1950), pp. 65-75.

11. Friedman, B., The iterative solution of elliptic partial difference equations, AEC Research and Development Report NYO 7698, 1957.

12. Frobenius, G., Über Matrizen aus nicht negative Elementen, Sitzungsberichte der Akademie der Wissenschaften zu Berlin (1912), pp. 456-477.

13. Geiringer, Hilda, On the solution of systems of linear equations by certain iterative methods, Reissner Anniversary volume, J. W. Edwards, Ann Arbor, Mich. (1944), pp. 365-393.

14. Gerschgorin, S., Über die Abgrenzung der Eigenwerten einer Matrix, Izvest. Akad. Nauk SSSR 7 (1931), pp. 749-754.

15. Heller, J., Simultaneous, successive and alternating direction iteration schemes, AEC Research and Development Report NYO-8675 (1958).

16. Householder, A. S., The approximate solution of matrix problems, Journal Assoc. Computing Mach. 5(1958), pp. 204-243.

17. Keller, Herbert B., On some iterative methods for solving elliptic difference equations, Quart. Appl. Math. 16 (1958), pp. 209-226.

18. Lanczos, Cornelius, Solution of systems of linear equations by minimized iterations, Journal Research Nat. Bureau of Standards 49 (1952), pp. 33-53.

19. von Mises, R., and Pollaczek-Geiringer, Praktische Verfahren der Gleichungsauflösung, Zeit. f. angew. Math. und Mech. 9 (1929), pp. 58-77, 152-164.

20. Murnaghan, Francis D., The Theory of Group Representations, Johns Hopkins Press, Baltimore, 1938.

21. Peaceman, D. W., and Rachford, H. H. Jr., The numerical solution of parabolic and elliptic differential equations, Journal Soc. Indust. Appl. Math. 3 (1955), pp. 28-41.

22. Perron, O., Zur Theorie der Matrices, Math. Ann 64 (1907), pp. 259-263.

23. Reich, Edgar, On the convergence of the classical iterative method of solving linear simultaneous equations, Ann. Math. Stat. 20 (1949), pp. 448-451.

24. Richardson, L. F., The approximate arithmetical solution by finite differences of physical problems involving differential equations, with an application to the stresses in a masonry dam, Phil. Trans. Royal Soc. A 210 (1910), pp. 307-357.

25. Romanovsky, V., Recherches sur les chaînes de Markoff, Acta Math. 66 (1936), pp. 147-251.

26. Stein, P., and Rosenberg, R.L., On the solution of linear simultaneous equations by iteration, Journal London Math. Soc. 23 (1948), pp. 111-118.

27. Stiefel, E., On solving Fredholm integral equations, Journal Soc. Indust. Appl. Math. 4 (1956), pp. 63-85.

28. Stieltjes, T.J., Sur les racines de l'equation $X_n = 0$, Acta Math. 9 (1887), pp. 385-400.

29. Taussky, Olga, A recurring theorem on determinants, Amer. Math. Monthly 56 (1949), pp. 672-676.

30. Todd, John, The condition of a certain matrix, Proc. Cambridge Philos. Soc. 46 (1950), pp. 116-118.

31. Varga, R.S., Numerical Solution of the Two-group Diffusion Equation in x-y Geometry, IRE Trans. of the Professional Group on Nuclear Science NS-4 (1957), pp. 52-62.

32. Varga, Richard S., p-cyclic matrices: a generalization of the Young-Frankel successive overrelaxation scheme, to appear in the Pacific Journal of Math.

33. Varga, Richard S., A comparison of the successive overrelaxation method and semi-iterative methods using Chebyshev polynomials, Journal Soc. Indust. Appl. Math. 5 (1957), pp. 39-46.

34. Wachspress, E.L., CURE: A generalized two-space-dimension multi-group coding for the IBM-704, Report KAPL-1724, Knolls Atomic Power Laboratory of the General Electric Company (1957).

35. Wielandt, Helmut, Unzerbegbare, nicht negative Matrizen, Math. Zeit. 52 (1950), pp. 642-648.

36. Windsor, Edith S., Iterative solutions of the biharmonic difference equations, Master's thesis, New York University (1957).

37. Wong, Y.K., Some properties of the proper values of a matrix, Proc. Amer. Math. Soc. 6 (1955), pp. 891-899.

38. Young, David, Iterative methods for solving partial difference equations of elliptic type, Trans. Amer. Math. Soc. 76 (1954), pp. 92-111.

39. Young, David, On Richardson's method for solving linear systems with positive definite matrices, Journal Math. and Physics 32 (1953), pp. 243-255.

40. Young, David, On the solution of linear systems by iteration, Proceedings of the Sixth Symposium in Applied Math, McGraw-Hill, New York, (1956), pp. 283-298.

DAVID YOUNG and LOUIS EHRLICH

Some Numerical Studies of Iterative Methods for Solving Elliptic Difference Equations

§1. Introduction

In the numerical solution by finite difference methods of boundary value problems involving elliptic partial differential equations, one covers the region with a mesh of horizontal and vertical lines and attemps to determine approximate values for the solution at the mesh points, the intersections of the mesh lines. The approximate values at the mesh points satisfy a system of linear algebraic equations, there being as many equations as interior points of the mesh. Although the existence of a unique solution of the linear system is usually easy to establish, nevertheless the computational problem of actually determining the solution may be very serious, particularly when, as is frequently the case, the number of equations is large. Iterative methods are frequently used. Starting with an arbitrary initial approximation to the solution one improves the values according to a prescribed procedure, repeating the process as often as necessary in order to achieve convergence. The proper choice of the iterative method to be used has a great influence on the amount of computational effort required to solve a given problem. With a slowly converging iterative method the amount of time required may be so large, even with a very fast computing machine, as to make the solution of the problem impractical.

The two iterative methods which are most frequently used at the present time are the successive overrelaxation method [3] and [7] and the Peaceman-Rachford method [4]. The successive overrelaxation method involves the successive modification of the approximate values of the solution at the individual points, a single value being modified at each step. For the usual finite difference analogue of the Dirichlet problem it can be shown that the number of complete iterations required to achieve a specified convergence is asymptotically proportional to h^{-1} as h approaches zero, where h is the mesh size.

Peaceman and Rachford [4] introduced the idea of simultaneously modifying the approximate values at all points of a line of mesh points, either a row or column. Values are modified alternately, first on rows and then on columns. For each such pair of iterations one selects and uses a number known as an iteration parameter. For the usual finite difference analogue of the Dirichlet problem, Peaceman and Rachford showed that the required number of iterations varies asymptotically as $|\log h|$, provided that the number of different iteration parameters is allowed to increase as h decreases. Varga [5] has shown that if a certain single iteration parameter is used for all iterations, then the number of iterations varies as h^{-1}. In the present paper it is shown that if one uses a certain set of m different iteration parameters, then the number of iterations varies as $h^{-1/m}$.

While the above statements concerning the successive overrelaxation method apply for rather general regions and even for other differential equations, for the Peaceman-Rachford method the theory has only been rigorously developed to apply to problems involving the rectangle. In Sec. 5 a simple example is given where the methods used in [4] would not apply. More generally, Birkhoff and Varga [1] have shown that for the case of the Dirichlet problem the methods used to develop the theory for the rectangle cannot be used for more general regions. In spite of all this, considerable success has been reported in using the Peaceman-Rachford method in cases where the theory is not known to apply.

During the past two years, the first-named author of the present paper has been engaged in a joint project with G. Birkhoff and R. Varga in an attempt to study the Peaceman-Rachford method. The methods of attack have been theoretical as well as numerical. The present paper is primarily concerned with a report of some numerical experiments which were carried out as part of this study. Helpful suggestions of G. Birkhoff and R. Varga are acknowledged.

The above-mentioned numerical experiments were performed in the IBM-704 computer at the Space Technology Laboratories in an attempt to determine the extent to which the theoretical results for the successive overrelaxation method and for the Peaceman-Rachford method would apply for non-rectangular regions. For the successive overrelaxation method the number of iterations was, as expected, approximately proportional to h^{-1}. For the Peaceman-Rachford method the hypothesis that the number of iterations was proportional to $h^{-1/m}$ for $m = 1, 2, 3$ was tested and found to hold fairly well for some regions which did not differ very much from the square. In other cases, although the hypothesis was not well satisfied, nevertheless, the number of iterations still appeared to vary like $h^{-\alpha}$ where $0 < \alpha < 1$. Also, except in one case, the number of iterations required for the square was, within one iteration, at least as large as that required for any of the other regions, the latter being subsets of the square. These observations suggest possible lines of approach in attempting to generalize the theory of the Peaceman-Rachford method to non-rectangular regions.

Because the analysis given in Sec. 4 is inexact, it was found that the observed rate of convergence for the Peaceman-Rachford method was approximately two and one-half times as great as that predicted by the theory. On the other hand, Wachspress [6] has developed a more refined analysis which is somewhat more accurate and which leads to an improved choice of iteration parameters resulting in fewer iterations.

In nearly every case the number of iterations required using the Peaceman-Rachford method was less than was required using the successive overrelaxation method. However, one must consider the fact that approximately three times as much machine time is required per double sweep of the Peaceman-Rachford method as is required per single iteration of the successive overrelaxation method. The successive overrelaxation method would appear to be preferable to the Peaceman-Rachford method for $h^{-1} \leqq 20$ unless one uses the Wachspress modification in which case the latter method appears superior for $h^{-1} = 20$. The Peaceman-Rachford method also appears to be preferable for all finer mesh sizes.

§2. A finite difference analogue of the Dirichlet problem

Let us consider the problem of finding the solution $U(x, y)$ of the Dirichlet problem corresponding to a closed bounded region R with boundary S. Evidently $U(x, y)$ satisfies Laplace's equation

$$\frac{\partial^2 U}{\partial x^2} + \frac{\partial^2 U}{\partial y^2} = 0 \tag{2.1}$$

in R and assumes prescribed continuous values in S. In setting up a finite difference analogue of the problem thus defined we consider a set L_h of points with coordinates (ih, jh) where the mesh size, h, is positive and where i and j are integers. Two points (ih, jh) and $(i'h, j'h)$ are said to be <u>adjacent</u> if $(i-i')^2 + (j-j')^2 = 1$. We let R_h denote the set of points of L_h which are in R and which have four adjacent points in $R + S$. The set S_h consists of points each of which is adjacent to some point of R_h but which does not itself belong to R_h. In this paper we will consider only regions such that S consists of lines which are either parallel to or which make a 45-degree angle with a coordinate axis. Moreover, we assume that $S_h \leq S$.

The usual finite difference analogue of the Dirichlet problem involves the determination of a function $u(x, y)$, defined on $R_h + S_h$, which assumes the prescribed values on S_h and which satisfies on R_h the difference equation

$$u(x+h, y) + u(x-h, y) + u(x, y+h) + u(x, y-h) - 4u(x, y) = 0 . \tag{2.2}$$

It is not difficult to show that the determinant of the corresponding system does not vanish. Consequently a unique solution exists. However, largely because so little is known about the difference between

$u(x, y)$ and $U(x, y)$ for a given value of h, one is tempted to choose as small a value of h as possible, thus obtaining a very large system. To solve such a large system one usually resorts to iterative methods. Starting with an initial approximation $u^{(0)}(x, y)$, which is arbitrary except that $u^{(0)}(x, y) = u(x, y)$ on S_h, one determines $u^{(1)}(x, y)$, $u^{(2)}(x, y)$, ... according to a prescribed procedure. Two such procedures are described below.

§3. The successive overrelaxation method

With the successive overrelaxation method one chooses an ordering of the points of R_h and modifies the approximate values at the points according to the formula

$$(3.1) \quad u^{(n+1)}(x, y) = \frac{\omega}{4}[\bar{u}(x+h, y) + \bar{u}(x-h, y) + \bar{u}(x, y+h) + \bar{u}(x, y-h)] - (\omega - 1)\, u^{(n)}(x, y)$$

where $\bar{u}(x', y')$ denotes $u^{(n+1)}(x', y')$ or $u^{(n)}(x', y')$ according to whether or not the point (x', y') precedes the point (x, y) in the ordering. In the usual ordering (x', y') follows (x, y) if either $y' > y$ or if $y' = y$ and $x' > x$. In this case (3.1) becomes

$$(3.2) \quad u^{(n+1)}(x, y) = \frac{\omega}{4}[u^{(n)}(x+h, y) + u^{(n+1)}(x-h, y) + u^{(n)}(x, y+h) + u^{(n+1)}(x, y-h)] - (\omega - 1)\, u^{(n)}(x, y) .$$

The parameter ω, which is known as the <u>relaxation factor</u>, is usually held fixed throughout the iteration process. In [7] it is shown that the optimum value of ω is given by

$$(3.3) \qquad \omega_b = 1 + \frac{\lambda}{(1 + \sqrt{1-\lambda})^2}$$

where λ is the spectral radius of the linear transformation defined by (3.2) with $\omega = 1$. In the case of a rectangle with horizontal and vertical side lengths $A = Ih$ and $B = Jh$, respectively, where I and J are integers, it can be shown that

$$(3.4) \qquad \lambda = \frac{1}{4}\left(\cos\frac{\pi}{I} + \cos\frac{\pi}{J}\right)^2 .$$

Moreover, for a region of the type we are considering and which is included in such a rectangle the corresponding value of λ is less than that given by (3.4).

It is also not difficult to show, [7], that as h approaches zero, the number of iterations required to achieve a specified convergence is approximately proportional to h^{-1}. This will be verified by the numerical experiments described below.

§4. The Peaceman-Rachford method

Each complete iteration consists of two partial iterations defined by

$$(4.1)\quad \begin{cases} u^{(n+\frac{1}{2})}(x,y) = u^{(n)}(x,y) - r_{n+1}[Hu^{(n+\frac{1}{2})} + Vu^{(n)}] \\ u^{(n+1)}(x,y) = u^{(n+\frac{1}{2})}(x,y) - r_{n+1}[Hu^{(n+\frac{1}{2})} + Vu^{(n+1)}] \end{cases}$$

where the operators H and V are defined by

$$(4.2)\quad \begin{cases} Hu(x,y) = 2u(x,y) - u(x+h,y) - u(x-h,y) \\ Vu(x,y) = 2u(x,y) - u(x,y+h) - u(x,y-h) \ . \end{cases}$$

Here r_{n+1} is a parameter whose selection will be discussed below. Usually one chooses m different values of r, say $r_1, r_2, \ldots, r_m$ and uses them in a cyclic order $r_1, r_2, \ldots, r_m, r_1, r_2, \ldots$. The first equation of (4.1) defines a row iteration; the second equation defines a column iteration. It would at first appear that the method would be very laborious since, for instance, the first equation of (4.1), being implicit in $u^{(n+\frac{1}{2})}$, involves the solution of a system of equations. However, the system involves a tridiagonal matrix and hence, as described in [4], can be solved using the Gauss elimination method with a number of operations proportional to the order of the system rather than to the cube of the order of the system as in the general case.

For the case of a rectangle a theoretical analysis of the rate of convergence is possible as shown in [4]. Let us assume that $R + S$ is the rectangle $0 \leqq x \leqq A$, $0 \leqq y \leqq B$ where $A = Ih$, $B = Jh$ and where I and J are integers. Letting $e^{(n)}(x,y) = u^{(n)}(x,y) - u(x,y)$, we note that $e^{(n)}(x,y)$ vanishes on the sides of the rectangle and satisfies (4.1). Let T_r denote the linear transformation which is defined by (4.1) with $r_{n+1} = r$ and which takes $e^{(n)}(x,y)$, considered as a vector in the $(I-1) \times (J-1)$ dimensional vector space of functions defined in R_h , into $e^{(n+1)}(x,y)$. The eigenvalues of T_r are given by

$$(4.3)\quad \lambda_{p,q} = \frac{1-r\mu_p}{1+r\mu_p}\ \frac{1-r\nu_q}{1+r\nu_q}\ , \quad (p=1,2,\ldots,I-1;\ q=1,2,\ldots,J-1)$$

where

$$(4.4)\quad \begin{cases} \mu_p = 4\sin^2 \dfrac{p\pi h}{2A}\ , \ (p = 1,\ 2,\ \ldots\ ,\ I-1) \\ \nu_q = 4\sin^2 \dfrac{q\pi h}{2B}\ , \ (p = 1, 2, \ldots\ ,\ J-1)\ . \end{cases}$$

The corresponding eigenvectors, which are independent of r, are given by

$$(4.5)\qquad v_{p,q} = \sin\frac{p\pi x}{A}\sin\frac{q\pi y}{B},\ (p = 1, 2, \ldots, I-1;\ q = 1, 2, \ldots, J-1).$$

Consequently for the product transformation $\prod_{k=1}^{m} T_{r_k}$ corresponding to the successive use of (4.1) with $r_1, r_2, \ldots, r_m$ the eigenvectors are given by (4.5) while the eigenvalues are given by

$$\prod_{k=1}^{m}\frac{1-r_k\mu_q}{1+r_k\mu_q}\ \frac{1-r_k\nu_q}{1+r_k\nu_q};\ (p=1, 2, \ldots, I-1;\ q=1, 2, \ldots, J-1).$$

For a given value of m one could optimize the choice of the r_k so as to minimize the maximum absolute value of the above expression with respect to p and q. As a practical matter, however, one seeks to minimize the expression

$$\max_{\substack{\alpha_1 \leq \mu \leq \beta_1 \\ \alpha_2 \leq \nu \leq \beta_2}} \prod_{k=1}^{m}\left|\frac{1-r_k\mu}{1+r_k\mu}\right|\left|\frac{1-r_k\nu}{1+r_k\nu}\right|$$

In order to simplify the analysis we use the fact that the previous expression does not exceed

$$\max_{a \leq t \leq b}\prod_{k=1}^{m}\left|\frac{1-r_k t}{1+r_k t}\right|$$

where $a = \mathrm{Min}(\alpha_1, \alpha_2)$, $b = \mathrm{Max}(\alpha_1, \alpha_2)$, or, by (4.4),

$$(4.6)\qquad \begin{cases} a = 4\sin^2\dfrac{\pi h}{2C} \\[2ex] b = 4\cos^2\dfrac{\pi h}{2C} \end{cases}$$

where $C = \mathrm{Max}(A, B)$.

Given a number ρ in the range $0 < \rho < 1$, it can be shown by the methods used in [4] that

$$(4.7)\qquad \max_{a \leq t \leq b}\prod_{k=1}^{m}\left|\frac{1-r_k t}{1+r_k t}\right| \leq \rho$$

provided the integer m satisfies the condition

$$(4.8) \qquad \left(\frac{1-\rho}{1+\rho}\right)^{2m} \leqq \frac{a}{b}$$

and provided that the m iteration parameters are given by

$$(4.9) \qquad r_k = \frac{1}{b}\left(\frac{1-\rho}{1+\rho}\right)^{1-2k}, \quad k = 1, 2, \ldots m .$$

The average rate of convergence* is given by

$$R = -\frac{1}{m} \log \rho .$$

Using (4.8) with the equality sign we have

$$(4.10) \qquad R = \frac{-2 \log \frac{1-\rho}{1+\rho} \log \rho}{\log (a/b)} .$$

The choice of ρ which maximizes R is determined by equating to zero the derivative of R with respect to zero. One obtains the equation

$$(4.11) \qquad \frac{1-\rho^2}{2} \log \frac{1-\rho}{1+\rho} = \rho \log \rho$$

which, as noted by Varga (private communication) has the exact solution $\rho = \sqrt{2} - 1 \doteq .414$. While the above analysis leading to the optimum determination of ρ is not given in [4], nevertheless, Douglas in [2] observed that the number of calculations required was minimized for ρ "around 0.4".** Using this value of ρ , or for that matter any fixed value of ρ in the range $0 < \rho < 1$, one can easily show, using (4.10) and (4.6), that as h tends to zero

$$R = O\left(\frac{1}{|\log h|}\right) .$$

Hence the number of iterations required to achieve a required accuracy varies as $|\log h|$. This represents a substantial theoretical improvement over the successive overrelaxation method where the number of iterations varies as h^{-1} .

In order to verify the preceding result on the Peaceman-Rachford method it would appear to be necessary to let h vary over a fairly wide range. Also, it would appear to be extremely difficult to generalize the result given above to non-rectangular regions. Consequently, it is felt that the following somewhat weaker results are of interest.

Varga [5] showed that for the rectangle if one chose a single suitable value of r , the number of iterations would be approximately proportional to h^{-1} ; thus the method in this form would be competitive with the successive overrelaxation method. It is possible to generalize this result to the case where a fixed number , m , of different values of r are used, the number being independent of h , even though the actual values of the r_k will vary with h. For a given value of the integer m we solve (4.8) for ρ, the inequality being replaced by an equality, obtaining

$$\rho = \frac{1-(a/b)^{1/2m}}{1+(a/b)^{1/2m}} . \tag{4.12}$$

Since the average rate of convergence is given by

$$R = -\frac{1}{m} \log \rho$$

it follows from (4.6) that, for small h, we have

$$R \doteq \frac{2}{m} (a/b)^{1/2m} \doteq \frac{2}{m} \left(\frac{\pi h}{2C}\right)^{1/m} . \tag{4.13}$$

Consequently, the number of iterations, which is approximately proportional to R^{-1}, varies approximately as $h^{-1/m}$.

We remark that the analysis outlined above is not sharp. Some numerical results described later indicate that the actual rate of convergence is considerably greater than that given by (4.13). Wachspress [6] has developed a more refined technique for choosing the r_k.

§5. Limitations on the theoretical analysis of the Peaceman-Rachford method

The analysis of the convergence of the Peaceman-Rachford method can be considered from a somewhat more general point of view. Consider the problem of solving the linear system

$$(H + V)u = d \tag{5.1}$$

where H and V are symmetric and positive definite and where $HV = VH$. The generalized Peaceman-Rachford method as applied to (5.1), as well as to somewhat more general systems, was considered by Wachspress [6]. That the linear system corresponding to the difference equation (2.2) falls in this category can easily be seen if we let the matrices H and V correspond respectively to the linear operators

$$H[u(x, y)] = 2u(x, y) - \overline{u}(x + h, y) - \overline{u}(x - h, y)$$

$$V[u(x, y)] = 2u(x, y) - \overline{u}(x, y + h) - \overline{u}(x, y - h)$$

where

$$\overline{u}(x, y) = \begin{cases} 0 & \text{if } (x, y) \text{ belongs to } S_h \\ u(x, y) & \text{if } (x, y) \text{ belongs to } R_h . \end{cases}$$

The vector d involves the prescribed values of $u(x, y)$ on S_h. One can verify directly that for a rectangle $HV = VH$. However, as shown by Birkhoff and Varga [1], the condition $HV = VH$ holds only for the rectangle.

The generalized Peaceman-Rachford method is defined by

$$(5.2)\quad \begin{cases} u_{n+\frac{1}{2}} = u_n - r_{n+1}[Hu_{n+\frac{1}{2}} + Vu_n - d] \\ u_{n+1} = u_{n+\frac{1}{2}} - r_{n+1}[Hu_{n+\frac{1}{2}} + Vu_{n+1} - d] . \end{cases}$$

It is assumed that the first of the equations (5.2) can be solved conveniently for $u_{n+\frac{1}{2}}$ and that the second can then be solved easily for u_{n+1}. In order to study the convergence of the method we eliminate $u_{n+\frac{1}{2}}$ from (5.2) obtaining

$$(5.3)\qquad u_{n+1} = Q_{r_{n+1}} u_n + c$$

where

$$(5.4)\quad \begin{cases} Q_{r_{n+1}} = (I + r_{n+1}V)^{-1}(I - r_{n+1}H)(I + r_{n+1}H)^{-1}(I - r_{n+1}V) \\ c = [(I + r_{n+1}V)^{-1}(I - r_{n+1}H)(I + r_{n+1}H)^{-1} + (I + r_{n+1}V)^{-1}]r_{n+1}d \end{cases}$$

The fact that the matrices H and V commute makes it possible to express the eigenvalues of $Q_{r_{n+1}}$ in terms of those of H and V. For it is well known that H and V have a common basis of eigenvectors. Thus, if μ and ν are eigenvalues of H and V, respectively, then

$$(5.5)\qquad \lambda_{r_{n+1}}(\mu, \nu) = \frac{(1-r_{n+1}\mu)(1-r_{n+1}\nu)}{(1+r_{n+1}\mu)(1+r_{n+1}\nu)}$$

is an eigenvalue of $Q_{r_{n+1}}$. Moreover

$$\prod_{n=1}^{m} \lambda_{r_n}(\mu, \nu)$$

is an eigenvalue of

$$\prod_{n=1}^{m} Q_{r_n} .$$

Consequently the analysis used in the previous section can be carried out, it being only necessary to determine upper and lower bounds for μ and ν.

The result of Birkhoff and Varga indicates that one cannot expect to duplicate the analysis of Sec. 4 for the case of a non-rectangular region. Possibly even more disturbing is the fact that in spite of the fact that the eigenvalues of H and V are real even in the non-rectangular case, nevertheless, in a very simple case an eigenvalue of Q_r can be shown to be complex. If the theory did "nearly" generalize

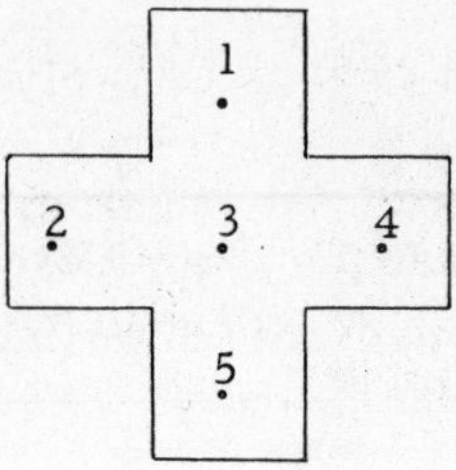

Fig. 1

to non-rectangular regions, one would expect from (5.5) that the eigenvalues of Q_r would be either real, or at least would have very small imaginary parts. However, let us consider the matrix

$$Q_r = (I + rV)^{-1}(I - rH)(I + rH)^{-1}(I - rV)$$

for $r = 1$ and for the region in Figure 1 containing only 5 interior mesh points where

$$H = \begin{pmatrix} 2 & 0 & 0 & 0 & 0 \\ 0 & 2 & -1 & 0 & 0 \\ 0 & -1 & 2 & -1 & 0 \\ 0 & 0 & -1 & 2 & 0 \\ 0 & 0 & 0 & 0 & 2 \end{pmatrix}$$

$$V = \begin{pmatrix} 2 & 0 & -1 & 0 & 0 \\ 0 & 2 & 0 & 0 & 0 \\ -1 & 0 & 2 & 0 & -1 \\ 0 & 0 & 0 & 2 & 0 \\ 0 & 0 & -1 & 0 & 2 \end{pmatrix} .$$

One can verify directly that the eigenvalues of Q_r are:

$$1/9,\ 1/9,\ .2164,\ -.05039 + .08909i,\ -.05039 - .08909i\ .$$

As a result of these considerations it would seem that one is justified in doubting whether the convergence of the Peaceman-Rachford method is as rapid for problems involving non-rectangular regions as it is for rectangular ones. In order to attempt to gain insight into this question it was decided to carry out some numerical experiments using the method. These experiments are described below.

§6. Numerical experiments

In order to test the applicability of the above theoretical results, several examples were solved on IBM 704 computer of the Space Technology Laboratories.

I. Unit square

$(h = \frac{1}{5}, \frac{1}{10}, \frac{1}{20}, \frac{1}{40})$

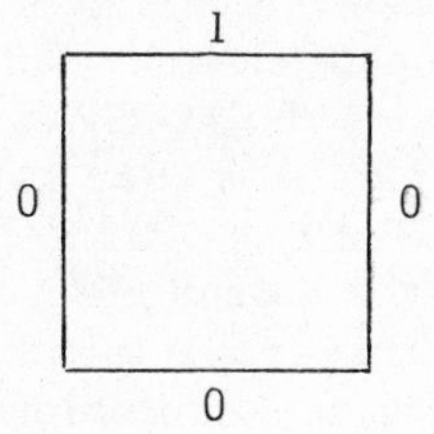

Fig. 2a

II. Unit square with $\frac{4}{10} \times \frac{4}{10}$ square removed from center.

$(h = \frac{1}{10}, \frac{1}{20}, \frac{1}{40})$

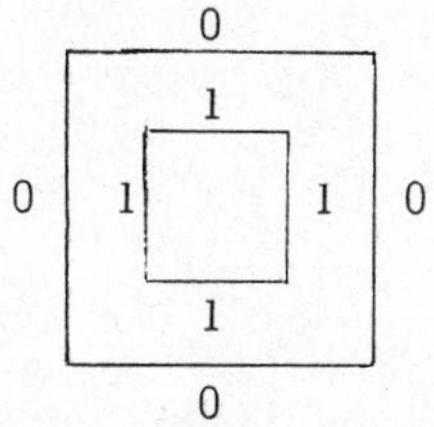

Fig. 2b

III. Unit square with $\frac{1}{5} \times \frac{1}{5}$ square removed from each corner.

$(h = \frac{1}{5}, \frac{1}{10}, \frac{1}{20}, \frac{1}{40})$

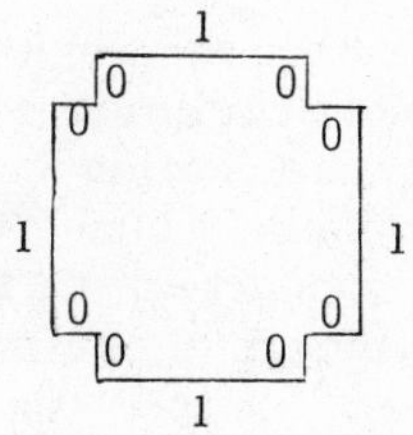

Fig. 2c

IV. Unit square with $\frac{1}{2} \times \frac{1}{2}$ square removed from one corner

$(h = \frac{1}{10}, \frac{1}{20}, \frac{1}{40})$

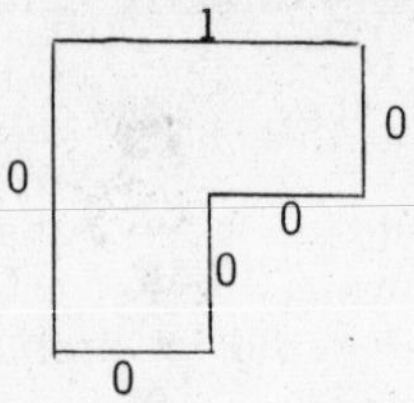

Fig. 2d

V. Right isosceles triangle with unit base

$(h = \frac{1}{5}, \frac{1}{10}, \frac{1}{20}, \frac{1}{40})$

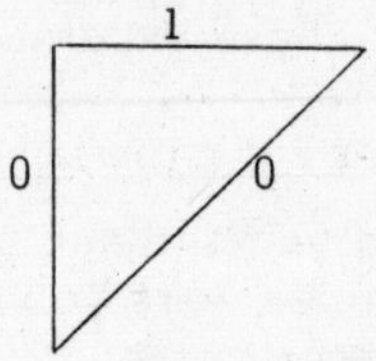

Fig. 2e

The boundary values are as shown in the figures. Several mesh sizes were used for each problem as indicated. The programming was performed using the FORTRAN automatic programming system.

The five problems were solved with mesh sizes $h = 1/40, 1/20, 1/10$, and, where possible, $h = 1/5$. For the successive overrelaxation method the values of ω which were used are indicated in Table II. These values were found by experiment to be close to optimal. For the Peaceman-Rachford method the number, m, of fixed iteration parameters was chosen as 1, 2, and 3. For given m the corresponding value of ρ was determined from (4.12) with $b = 4$. The values of r_k which were used are given in Table I. Formula (4.9) was used with $b = 4$.

The number of iterations which were required to make

$$|u^{(n)}(x,y) - u^{(n-1)}(x,y)| < 10^{-6}$$

for all (x, y) in R_h, starting with $u^{(0)}(x, y) = 0$ for all (x, y) in R_h, is given in Table II ***. The results are plotted in Figures 3 - 7, the logarithm of N, the number of iterations, being plotted against $\log h^{-1}$.

§7. Analysis of results

According to the theory, the slope of the graph of $\log N$ versus $\log h^{-1}$ should be a straight line. The slope should be unity for the successive overrelaxation method. For the Peaceman-Rachford method the slope should be $(1/m)$, where m is the number of different values of r_k. Inspection of Figures 3 - 7 does indeed reveal that the graphs are approximately straight lines with the following slopes:

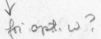

for opt. ω?

Case	Successive Overrelaxation	Peaceman-Rachford m = 1	m = 2	m = 3
I	1.024	.923	.571	.369
II	.941	1.044	.610	.666
III	1.061	.948	.570	.377
IV	.975	.982	.580	.370
V	1.103	1.082	.625	.574

For the successive overrelaxation method and for the Peaceman-Rachford method with $m = 1$ the slopes are quite close to unity. For the Peaceman-Rachford method with $m = 2$ and $m = 3$ the slopes are in fairly good agreement with m^{-1} for Cases I, III, and IV, for which the corresponding regions are close to or are actually square. The agreement is not as good for Cases II and V which involve regions which are quite different from the square. Nevertheless the actual number of iterations is smaller for $m = 2$ and still smaller for $m = 3$. Based on these results it seems reasonable to expect that it might be possible to show for a general region that for each $m > 1$ the number of iterations required using the Peaceman-Rachford method with m values of r_k is approximately proportional to $h^{-\alpha(m)}$ where $0 < \alpha(m) < 1$ and, possibly, where $\alpha(m)$ is a non-increasing function of m. Ideally, of course, $\alpha(m)$ would equal m^{-1}, but this does not appear to be the case.

Let us next consider the absolute number of iterations required in each case. One would normally expect that the theoretical number of iterations, N_T, would be given approximately by the following formula

$$N_T = \frac{-\log \sigma}{R} \tag{7.1}$$

where R is the rate of convergence and where σ is the factor by which the error is to be reduced. Since the error is to be reduced by approximately 10^{-6}, it follows that

$$-\log \sigma = \log 10^6 \doteq 13.8 . \tag{7.2}$$

Moreover, we have

$$R = \begin{cases} -\log(\omega - 1) & \text{for the successive overrelaxation method} \\ -\dfrac{1}{m}\log \rho \doteq \dfrac{2}{m}\left(\dfrac{\pi h}{2}\right)^{1/m} & \text{for the Peaceman-Rachford method} \end{cases} \tag{7.3}$$

the latter formula holding for the unit square, by (4.13).

For Case I with $h^{-1} = 20$ let us compute N_T using (7.1), (7.2), and (7.3). We obtain the following results:

Method	N_T	N	N_T/N
successive overrelaxation	46	53	.865
Peaceman-Rachford m = 1	88	39	2.26
Peaceman-Rachford m = 2	50	20	2.50
Peaceman-Rachford m = 3	48	19	2.52

Thus for the Peaceman-Rachford method the theoretical number of iterations is approximately two and one-half times the actual number while for the successive overrelaxation method the actual number of iterations slightly exceeds N_T . This ratio of two and one-half for the Peaceman-Rachford method holds fairly generally for the other cases and can be explained by noting the inexactness of the analysis of Sec. 4. Using the results of a more sophisticated analysis of Wachspress, [6], Case I was run with nine selected iteration parameters. The number of iterations was reduced to ten. It should be noted that the analysis of Sec. 4 predicts that $m = 3$ is the optimum number of iteration parameters to be used. For $h^{-1} = 40$ the theory indicates that $m = 4$ is better. This is borne out as shown in Table II, although the difference is not large except for Case II.

For the successive overrelaxation method the number of iterations required for Case I involving the square is at least as large (to within one iteration which can be explained as rounding) as that required for any of the other cases involving regions included in the square. In [8] it was observed, and is proven in [7], that if the same ω is used in all cases, then the rate of convergence is smaller for the square than for any sub-region of the square. If such a result could be proved for the Peaceman-Rachford method it would represent a substantial advance in the theory. However, although in most cases the number of iterations for the square is as large (to within one) as that for any of the regions, nevertheless for $h^{-1} = 40$ and for $m = 1, 3$ the number of iterations required for Case II, involving the hollow square, was considerably greater than for Case I. In spite of this it seems reasonable to expect that one could show that for a given set of iteration parameters the rate of convergence of the Peaceman-Rachford method for the square was no more than some constant, q , times that for any included region where q is independent of h , though probably not independent of m .

As for the relative merits of the successive overrelaxation method versus the Peaceman-Rachford method one must take into account the fact that each double sweep of the latter method requires at least twice as much computational effort as a single iteration of the former method. Actually, on the program used in this investigation the ratio was more nearly three. For $h^{-1} = 40$ and probably also for $h^{-1} = 20$ the Peaceman-Rachford method would appear to be preferable.

NOTE

*See [7] for a definition of the rate of convergence of an iterative process involving a single linear operator.

** A private communication from J. Douglas has since revealed that his method for determining the optimum value of ρ was actually the same as that described here.

***Both R. Varga and J. Douglas have pointed out some of the disadvantages of this procedure for stopping the iteration process. If r is either very large or very small, the condition could be satisfied even when convergence has not been obtained. Although it is believed that this would not seriously affect the results for the cases studied in this paper, nevertheless, it is planned to run additional cases with an improved stopping condition.

BIBLIOGRAPHY

1. Garrett Birkhoff and Richard S. Varga, Implicit alternating direction methods, Report WAPD-T-650, Bettis Plant, Westinghouse Electric Corporation, Pittsburgh, Pa., October 1957.
2. Jim Douglas, Jr., A note on the alternating direction implicit method for the numerical solution of heat flow problems, Humble Oil Co. Report, Houston, Texas.
3. S. Frankel, Convergence rates of iterative treatments of partial differential equations, M.T.A.C. vol. 4, pp. 65-75(1950).
4. D. W. Peaceman and H. H. Rachford, Jr., The numerical solution of parabolic and elliptic differential equations, J. Soc. Indust. Appl. Math., vol. 3, pp. 28-41 (1955).
5. R. S. Varga, Remarks on Peaceman-Rachford iteration, Report WAPD-TM-139, Bettis Plant, Westinghouse Electric Corporation, Pittsburgh, Pa., 1958.
6. E. L. Wachspress, CURE: a generalized two-space-dimension multigroup coding for the IBM 704, Report KAPL 1724, Knolls Atomic Power Laboratory, General Electric Co., Schenectady, N. Y., April 30, 1957.
7. David Young, Iterative methods for solving partial difference equations of elliptic type, Trans. Amer. Math. Soc., vol. 76, pp. 92-111 (1954).
8. David Young, Ordvac solutions of the Dirichlet problem, Jour. Assoc. for Computing Machinery, vol. 2, pp. 137-161 (1955).

TABLE I

$$r_k = \frac{1}{4}\left(\sin\frac{\pi h}{2}\right)^{\frac{1-2k}{m}}; \quad k = 1, 2, \ldots, m$$

h	m	r_k ; k = 1, 2, ... , m
$\frac{1}{5}$	1	.80901702
	2	.44972626; 1.4553467
	3	.36978210; .80901702; 1.7699843
	4	.33530839; .60318876; 1.0850807; 1.9519599
$\frac{1}{10}$	1	1.5981133
	2	.63208254; 4.0405582
	3	.46397638; 1.5981133; 5.5045179
	4	.39751810; 1.0050569; 2.5411159; 6.4247800
$\frac{1}{20}$	1	3.1863748
	2	.89252098; 11.375625
	3	.58397235; 3.1863748; 17.386068
	4	.47236665; 1.6863885; 6,0205486; 21.493863
$\frac{1}{40}$	1	6.3678399
	2	1.2617289; 32.137951
	3	.73557005; 6.3678399; 5.5126471
	4	.56163354; 2.8345172; 14.305569; 72.199006

TABLE II

	$h^{-1} = 5$				$h^{-1} = 10$				$h^{-1} = 20$				$h^{-1} = 40$				
	m				m				m				m				
Case	1	2	3	SOR	1	2	3	SOR	1	2	3	SOR	1	2	3	4	SOR
I	11	9	10	12 (ω=1.27)	21	15	13	26 (ω=1.54)	39	20	19	53 (ω=1.74)	75	29	22	21	103 (ω=1.86)
II					19	13	11	15 (ω=1.25)	40	21	18	29 (ω=1.58)	81	30	28	22	55 (ω=1.72)
III	9	9	10	11 (ω=1.22)	18	14	13	24 (ω=1.50)	34	20	16	50 (ω=1.71)	64	29	22	21	100 (ω=1.84)
IV					19	13	13	23 (ω=1.41)	38	20	17	46 (ω=1.64)	74	29	22	22	89 (ω=1.80)
V	7	8	8	8 (ω=1.10)	16	11	11	20 (ω=1.35)	34	18	15	42 (ω=1.59)	71	27	22	20	84 (ω=1.77)

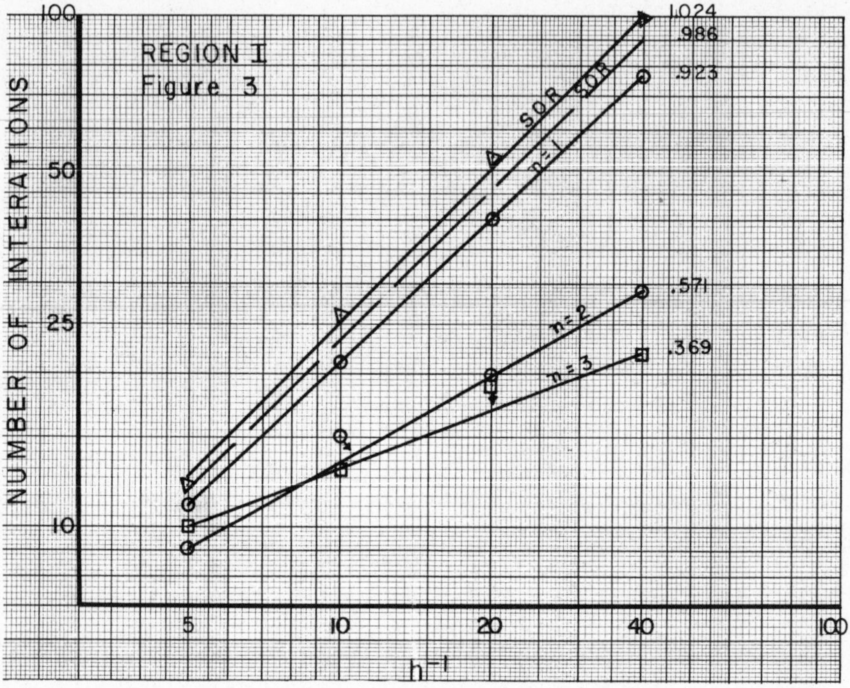
REGION I
Figure 3
NUMBER OF INTERATIONS
h⁻¹
SOR
SOR
n=1
n=2
n=3
1.024
.986
.923
.571
.369
100
50
25
10
5
10
20
40
100

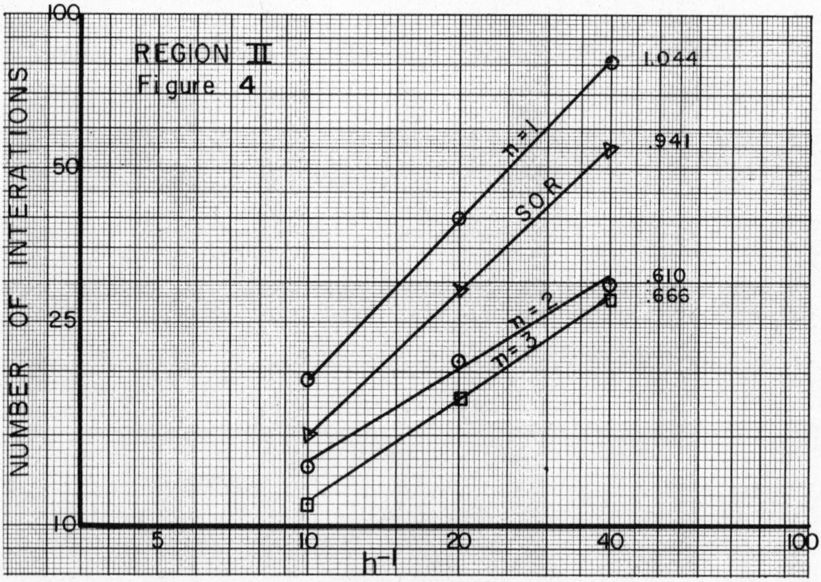
REGION II
Figure 4
NUMBER OF INTERATIONS
h⁻¹
n=1
SOR
n=2
n=3
1.044
.941
.610
.666
100
50
25
10
5
10
20
40
100

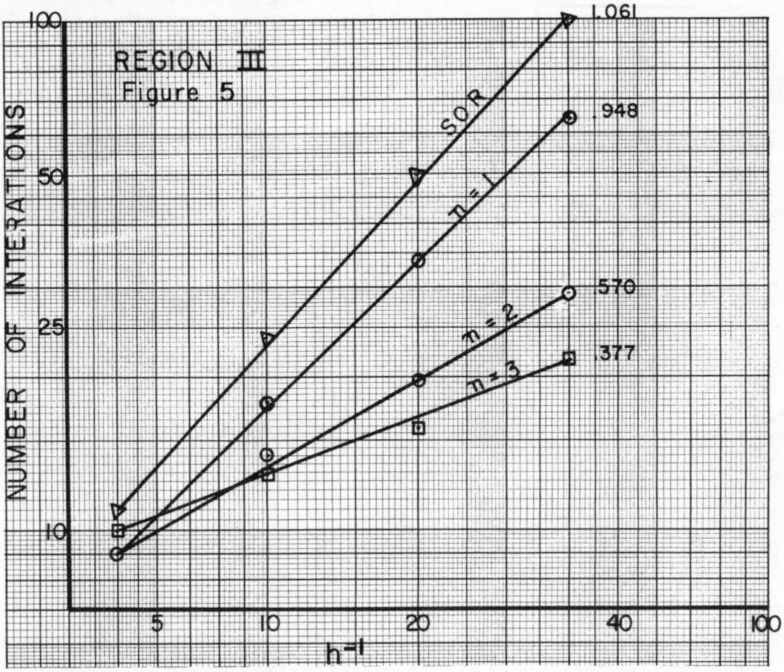
REGION III
Figure 5
NUMBER OF INTERATIONS
100
50
25
10
5
10
20
40
100
h^-1
SOR
n = 1
n = 2
n = 3
1.061
.948
.570
.377

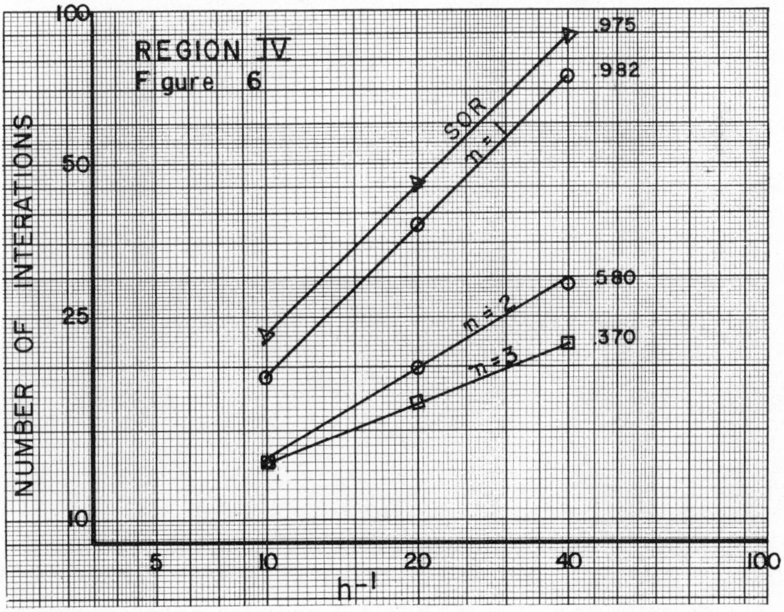
REGION IV
Figure 6
NUMBER OF INTERATIONS
100
50
25
10
5
10
20
40
100
h^-1
SOR
n = 1
n = 2
n = 3
.975
.982
.580
.370

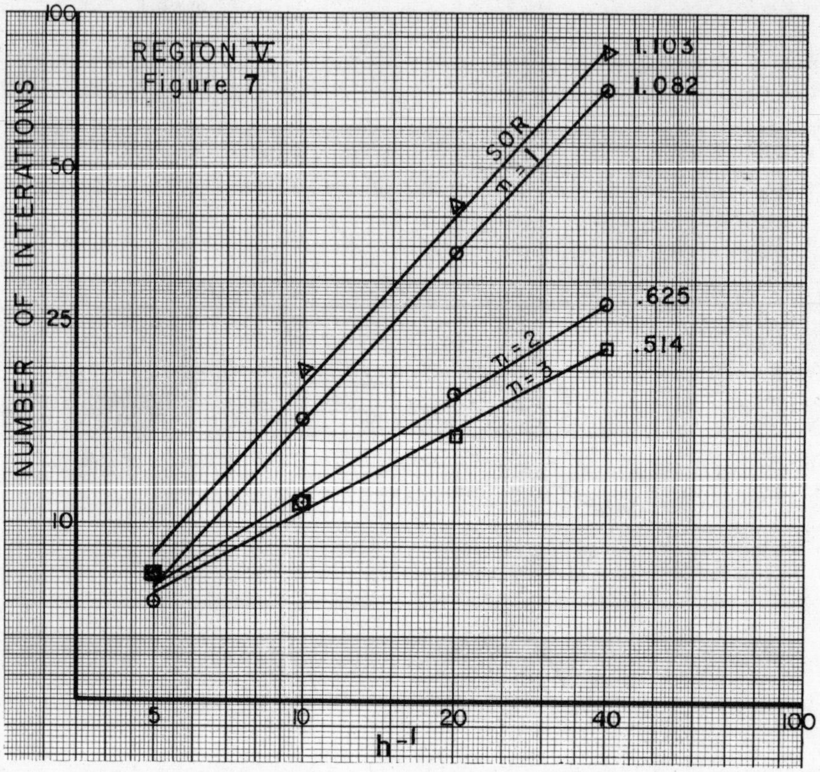
REGION V
Figure 7
NUMBER OF INTERATIONS
h⁻¹
SOR
n = 1
n = 2
n = 3
1.103
1.082
.625
.514
100
50
25
10
5
10
20
40
100

GARRETT BIRKHOFF

Albedo Functions for Elliptic Equations

I. INTRODUCTION

§1. Basic problems

The aim of this paper is to call attention to integral boundary value conditions for elliptic partial differential equations, to explain their physical significance, and to derive some preliminary mathematical theorems about them.

Let there be given a self-adjoint elliptic DE of the form

$$-\nabla \cdot (D \nabla \phi) = (\nu \Sigma_f - \Sigma_a)\phi + S , \quad D > 0 , \tag{1}$$

where D, Σ_f, Σ_a and S denote nonnegative functions of position, ν is a constant, and ϕ is the unknown function to be determined. I shall be especially concerned with integral boundary conditions of the form

$$\phi(y) + \iint A(y,\eta)\ D(\eta) \frac{\partial \phi}{\partial n}(\eta)\, dS = g(y) . \tag{2}$$

I know of few published discussions of boundary conditions of the form (2), from either the mathematical or the physical point of view.[1] I shall also be concerned with the usual interface conditions

$$\phi \text{ and } D\frac{\partial \phi}{\partial n} \text{ are continuous,} \tag{3}$$

across boundaries on which D, Σ_f, or Σ_a change discontinuously

Obviously, the boundary condition (2) contains as a singular limiting case $A(y,\eta) = h(y)\delta(y-\eta)$, the usual "mixed" boundary condition of Fourier

$$\phi(y) + d(y)\frac{\partial \phi}{\partial n}(y) = \gamma(y) . \tag{2'}$$

This is just the case that the kernel $A(y,\eta)$ is concentrated on the "diagonal" $y = \eta$, so that $\delta(y-\eta)$ is a suitably normalized Dirac delta-function.

II. FAMILIAR MATHEMATICAL ANALOGS

§2. Riemann-Hilbert problem

In §§2 - 7, I shall discuss boundary value problems defined by (1) in a given connected domain $\mathscr{C}$, and (2) on the boundary $\mathscr{G}$ of $\mathscr{C}$. This can be considered as a natural generalization of the Riemann-Hilbert problem.[2] In this problem, one is given a linear relation

(4) $$a(s)u(s) + b(s)v(s) + c(s) = 0$$

between the real and imaginary parts of a complex-valued function $w = u + iv = f(s)$ on the boundary $\mathscr{G}$ of a region $\mathscr{C}$, and one looks for a function $w = f(z)$ analytic in $\mathscr{C}$ and satisfying (4). The functions $a(s)$, $b(s)$ and $c(s)$ are assumed to be continuously differentiable.

In treating this problem, Hilbert[2] worked with the identities $\nabla^2 u = \nabla^2 v = 0$, and [4, p. 85]

(5) $$v(s) = \frac{1}{2\pi} \oint \frac{\partial G}{\partial \sigma} (\sigma, s) u(\sigma) d\sigma ,$$

where ℓ is the length of $\mathscr{G}$, making $\oint v(\sigma) d\sigma = 0$ by a normalization. If one substitutes (5) into (4), one clearly gets a special case of (2), with $D = 1$.

Moreover, in [4, p. 87, (8)] Hilbert stressed the equivalence of regularity in the exterior $\mathscr{R}$ of $\mathscr{G}$, to the condition

(6) $$u(s) = -\frac{1}{2\pi} \oint G(s, \sigma) \frac{\partial u}{\partial n} ds \quad , \text{ if } \oint u(s) ds = 0 .$$

Hilbert did not relate his problem to physical concepts, but Muskhelishvili[3] has applied the same ideas to many problems in elasticity theory. One can regard (6) as defining naturally a special case of (2) for an infinite "reflector" .

The most important idea of the present paper can be interpreted as a straightforward generalization of (6). In this generalization, Hilbert's condition $\nabla^2 u = 0$ in $\mathscr{R}$ is replaced by (1), and $\mathscr{R}$ itself is allowed to be any domain surrounding $\mathscr{C}$, in the plane or in space.

The necessity for adjoining the conditions

$$\oint u(s) ds = \oint v(s) ds = 0$$

to (5) and (6), in the Riemann-Hilbert problem, comes from the fact that the perfect diffusion problem is singular if the plane (cf. §10), for the exterior problem. Inside bounded regions, the perfect diffusion problem (the case $\Sigma_a = \Sigma_f = 0$) is singular in any number of dimensions.

§3. Ordinary DE's

In the special case of one independent variable x and a finite domain $a \leq x \leq b$, evidently (1) reduces to the ordinary DE

$$0 = \frac{d}{dx}\left(D(x)\frac{d\phi}{dx}\right) + [\nu\Sigma_f(x) - \Sigma_s(x)]\phi + S(x) = 0 \ , \quad D(x) > 0 \ . \tag{7}$$

When $S(x) \equiv 0$, the general boundary condition (2), rewritten as

$$\begin{aligned} &\phi(a) - A_{11}D(a)\phi'(a) + A_{12}D(b)\phi'(b) = 0 \\ &\phi(b) - A_{21}D(a)\phi'(a) + A_{22}D(b)\phi'(b) = 0 \ , \end{aligned} \tag{8}$$

defines with (7) precisely the general second-order Sturm-Liouville system. Note that the system (7)-(8) is self-adjoint if and only if the matrix $\|A_{ij}\|$ is symmetric.[4] Therefore, if $\|A_{ij}\|$ is symmetric, (7) (8) has only real eigenvalues, and a basis of real eigenfunctions.

The case of separated endpoint conditions is, of course, simply that of a diagonal matrix ($A_{ij} = 0$ if $i \neq j$); it generalizes to the usual "mixed boundary condition" (2') for elliptic DE's. In this case, it is well known that, for $\Sigma_s \geqq 0$ and $A_{ii} \geqq 0$, all eigenvalues ν_k of (8) are positive. In particular, if $\nu \leqq 0$, then (7)-(8) has no non-trivial solution. Equivalently, one can show that if $\nu \leqq 0$, $\Sigma_s \geqq 0$, $\Sigma_f \geqq 0$, $A_{ii} \geqq 0$, then the boundary value problem (7)-(8) is well-set for diagonal $\|A_{ij}\|$. The same conclusion holds for any self-adjoint system (1), (2'), if $\nu \leqq 0$, $\Sigma_s \geqq 0$, $\Sigma_f \geqq 0$, and $d(y) \geqq 0$; this will be shown in §5. I will now show that this uniqueness theorem fails unless $\|A_{ij}\|$ is diagonal.

Example 1. Consider the system $\phi'' - \phi = 0$ on $-1 \leqq x \leqq 1$, subject to the boundary conditions $\phi(-1) + C\phi'(1) = \phi(1) - C\phi'(-1) = 0$, where $C = \coth 1$. Evidently $\phi = \cosh x$ satisfies this self-adjoint homogeneous Sturm-Liouville system (with $D = \Sigma_f = 1$, $\nu = -1$, $\Sigma_s = 0$, $A_{ii} = C$), as well as $\phi = 0$.

Though ν is negative in Example 1, this would be impossible if $\|A_{ij}\|$ were positive definite. The corresponding result will be proved more generally below, for partial DE's (1) and boundary conditions (2).

Indeed, the reader may find it suggestive to think of (2) as a direct generalization of (8), the matrix $\|A_{ij}\|$ in (8) being replaced by an integral kernel in (2).

§4. Green's identities

As is well known[5], one can easily prove analogs of Green's identities for general self-adjoint linear elliptic DE's (1), which are homogeneous in the sense that $S = 0$ in (1).

We begin by recalling Green's first identity

$$\nabla \cdot (\phi D \nabla\psi) = D(\nabla\phi \cdot \nabla\psi) + \phi\nabla \cdot (D\nabla\psi) \ , \tag{12}$$

whence, by the Divergence Theorem

$$(13)\qquad \iint_{\mathscr{G}} \phi\, D \frac{\partial\psi}{\partial n}\, dS = \iiint_{\mathscr{C}} D(\nabla\phi \cdot \nabla\psi) dR + \iiint_{\mathscr{C}} \phi \nabla \cdot (D\nabla\psi) dR \ .$$

Setting $\psi = \phi$, we obtain the following consequence of (1):

$$(14)\qquad \iint_{\mathscr{G}} \phi\, D \frac{\partial\phi}{\partial n}\, dS = \iiint_{\mathscr{C}} \{D\nabla\phi \cdot \nabla\phi + (\Sigma_a - \nu\Sigma_f)\phi^2\} dR \ .$$

Evidently, if $D > 0$, $\Sigma_a \geqq 0$, $\Sigma_f \leqq 0$ and $S = 0$ ("source-free reactor containing no fissionable material"), then the right side of (14) is positive or zero, zero only being possible if $\phi \equiv 0$. Hence, if $\phi \equiv 0$ on $\mathscr{G}$, $\phi \equiv 0$ in $\mathscr{C}$; and if $\partial\phi/\partial n \equiv 0$ on $\mathscr{G}$, $\phi = \text{const.}$ in $\mathscr{C}$, the constant being zero unless $\Sigma_a \equiv \nu\Sigma_f \equiv 0$. These imply familiar [2, p. 213] uniqueness theorems for (1) in $\mathscr{C}$, with respect to given ϕ or $\partial\phi/\partial n$ on $\mathscr{G}$, the restriction $S = 0$ being dropped.

More interesting is Green's second identity

$$(15)\qquad \iiint_{\mathscr{C}} \{\phi\nabla \cdot (D\nabla\psi) - \psi\nabla \cdot (D\nabla\phi)\} dR = \iint_{\mathscr{G}} \{\phi D \frac{\partial\psi}{\partial n} - \psi D \frac{\partial\phi}{\partial n}\} dS \ .$$

If ϕ and ψ both satisfy (1) in $\mathscr{C}$, with $S = 0$, then the left side of (15) vanishes because the integrand vanishes identically, and so

$$(16)\qquad \iint_{\mathscr{G}} \phi D \frac{\partial\psi}{\partial n}\, dS = \iint_{\mathscr{G}} \psi D \frac{\partial\phi}{\partial n}\, dS = [\phi, \psi]_{\mathscr{C}} \ .$$

By (13) and (1), both integrals in (16) are equal to the generalized Dirichlet integral

$$(17)\qquad [\phi, \psi]_{\mathscr{C}} = \iiint_{\mathscr{C}} \{D(\nabla\phi \cdot \nabla\psi) + (\Sigma_a - \nu\Sigma_f)\phi\psi\} dR = [\psi, \phi]_{\mathscr{C}} \ .$$

We can summarize the preceding results in the following theorem.

Theorem 1. If ϕ and ψ satisfy (1), with $S = 0$, in a region $\mathscr{C}$ with boundary $\mathscr{G}$, then (14)-(17) hold.

Corollary 1. If also ϕ and ψ satisfy (2) on $\mathscr{G}$, with $g = 0$, then

$$(18)\qquad [\phi, \psi]_{\mathscr{C}} = - \iiiint_{\mathscr{G}\times\mathscr{G}} A(y,\eta) D(y) D(\eta) \frac{\partial\phi}{\partial n}(y) \frac{\partial\psi}{\partial n}(\eta) dS(y) dS(\eta) \ .$$

If $A(y, \eta)$ is nonnegative definite, then the right side of (18) is nonpositive. But the left side is nonnegative. Since the difference of two solutions of (1)-(2) satisfies (1)-(2) with $S = g = 0$, this proves

Corollary 2. If $A(y, \eta)$ is nonnegative definite, then, with trivial exceptions, the boundary value problem (1)-(2) has at most one solution.

§5. Spectral theory

We shall now show that the boundary value problems defined by the differential operators of (1)

(19) $L[\phi] = -\nabla \cdot (D\nabla\phi) + \Sigma_a\phi$ and $L_\nu[\phi] = L[\phi] - \nu\Sigma_f\phi$,

with $S(x) = 0$, are self-adjoint relative to boundary conditions of the form (2), if $g(y) = 0$, and

(20) $$A(y, \eta) = A(\eta, y) .$$

From this fact, elementary spectral theorems follow immediately.

Consider the "space" of all functions $\phi, \psi, \ldots$ of class C^2 in $\mathscr{C}$, satisfying (2) on the boundary $\mathscr{G}$, relative to the usual complex inner product

(21) $$(\phi, \psi)_{\mathscr{C}} = \iiint_{\mathscr{C}} \phi(x)\psi^*(x)dR(x) .$$

This is evidently the Hermitian analog of a Euclidean vector space[6]; it is however not complete, because of (2). Thus the space is not a complex Hilbert space.

In this space, the operators (19) are easily seen to be self-adjoint. For, by definition

$$(\phi, L[\psi])_{\mathscr{C}} = \iiint_{\mathscr{C}} \{\phi\nabla\cdot(D\nabla\psi^*) + \Sigma_a\phi\psi^*\}dR$$
$$= \iint_{\mathscr{G}} \phi D \frac{\partial\psi^*}{\partial n} + \iiint_{\mathscr{C}} \{D(\nabla\phi\cdot\nabla\psi^*) + \Sigma_a\phi\psi^*\}dR ,$$

by (13). Now using (2) on ϕ and (18), we get

(22) $$(\phi, L[\psi])_{\mathscr{C}} = \iiiint_{\mathscr{G}\times\mathscr{G}} A(y, \eta)D(y)D(\eta)\frac{\partial\phi}{\partial n}(y)\frac{\partial\psi^*}{\partial n}(\eta)dS(y)dS(\eta)$$
$$+ \iiint_{\mathscr{C}} \{D(\nabla\phi\cdot\nabla\psi^*) + \Sigma_a\phi\psi^*\}dR .$$

By exactly the same argument, the right side can also be shown to equal $(L[\phi],\psi)_{\mathscr{C}}$. Hence

(23) $$(\phi, L[\psi])_{\mathscr{C}} = (L[\phi], \psi)_{\mathscr{C}} ,$$ assuming (2) and (20).

The same argument applies also to L_ν in (19).

The usual elementary manipulations[7] now lead to

Theorem 2. The Sturm-Liouville system defined by the DE

(24) $$L[\phi] = \nu\Sigma_f\phi \quad \text{in } \mathscr{C} ,$$

and the boundary conditions (2) and (20) on $\mathscr{G}$, with $g(y) = 0$ in (2), has only real eigenvalues of rank one; moreover eigenfunctions which correspond to distinct eigenvalues are orthogonal with respect to the weighting function $\Sigma_f(x)$.

With a little more effort, we can prove

Theorem 3. If, in (20), $A(y,\eta)$ is positive definite, then all the eigenvalues of (24) are positive.

For, setting $\psi = \phi$ and $L[\psi] = \nu\Sigma_f\phi$ in (22), we get

$$\nu(\Sigma_f\phi, \phi)_{\mathscr{C}} = (\phi, L[\phi]_{\mathscr{C}}) > 0 \quad , \tag{25}$$

since every integrand in the right side of (22) is identically nonnegative, and some term is positive unless $\phi \equiv 0$. But $(\Sigma_f\phi, \phi)_{\mathscr{C}} > 0$ for the same reason; hence ν , as the ratio of two positive real numbers, must be positive.

Corollary. If $\nu\Sigma_f \leqq \Sigma_a$ identically in $\mathscr{C}$, and $A(y,\eta) = A(\eta, y)$ is positive definite, then $L_\nu[\phi] = 0$ has no non-zero solution satisfying (2), with $g(y) = 0$.

The preceding formulas are evidently very analogous to those of §4. Indeed, it is obvious from (17) that if $L[\phi] = 0$

$$(\phi, L_\nu[\psi])_{\mathscr{C}} = [\phi, \psi^*]_{\mathscr{C}} \quad . \tag{26}$$

§6. Variational principles

We shall now give to the boundary value problem (1), (2) a variational formulation. To do this, we consider the Euclidean vector space $\mathscr{F}$ of all real functions ϕ, ψ which are of class[8] C^2 on $\mathscr{C} \cup \mathscr{G}$. In $\mathscr{F}$, $(\phi,\psi)_{\mathscr{C}} = (\phi, \psi^*)_{\mathscr{C}}$; $[\phi,\psi]_{\mathscr{C}}$, as defined by (17), exists for all ϕ, ψ ; moreover so does $(\phi, L[\psi])_{\mathscr{C}}$. Finally, so does

$$[\phi,\psi]_{\mathscr{G}} = \iiiint_{\mathscr{G}\times\mathscr{G}} A(y,\eta) D(y) D(\eta) \frac{\partial\phi}{\partial n}(y) \frac{\partial\phi}{\partial n}(\eta) dS(y) dS(\eta) \quad . \tag{27}$$

We shall use all the preceding "inner products".

First, consider the quadratic functional

$$J[\phi] = \tfrac{1}{2}\{[\phi,\phi]_{\mathscr{C}} + [\phi,\phi]_{\mathscr{G}}\} \quad \text{with} \quad \nu = 0 \quad . \tag{28}$$

The last term in (28) is analogous to the "Dirichletsche Randteil" which has been considered by Kamke[9] for ordinary differential equations (cf. §3). Taking the first variation of (28), we get

$$\delta J = [\delta\phi, \phi]_{\mathscr{C}} + [\delta\phi, \phi]_{\mathscr{G}} \ .$$

Comparing the preceding expression with (2.2), and subtracting $\nu(\Sigma_f\phi, \phi)_{\mathscr{C}}$ from both sides, we get the basic identity

$$\delta J = (\delta\phi, \ L_\nu[\phi])_{\mathscr{C}} \quad , \tag{29}$$

valid for all $\delta\phi \in \mathscr{F}$ satisfying (2) on $\mathscr{G}$ with $g(y) = 0$. We conclude

Theorem 4. A function $\phi \in \mathscr{F}$ extremalizes $J[\phi]$, in the class of all functions satisfying (2) with given $A(y, \eta) = A(\eta, y)$ and $g(y)$, if and only if ϕ satisfies (1) with $S = 0$.

Remark. If A is positive definite and $\nu \geq 0$, then the second variation in (28) is positive, and one can prove that $J[\phi]$ is minimized by the above solution. That is, $J[\phi] < J[\phi + \psi]$ unless $\psi \equiv 0$.

In the case $g = 0$ of homogeneous boundary conditions, an analog of the usual[10] variational characterization of eigenfunctions can also be made. Consider the Rayleigh quotient

$$(30) \qquad \rho[\phi] = (\phi, L[\phi])_{\mathscr{C}} \Big/ (\phi, \Sigma_f \phi)_{\mathscr{C}} = J[\phi] \Big/ (\phi, \Sigma_f \phi)_{\mathscr{C}} .$$

Using the symmetry relations $(\phi, L[\delta\phi])_{\mathscr{C}} = (L[\delta\phi], \delta\phi)_{\mathscr{C}}$ and $(\Sigma_f \phi, \delta\phi)_{\mathscr{C}} = (\phi, \Sigma_f \delta\phi)_{\mathscr{C}}$ valid by (23) for real $\phi, \delta\phi$, we have

$$\tfrac{1}{2}\delta\rho = \frac{(\phi, \Sigma_f \phi)(\delta\phi, L[\phi]) - (\phi, L[\phi])(\delta\phi, \Sigma_f \phi)}{(\Sigma_f \phi, \phi)^2} .$$

If $L[\phi] = \nu \Sigma_f \phi$, then the numerator clearly vanishes above. With a little more care, one can prove the converse. Hence

Theorem 5. Equation (1) in $\mathscr{C}$, with $S = 0$, is equivalent to the extremal condition $\delta\rho = 0$ in (30), for functions $\phi \in \mathscr{F}$ satisfying (2) on $\mathscr{G}$ with $g = 0$.

III. ALBEDO FUNCTION: PHYSICAL BACKGROUND

§7. Neutron reflectors

An important generalization of the boundary value problem (1), (2) arises naturally in nuclear reactor theory[11]. The geometry of interest involves a central core $\mathscr{C}$, surrounded by a reflector $\mathscr{R}$. I shall denote the interface between $\mathscr{C}$ and $\mathscr{R}$ by $\mathscr{G}$, and the outer boundary of $\mathscr{R}$ by $\mathscr{G}_0$, as indicated in Fig. 1. The generalization is as follows.

Problem I. Find a function $\phi(x)$ which satisfies Eq. (1) in $\mathscr{C}$ and, for different D, Σ_f, Σ_s, and S, in $\mathscr{R}$, which satisfies (3) across $\mathscr{G}$, and (2') on $\mathscr{G}_0$.

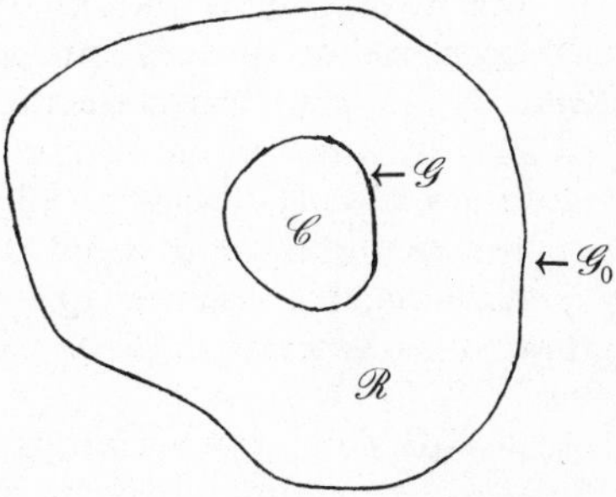

Fig. 1

This problem arises in the so-called "one-group diffusion" approximation of reactor statics. Specifically [1, pp. 129-136], (1) is the usual one-group diffusion equation, with "diffusion coefficient" D, absorption and fission "macroscopic cross-sections" Σ_a and Σ_f "source strength" S, and "neutron yield per fission" ν . The "core" $\mathscr{C}$ is supposed to contain fissionable material ("fuel"), and the reflector $\mathscr{R}$ is supposed to improve the neutron economy by reducing neutron leakage. Typically, $S = \Sigma_f = 0$ in $\mathscr{R}$, so that (1) assumes there the simplified form

$$(1^*) \qquad L[\phi] = -\nabla \cdot (D\nabla\phi) + \Sigma_a\phi = 0 \quad \text{in } \mathscr{R} .$$

On $\mathscr{G}_0$, (2') is usually assumed, the "extrapolation distance" d being a positive number equal to about $0.71\lambda_t$, where λ_t is the transport mean free path [1, pp. 104-105]. In the limiting case $\lambda_t = 0$ of pure diffusion theory, clearly $d = 0$, and so (2') reduces to

$$(3^*) \qquad \phi = 0 \quad \text{on } \mathscr{G}_0 .$$

However, the problems of §1 have simpler basic interpretations, if we do not pass to the limit $\lambda_t = 0$ of "zero mean free (neutron) path" quite so directly. The simplest basic idea is that of reflection coefficient or albedo β , introduced in 1936 by Fermi and Amaldi[12] in the preceding context, but with $\lambda_t > 0$. By this is meant the fraction of neutrons entering the reflector which are reflected (by multiple scattering) back to the core [1, p. 130]. This fraction $\beta = \beta(\mathscr{R})$ plays an important role in the neutron economy, and provides a rough measure of the effectiveness of a given reflector $\mathscr{R}$.

Amaldi and Fermi approximated the effect of the reflector on the core by the boundary condition [1, (5.98.2)]

$$(31) \qquad (1-\beta)\phi + 2(1+\beta)D\frac{\partial\phi}{\partial n} = 0 \quad \text{on } \mathscr{G} ,$$

of the familiar "mixed" form of Fourier. This is similar to (3'), but with an increased "extrapolation distance". The essence of their conclusion was the equivalence of the reflector to the assumption of (31).

This conclusion is very remarkable: it replaces the three conditions (1) in $\mathscr{R}$, (3) on $\mathscr{G}$, and (2') on $\mathscr{G}_0$ by the single condition (31) on $\mathscr{G}$.

Unfortunately, it is only approximate: obviously, neutrons entering $\mathscr{R}$ from $\mathscr{C}$ at η will, in general, return to $\mathscr{C}$ from $\mathscr{R}$ at a different point y . My first main idea is that, in the limiting[13] case $\lambda_t = 0$ of pure diffusion, the single condition (2) on $\mathscr{G}$ (with $g = 0$) is exactly equivalent to (1) in $\mathscr{R}$, (3) on $\mathscr{G}$, and (2') on $\mathscr{G}_0$. The verification of this result is equivalent to solving the following problem.

Problem II. Find an albedo function $A(y,\eta) = A(\eta, y)$ on $\mathscr{G}$, such that $\phi(x)$ satisfies (1) in $\mathscr{R}$ and (2') on $\mathscr{G}_0$ only if it satisfies (2) on $\mathscr{G}$.

I shall now, therefore, turn to the physical interpretation of the "albedo" concept in the limiting case of pure diffusion.

§8. Brownian movement

It is not easy to interpret the ideas of Fermi and Amaldi[2] within the framework of ideal diffusion theory, to which alone (1) is rigorously applicable. As is well known, this limiting case corresponds to Brownian movement, for which a rigorous theory was first provided by Norbert Wiener less than thirty years ago!

In ideal Brownian movement, a particle which crosses a given plane will, with probability one, recross it infinitely often, infinitely nearby, in an infinitely short time. Hence, if we try to define $A(y,\eta)$ as the probability that a particle leaving $\mathscr{C}$ at η will return to it from $\mathscr{R}$ at y, we will have simply $A(y,\eta) = \delta(y-\eta)$. In particular, if we can assign any probability to "successive crossings" of $\mathscr{G}$, we should set $\beta = 1$.

This can be seen in another way as follows. In the passage from transport theory to Brownian movement, $D = \lambda_t/3$ approaches zero, while the "diffusion length" $\kappa^{-1} = (D/\Sigma_a)^{\frac{1}{2}}$ is held constant. (Note that, in (1), it is only the ratio $\kappa^2 = \Sigma_a/D$ which matters, whereas Σ_a and D have well-defined independent meanings in transport theory with $\lambda_t > 0$.) Consequently, by (31), $\beta \uparrow 1$. (In particular, for slab reflectors, by [1, (5. 100. 1)],

$$\beta = (1-2\kappa D \coth \kappa a)/(1+2\kappa D \coth \kappa a) \uparrow 1.)$$

Hence, as $\lambda_t \downarrow 0$, $\Sigma_a \downarrow 0$, also, while[14] $\Sigma_a \uparrow +\infty$.

A rigorous probabilistic discussion of the passage from the simple "albedo" definition of Fermi and Amaldi to the limiting $A(y,\eta)$ defined by (2) would, indeed, be fairly sophisticated. I shall content myself with a direct intuitive interpretation of $A(y,\eta)$, in terms of particle diffusion (e.g., of neutrons). In doing this, it will be most suggestive to think of ϕ as representing particle density $N = \phi/v$.

Consider a unit source of particles placed at $\eta \in \mathscr{G}$, just inside $\mathscr{R}$. Let us replace $\mathscr{C}$ by a perfect reflector, so that $\partial\phi/\partial n \equiv 0$ on $\mathscr{G}$ in $\mathscr{R}$. (Using (3), this can be achieved by making $D = 0$ in $\mathscr{C}$.) This will permit particles to leak out of $\mathscr{R}$ through $\mathscr{G}_0$; the net flux through a small hemisphere surrounding y in $\mathscr{R}$ will therefore be (cf. Fig. 2)

$$\iint D \frac{\partial\phi}{\partial n}\, dS = 1, \tag{32}$$

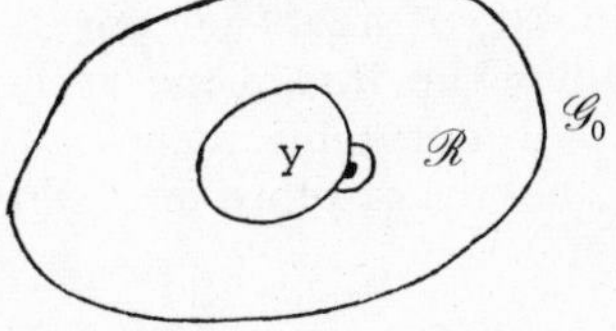

Fig. 2

where $D\nabla\phi$ represents the current [1, p. 92].

Macroscopically, the resulting $\phi(\xi) = A(\eta, x)$ will evidently have a dipole singularity near η inside $\mathscr{R}$, will satisfy $\partial\phi/\partial n = 0$

elsewhere on $\mathscr{G}$, and (2') on $\mathscr{G}_0$, with $\gamma = 0$. Therefore, a continuously distributed source with density $D\partial\phi/\partial n$ per unit area on $\mathscr{G}$, should satisfy (1) in $\mathscr{R}$, (2') on $\mathscr{G}_0$ (with $\gamma = 0$) , and (2) on $\mathscr{G}$, for any given $\partial\phi/\partial n$.

Intuitively, therefore, it seems reasonable to suppose that $A(x, \eta)$ can be constructed as a well-defined function in $\mathscr{R}$. Letting D be very small in $\mathscr{C}$, its extension to $\mathscr{C}$ by continuity (2) of ϕ would also seem clearly indicated; for fixed finite particle velocity v , this amounts to having long lifetimes in $\mathscr{R}$ and short lifetimes in $\mathscr{C}$.

§9. Heat conduction

The analogy between mass diffusion and heat conduction is well known; we shall now interpret the "albedo function" $A(y, \eta)$ in the context of heat conduction. In this context, ϕ refers to temperature $D = k$ to thermal conductivity (in an isotropic medium). The interface condition (3) is standard while Σ_a in (1) may be interpreted as a coefficient of heat transfer for radiation[15]. Though $\nu\Sigma_f$ can be interpreted in terms of temperature-dependent chemical reactions, I shall suppose $\nu\Sigma_f = 0$, which would ordinarily be the case.

In Fig. 1, we now interpret $\mathscr{R}$ as a layer of insulation wrapped around the heat source $\mathscr{C}$; $\mathscr{G}$ is the inner surface of this layer; $\mathscr{G}_0$ is the outer surface exposed to the air; (2) is just Newton's Law of Cooling. Then $A(x, \eta)$ can be defined on $\mathscr{R} \times \mathscr{G}$ in physical language as follows.

Let $\mathscr{R}$ be supposed perfectly insulated along $\mathscr{G}$; let a heat source of unit strength be placed at $\eta \in \mathscr{G}$ just inside $\mathscr{R}$; and let heat diffuse through $\mathscr{R}$, leaking out at $\mathscr{G}$. Then, in thermal equilibrium, the temperature will satisfy the mathematical conditions of §4, and so realize $A(x, \eta)$ inside $\mathscr{R}$.

Since, as is well known [2, p. 214], either of ϕ or $\partial\phi/\partial n$ determines the other on the boundary, there is only one $A(x, \eta)$ with the preceding properties. Therefore, any solution of (1) in $\mathscr{R}$ which satisfies (2') on $\mathscr{G}_0$ (with $\gamma = 0$) must satisfy (2) on $\mathscr{G}$. This gives a second physical realization of the reflector function; in the present context, it might suggestively be called the insulation function, describing the insulating value of $\mathscr{R}$.

A direct application to reactor heat transfer can be had by letting $\mathscr{C}$ be a fuel plate and $\mathscr{R}$ the cladding, and letting a coolant flow past $\mathscr{G}_0$.

§10. Containment

In the case $\nu\Sigma_f = \Sigma_a = 0$ corresponding to pure diffusion without internal absorption, the "reflector function" $A(x, \eta)$ also has a natural hydrodynamical interpretation. In this interpretation, $\mathscr{R}$ consists of an incompressible fluid of density $\rho(x) = 1/D(x)$, surrounding a movable boundary $\mathscr{G}$ as in Fig. 1. One can suppose that the normal velocity of $\mathcal{G}$ is controllable at will; the special cases corresponding to rigid translation and rotation of $\mathcal{G}$ (i.e., of $\mathcal{C}$) will then give the theory of induced mass in a fluid of variable density[16]; that corresponding to expansion (with ϕ = const. on $\mathcal{G}$) to the initial acceleration of water in an underwater explosion.

In the hydrodynamical interpretation, $\phi(x) = p(x)$ is the pressure, and $a(x) = D\nabla p(x) = \rho^{-1}\nabla p(x)$ is the initial acceleration. Hence, in this example, $(\phi, \phi)_{\mathcal{R}}$ is

$$(33) \qquad \iiint_{\mathcal{R}} \rho(a\cdot a)dR = \iiint D(\nabla\phi\cdot\nabla\phi)dR \ ,$$

the kinetic energy integral (or, more precisely, its second time derivative). The "boundary parts" $(\phi, \phi)_{\mathcal{G}}$ and $(\phi, \phi)_{\mathcal{G}_0}$ express work done on the boundary.

The case $\phi = p_1$ = const. on $\mathcal{G}$, $\phi = 0$ on $\mathcal{G}_0$ of an underwater explosion is interesting; p_1 gives a measure of the containment effect of the fluid in $\mathcal{R}$, for a given volumetric expansion. The case that $\mathcal{G}_0$ consists partly of a fixed surface (on which $\partial\phi/\partial n = 0$) and partly of a free surface (with $\phi = p_0$) is of especial interest. So is the case ρ = const., corresponding to a homogeneous fluid; in this case $A(x, \eta)$ depends only on the geometry of $\mathcal{R}$.

Another important application is to the theory of the natural vibration frequencies of a floating elastic body (surface ship)[17].

The case that $\mathcal{R}$ extends to infinity is also especially interesting. It is suggestive to note that, in this case, $A(x, \eta)$ is not defined in two dimensions; this is a corollary of the underwater explosion paradox (expansion requires infinite kinetic energy at infinity). It corresponds to the well-known fact that, in two-dimensional Brownian motion, a particle will return to every neighborhood of its source, infinitely often, after an arbitrarily long time. As a result, if there were no absorption or leakage (if $\Sigma_a = 0$), a neutron (or heat) source would build up an infinitely high neutron density (or temperature).

In three dimensions, or if $\Sigma_a > 0$ in two dimensions, this difficulty does not arise.

§11. Capacity

As a final physical interpretation of $A(x, \eta)$, related to the preceding, consider a charged domain $\mathcal{C}$, surrounded by a dielectric medium $\mathcal{R}$ with inductive capacity $K(x)$, whose outer boundary $\mathcal{G}_0$ (cf. Fig. 1) is grounded so that the electrostatic potential $E(x) = 0$ on $\mathcal{G}$.

In $\mathcal{C}$, (1) will hold with $\phi(x) = E(x)$, $S = -4\pi\rho(x)$ equal to the charge density, and $D = K(x)$ the inductive capacity[18]. In this interpretation, $\Sigma_a = \nu\Sigma_f = 0$ again. On $\mathcal{G}$, (3) holds; in $\mathcal{R}$, (1) holds again with $S = 0$.

If we knew the "albedo function" $A(x, \eta)$, we could therefore again reduce the preceding boundary value problem for $\mathcal{C} \cup \mathcal{R}$, to one for

$\mathscr{C}$ involving the boundary condition (3).

A special case of some interest occurs when $\mathscr{C}$ is a conductor. In this case, $\phi = E$ is a constant on $\mathscr{G}$. The following generalized conductor problem is then of interest: given $\phi = 1$ on $\mathscr{G}$, (1) in $\mathscr{R}$ (which could constitute the entire exterior of $\mathscr{G}$), and $\phi = 0$ on $\mathscr{G}_0$ (which would then reduce to the point at infinity), what is the charge distribution $2\pi K \partial\phi/\partial n$ on $\mathscr{G}$?

When this problem is solved, Problem I can also be solved easily in the homogeneous case $k \equiv 1$, by integrating the elementary potential $1/r$ of a simple source. The generalized conductor problem can also be stated in purely mathematical terms, as a special case of the inverse of Problem II.

Problem II'. Given ϕ on $\mathscr{G}$, (1) in $\mathscr{R}$, and (2') on $\mathscr{G}_0$, what is $\partial\phi/\partial n$ on $\mathscr{G}$?

IV. ALBEDO FUNCTION: MATHEMATICAL THEORY

§12. Basic definition

The physical ideas of §§ 8, 9 (cf. Fig. 2) suggest directly the following basic definition.

Definition. By the albedo function for a region $\mathscr{R}$, for the DE (1) in $\mathscr{R}$ with $S = \Sigma_f = 0$, and the condition (2') with $\gamma = 0$ on a portion $\mathscr{G}_0$ of the boundary $\partial\mathscr{R}$ of $\mathscr{R}$ (the "outer boundary" of $\mathscr{R}$), is meant a function $A(y, \eta)$ defined on $\mathscr{G} \times \mathscr{G}$, where $\mathscr{G} = \partial\mathscr{R} - \mathscr{G}_0$ (cf. Fig. 1) which, for each fixed $y \in \mathscr{G}$: (i) has a simple source of unit strength at y, satisfies $\partial A/\partial\nu = 0$ elsewhere on $\mathscr{G}$, (ii) satisfies (1) in $\mathscr{R}$ which $S = \Sigma_f = 0$, and (iii) satisfies (2') on $\mathscr{G}_0$ with $\gamma = 0$.

For $\nabla^2 \phi = 0$ and the boundary condition (2') on $\mathscr{G}_0$, the albedo function is clearly a limiting form of Robin's function.[19] Thus, albedo functions are limits of "fundamental solutions" of (1) in $\mathscr{R}$, with respect to (2) on $\mathscr{G}_0$ and $\partial A/\partial\nu = 0$ on $\mathscr{G}$.

Theorem 6. If $\phi(x)$ satisfies (1) in $\mathscr{R}$ with $S = \Sigma_f = 0$, and (2') on $\mathscr{G}_0$ with $\gamma = 0$, then $\phi(x)$ satisfies (2) on $\mathscr{G}$ with respect to any albedo function for the given partial boundary value problem in $\mathscr{R}$.

Proof: The proof is, for each y, a straightforward application of the identities of Part II, applied to $\mathscr{R}$ instead of $\mathscr{C}$. First, by (16), letting $\mathscr{G}'$ be $\mathscr{G}$ with a small circle around y of radius r replaced by a small near-hemisphere in $\mathscr{R}$ with center y,

$$(34) \qquad 0 = \iint_{\mathscr{G}' \cup \mathscr{G}_0} \left\{ \frac{\partial A}{\partial\nu}(y,\eta)\, \phi(\eta) - A(y,\eta) \frac{\partial\phi}{\partial n}(\eta) \right\} D(\eta)\, dS(\eta) .$$

The expression in braces vanishes identically on $\mathscr{G}_0$, since both ϕ and A satisfy (2') there with $\gamma = 0$,

$$\phi \frac{\partial A}{\partial \nu} = -d \frac{\partial \phi}{\partial \nu} \frac{\partial A}{\partial \nu} = A \frac{\partial \phi}{\partial n} .$$

On $\mathscr{G}$, $\partial A/\partial \nu \equiv 0$; hence the contribution to the left-hand term in (34) comes entirely from the hemispherical portion of $\mathscr{G}'$. This contribution, for a unit source[20], is just $\phi(y)$. Hence, substituting into (34), and passing to the limit as $r \downarrow 0$, we get

$$(34^*) \qquad \phi(y) - \iint_{\mathscr{G}} A(y, \eta) \frac{\partial \phi}{\partial n}(\eta)\, D(\eta) dS(\eta) = 0 .$$

The reversal of sign in passing from (34*) to (2) is easily explained by (3): outward normals go into inward normals, as one crosses $\mathscr{G}$ from $\mathscr{R}$ to $\mathscr{C}$.

By very slight modifications, the preceding definition and theorem can be extended to the case that ϕ satisfies (2) on $\mathscr{G}_0$.

§13. Existence of albedo function

For boundary conditions of the form (2'), it is quite easy to prove the existence of an albedo function. Thus, in the classical case of the Laplace equation $\nabla^2 \phi = 0$ in three dimensions, the expression $1/2\pi r + \psi$ will satisfy the conditions of §12, provided

$$\partial\psi/\partial n = - \frac{\partial}{\partial n} (1/2\pi r) \qquad \text{on } \mathscr{G}$$

and $d(\partial\psi/\partial n) + \psi = -[d\partial(1/2\pi r)/\partial n + (1/2\pi r)]$ on $\mathscr{G}_0$. This boundary value problem has a solution, by standard theorems of potential theory [2, p. 315].

In the case of other self-adjoint elliptic equations of the form (1), the existence of an albedo function can be proved by similar methods. Namely, one can construct a Robin's function with source at any $y \in \mathscr{G}$ on an extension of $\mathscr{R}$ across $\mathscr{G}$, by extending (1) smoothly across this domain. Under very general conditions[21], one can then "correct" this simple source by a function ψ satisfying $\partial\psi/\partial n = f(\eta)$ on $\mathscr{G}$ and (2') on $\mathscr{G}_0$.

Furthermore, the albedo function so constructed is uniformly integrable, though its kernel is singular on the diagonal $y = \eta$. Therefore, it acts as a bounded linear operator from the space of bounded measurable $\partial\phi/\partial n(\eta)$ to the space of bounded measurable $\phi(y)$. The inverse operator, referred to in Problem II', is unbounded and its kernel is non-integrable[22]. We have thus sketched the proof of

Theorem 7. The albedo function $A(y,\eta)$ exists, for any sufficiently regular $\mathscr{R}$, $\mathscr{G}_0$, $\mathscr{G}$, positive function D and nonnegative Σ_a , and $d \geq 0$.

In the limiting case that (2') degenerates to $\partial\phi/\partial n = 0$ on $\mathscr{G}_0$ $(d = \infty)$, the problem is singular, as noted at the end of §2. Actually, it seems certain that (2') on $\mathscr{G}_0$ could be replaced by a boundary condition of the "integral" form (2), for any positive definite symmetric kernel $A(y, \eta)$.

§14. Properties of albedo function

The albedo function, as defined in §12 and constructed in §13, has two basic general properties.

Theorem 8. If (2) on $\mathcal{G}$ is implied by (1) in $\mathcal{R}$ and (2') on $\mathcal{G}_0$, with $S = 0$ in (1) and $d \geqq 0$ and $\gamma = 0$ in (2'), and if $\Sigma_f = 0$ in $\mathcal{R}$, then $A(y, \eta)$ is positive definite on $\mathcal{G}$.

Proof. In the proof, we assume as before[21] that (1) in $\mathcal{R}$ and (2') on $\mathcal{G}_0$ can be solved, for any $D\ \partial\phi/\partial n$ on $\mathcal{G}$. We now apply (14) to $\mathcal{R}$, getting

$$\iint_{\mathcal{G}\cup\mathcal{G}_0} \phi D \frac{\partial\phi}{\partial n}\, dS = \iiint_{\mathcal{R}} \{D\nabla\phi\cdot\nabla\phi + \Sigma_a \phi^2\}\, dR \geqq 0 .$$

Using (2') on $\mathcal{G}_0$, (2) on $\mathcal{G}$, and transposing, we have

$$(35)\qquad \iiiint_{\mathcal{G}} A(y,\eta) D(y) \frac{\partial\phi}{\partial n}(y)\ D(\eta)\frac{\partial\phi}{\partial n}(\eta) dS(y) dS(\eta)$$

$$= \iint_{\mathcal{G}_0} d(y)\ \phi^2(y) dS(y) + \iiint_{\mathcal{R}} \{D\nabla\phi\cdot\nabla\phi + \Sigma_a \phi^2\}\, dR \geqq 0 ,$$

equality occurring only in the trivial cases $\phi \equiv 0$ or $\Sigma_a \equiv 0$, ϕ = const. This completes the proof.

Those acquainted with reactor theory will readily recognize the condition of positive definiteness of $A(y, \eta)$ as corresponding to the subcriticality of the reactor domain $\mathcal{R}$ in question. However, I shall not elaborate on this connection here.

Again, applying (17) to $\mathcal{R}$, we get

$$(36)\qquad \iint_{\mathcal{G}} \phi D \frac{\partial\psi}{\partial n}\, dS + \iint_{\mathcal{G}_0} \phi D \frac{\partial\psi}{\partial n}\, dS$$

$$= \iiint_{\mathcal{R}} \{D(\nabla\phi\cdot\nabla\psi) + (\Sigma_a - \nu\Sigma_f)\phi\psi\}\, dR ,$$

provided $S \equiv 0$ in $\mathcal{R}$. Now substitute the boundary conditions (2) into (16) and (36).

We see that, if ϕ and ψ satisfy (1) in $\mathcal{R}$ which $S = 0$, and (2) on $\mathcal{G}_0$, then

$$(37)\qquad 0 = [\phi, \psi]_{\mathcal{R}} - [\psi, \phi]_{\mathcal{R}}$$

$$= \iiiint_{\mathcal{G}\times\mathcal{G}} D(y) \frac{\partial\psi}{\partial n}(y)\ [A(y,\eta) - A(\eta, y)]\ D(\eta) \frac{\partial\phi}{\partial n}(\eta) dS(y) dS(\eta) ,$$

since (2') makes the corresponding integral over $\mathcal{G}_0 \times \mathcal{G}_0$, with $\gamma(y) \equiv 0$, vanish. From the symmetry (17), it follows that if (1) and (2)-(2') have a solution in $\mathcal{R}$ for general boundary normal derivatives $D\frac{\partial\phi}{\partial n}$ and $D\frac{\partial\psi}{\partial n}$ ("neutron currents") on $\mathcal{G}$, then

$$A(y, \eta) = A(\eta, y) \quad \text{on} \quad \mathcal{G} \times \mathcal{G} \quad . \tag{38}$$

In words, the reflector function $A(y, \eta)$ is symmetric.

This proof can, no doubt, be made rigorous by an appeal to appropriate existence theorems. It is also suggestive to think of it in terms of the principle of the reversibility of diffusion. It is a limiting case of the Optical Reciprocity Theorem of neutron transport theory, in the one-group approximation. In pure diffusion (with finite mean free path and no "slowing down"), the reverse of every particle (e.g., neutron) trajectory is an equally probable trajectory.

The proof of (38) extends without change to the case that (2) holds on $\mathcal{G}_0$, with $A(y, \eta) = A(\eta, y)$ on $\mathcal{G}_0 \times \mathcal{G}_0$. The physical reason for the symmetry is the same as before.

To complete the proof of the above results, it would suffice[21] to prove the Fredholm alternative for boundary conditions of the form (2).

The author wishes to thank Dr. T. W. Mulliken for correcting several errata, and to thank Profs. Felix Browder and J. B. Diaz for supplying references.

NOTES

1. See M.I. Visik, Doklady SSSR 82 (1952), 181-184; A. Shapiro, Izv. Akad. Nauk 17 (1953), 539-562; J. L. Lions, Acta Math. 94 (1955), 13-153; F. Browder, Comm. pure appl. math. 9(1956), 351-361.
2. See [4] and N.I. Muskhelishvili, "Singular integral equations", Groningen, 1953.
3. N. I. Muskhelishvili, "...mathematical theory of elasticity", Groningen, 1953, Chs. 23-25.
4. E. A. Coddington and N. Levinson, "Ordinary differential equations", Ch. 7. Note that $\partial\phi/\partial n(a) = -\phi'(a)$, whereas $\partial\phi/\partial n(b) = \phi'(b)$.
5. Enzykl. Math. Wiss. The proofs are exactly as in [2, Ch. VIII].
6. G. Birkhoff and S. MacLane, "Survey of modern algebra", rev. ed., Ch. IX, §12.
7. See for example B. Friedman, "Principles of applied mathematics", Wiley, 1956, pp. 94-96.
8. I have not studied possible ways to weaken this condition (e.g., to class C^2 on $\mathcal{C}$ and class C^1 on $\mathcal{G}$). In this connection, see H. Weyl, Duke Math. J. 7 (1940), 411-444.
9. E. Kamke, Math. Zeits. 46 (1940), 231-286 and 48(1942), 67-100; see also L. Collatz, "Eigenwertprobleme und ihre numerische Behandlung", Leipzig, 1944, p. 65 ff.
10. B. Friedman, op. cit. in ftnt. 7, pp. 208-209; Collatz, op. cit. in ftnt. 9, §15.
11. It was in this connection that the author became interested in albedo functions, in 1955-56 while working with Dr. R. S. Varga of

the Atomic Power Division of the Westinghouse Electric Company.

12. E. Amaldi and E. Fermi, Phys. Rev. 50 (1936), 899.

13. Generalizations of the ideas and conclusions presented below to transport theory and to slowing down ("moderation") will, obviously, involve greater complications and corresponding mathematical exertion.

14. Since $3D = \lambda_t = 1/\Sigma_a(1 - \bar{\mu}_0)$, as in [1, p. 98].

15. See H. S. Carslaw and J. C. Jaeger, "Conduction of heat in solids", Oxford, 1947, Sec. 64. For our (2), see ibid., p. 14; for (3) see p. 17.

16. G. Birkhoff, Quar. Appl. Math. 11 (1953), 109-110. For underwater explosions, see R. H. Cole, "Underwater Explosions", Princeton, 1948, Ch. 8, and refs. given there. Though there are some interconnections, the problem treated in the present paper is not the "induced potential" problem which I discussed on pp. 88-96 of the von Mises Anniversary Volume, Academic Press, 1954.

17. F. M. Lewis, Trans. Nav. Arch. Marine Eng. 37 (1929), 1-18; E. B. Moullin, Proc. Camb. Phil. Soc. 24 (1928), 400-413 and 531-538.

18. J. H. Jeans, "Electricity and magnetism", fifth ed., Cambridge Univ. Press, 1941, Sec. 132. The equations go back to Poisson. For (2), see Sec. 137.

19. S. Bergman and M. Schiffer, "Kernel functions and elliptic differential equations", Academic Press, 1953, p. 11. We treat the limiting case that $\lambda(P) = 0$ on $\mathcal{G}$.

20. We normalize so that the flux through the hemisphere is one.

21. F. Browder, Proc. Nat. Acad. Sci. 39 (1953), 185-190.

22. This is why, in (27), a bilinear expression in $\partial\phi/\partial n$ was used instead of one in ϕ . Prof. Friedrichs has observed orally that an expression in ϕ would lead to more smoothly defined purely variational problems, if the kernel were equally regular.

REFERENCES

[1] S. Glasstone and M. Edlund, "The elements of nuclear reactor theory", van Nostrand, 1952.

[2] O. D. Kellogg, "Foundations of potential theory", Springer, 1929.

[3] F. Pockels, "Über die partielle Differentialgleichung $\Delta u + k^2 u = 0$ in der mathematischen Physik", Teubner, 1891.

[4] D. Hilbert, "Intergralgleichungen", Teubner, 1912, Ch. 10.

JIM DOUGLAS, JR.

A Numerical Method for Analytic Continuation

§1. Introduction

Analytic continuation is one of the oldest subjects of study in analysis. It is well known that the values of an analytic function on a circle determine the function exactly throughout its domain of analyticity. However, the situation is entirely different if the values on the circle are known only approximately. It is still true that an approximation to the function can be obtained inside the circle, but continuation of the function outside the circle may be very much in error; in fact, the circle may be a cut for the approximation. Unfortunately, any physical measurement is subject to error; thus, the continuation of a physically determined analytic function may lead to considerable difficulties. Without more information than just approximate values on a circle (or, of course, on any other reasonable, closed curve), the continuation may be impossible.

Consequently, we are lead to adding additional hypotheses regarding the information known about the function. In many physical problems, it is known that the function is analytic in a specific, larger region and that the function is bounded in modulus in the larger region by a constant that can be estimated in advance. Under these conditions, the Stieltjes-Vitali theorem implies immediately that, if we can extend the approximate data to an analytic function in the larger region so that the approximation is also bounded by the same constant, the error in the approximation tends to zero as the error in the data tends to zero. It is precisely a problem of this type that will be discussed here.

Let $f(z)$ be analytic in the disk $0 \leqq |z| \leqq 1$, and let

$$(1.1)\qquad \begin{cases} \max\limits_{|z| \leqq 1} |f(z)| \leqq m_0 , \\ \max\limits_{|z| \leqq 1} |f'(z)| \leqq m_1 , \\ \max\limits_{|z| \leqq 1} |f''(z)| \leqq m_2 . \end{cases}$$

Note that, if $f(z)$ is merely bounded in a slightly larger disk, bounds on $f'(z)$ and $f''(z)$ could be derived from the bound on $f(z)$. For convenience, we shall assume (1.1). Assume that, on the points

(1.2) $$s_j = \rho \exp(2\pi ij/p) \ , \ j = 0, 1, \ldots, p-1 \ ,$$

approximate values $g_\epsilon(s_j)$ are known:

(1.3) $$|g_\epsilon(s_j) - f(s_j)| \leq \epsilon \ , \ j = 0, \ldots, p-1 \ .$$

The problem is to approximate $f(z)$ in $|z| < 1$. The method of approximation to be used is similar to that of [2] for a problem in harmonic continuation.

Let

(1.4) $$F(z, \{a_k\}) = \frac{1}{2\pi i} \sum_{k=0}^{n-1} \frac{a_k \Delta t_k}{t_k - z} \ ,$$

where

(1.5) $$|a_k| \leq m_0 \ , \ k = 0, \ldots, n-1 \ ,$$

and

(1.6) $$\begin{cases} t_k = \exp(2\pi ik/n) \ , \ k = 0, \ldots, n-1 \ , \\ \Delta t_k = t_{k+\frac{1}{2}} - t_{k-\frac{1}{2}} \ . \end{cases}$$

Clearly, $F(z, \{a_k\})$ is a Riemann sum analogue of the Cauchy integral. The restraint (1.5) implies the boundedness and, hence, the normality of this family of functions in $|z| \leq R < 1$. Let

(1.7) $$e(\{a_k\}) = \max_j |g_\epsilon(s_j) - F(s_j, \{a_k\})| \ .$$

There exists $\{a_k^*\}$ such that

(1.8) $$e(\{a_k^*\}) = \inf_{\{a_k\}} e(\{a_k\}) \ .$$

Let

(1.9) $$F(z, n, p, \epsilon) = F(z, \{a_k^*\}) \ .$$

Then, $F(z, n, p, \epsilon)$ is an approximate analytic continuation $f(z)$ in $|z| < 1$.

Both a priori and a posteriori bounds for

(1.10) $$\max_{|z| = R} |f(z) - F(z, n, p, \epsilon)|$$

will be derived. It will be shown that the method is essentially a linear programming problem.

The analytic continuation problem is a special case of a large class of improper boundary problems. Cauchy's problem for elliptic equations and the backward solution of the heat equation are other examples. John, Pucci, Landis, Lavrentiev, and others have treated problems of this nature. See [4] for references. The general method of this paper may be applied to certain of these problems.

§2. Preliminary lemmas

For the sake of preserving the simplicity of the arguments later, let us collect a few lemmas.

Lemma 2.1. If $F^{(j)}(z, \{a_k\})$ denotes the j-th derivative of $F(z, \{a_k\})$, then

$$\max_{|z| \le \rho} |F^{(j)}(z, \{a_k\})| \le \frac{m_0 j!}{(1-\rho)^{j+1}} .$$

Proof. This follows immediately from the form of derivatives of $F(z, \{a_k\})$ and the bound on $|a_k|$.

Lemma 2.2. Let

$$G(\rho, R) = \sup \left\{ \left| \frac{1}{2\pi i} \oint_{|t|=R} \frac{a(t)dt}{t-z} \right| : |a(t)| \le m_0, |z| \le \rho < R \right\}.$$

Then

$$G(\rho, R) = \frac{Rm_0}{\pi} \int_0^\pi \frac{d\theta}{\sqrt{R^2 + \rho^2 - 2R\rho\cos\theta}}$$

$$\le \frac{m_0}{\pi\sqrt{1-\frac{\pi^2}{48}}} \sqrt{\frac{R}{\rho}} \log\left(\frac{\frac{\pi}{2}\sqrt{(1-\frac{\pi^2}{48})R\rho} + \sqrt{(R-\rho)^2 + \frac{\pi^2}{4}(1-\frac{\pi^2}{48})R\rho}}{R-\rho} \right) + \frac{m_0 R}{2\sqrt{R^2+\rho^2}}.$$

Proof. First,

$$\left| \frac{1}{2\pi i} \oint_{t=R} \frac{a(t)dt}{t-z} \right| \le \frac{1}{2\pi} \oint_{|t|=R} \frac{m_0|dt|}{|t-z|}$$

$$= \frac{Rm_0}{2\pi} \int_0^{2\pi} \frac{d\theta}{|R\rho^{i\theta} - z|}$$

$$\le \frac{Rm_0}{\pi} \int_0^\pi \frac{d\theta}{\sqrt{R^2 + \rho^2 - 2R\rho\cos\theta}} .$$

However, if $z = \rho$ and $a(t) = m_0 \exp\{i(-\theta + \arg(t-\rho))\}$, then equality holds. Thus, the precise evaluation of $G(\rho, R)$ holds.

Next, consider the estimate:

$$\int_0^{\pi} \frac{d\theta}{\sqrt{R^2+\rho^2-2R\rho\cos\theta}} = \int_0^{\pi/2} \frac{d\theta}{\sqrt{R^2+\rho^2-2R\rho\cos\theta}} + \int_{\pi/2}^{\pi} \frac{d\theta}{\sqrt{R^2+\rho^2-2R\rho\cos\theta}}$$

$$< \int_0^{\pi/2} \frac{d\theta}{\sqrt{R^2+\rho^2-2R\rho\cos\theta}} + \frac{\pi}{2\sqrt{R^2+\rho^2}} \quad .$$

As $\cos\theta \le 1-\theta^2/2+\theta^4/24 \le 1-(1-\frac{\pi^2}{48})\,\theta^2/2$ for $0 \le \theta \le \pi/2$,

$$\int_0^{\pi/2} \frac{d\theta}{\sqrt{R^2+\rho^2-2R\rho\cos\theta}} \le \int_0^{\pi/2} \frac{d\theta}{\sqrt{(R-\rho)^2+(1-\frac{\pi^2}{48})R\rho\theta^2}}$$

$$= \frac{1}{\sqrt{(1-\frac{\pi^2}{48})R\rho}} \log \frac{\frac{\pi}{2}\sqrt{(1-\frac{\pi^2}{48})R\rho}+\sqrt{(R-\rho)^2+\frac{\pi^2}{4}(1-\frac{\pi^2}{48})R\rho}}{R-\rho} .$$

Thus, the estimate holds. It is clear that the factor $1-\pi^2/48$ can be made aribtrarily close to one, but with a corresponding increase in the additive constant.

Lemma 2.3. Let

$$H(\rho) = \sup \left\{ \left| \frac{1}{2\pi i} \sum_{k=0}^{n-1} \frac{a_k \Delta t_k}{t_k - z} \right| : |a_k| \le m_0 ,\ |z| \le \rho < 1 \right\}$$

$$= \sup \ \{ |F(z, \{a_k\})| : |z| \le \rho < 1 \} \ .$$

Then,

$$H(\rho) \le \frac{2m_0}{(1-\rho)n} + G(\rho, 1) \ .$$

Proof. By symmetry,

$$H(\rho) \le \frac{2m_0 |\Delta t_0|}{2\pi(1-\rho)} + \frac{m_0}{\pi} \sum_{k=1}^{n/2} \frac{|\Delta t_k|}{|t_k-\rho|}$$

$$\le \frac{2m_0}{(1-\rho)n} + G(\rho, 1) \ .$$

Thus, we have derived a bound for $F(z, n, p, \epsilon)$ in $|z| < 1$. It will also be necessary to know a bound for $F(z, n, p, \epsilon) - f(z)$ on the circle $|z| = \rho$, knowing bounds at the nodal points only.

Lemma 2.4. Let $u(z)$ be analytic in $|z| \leq \rho$, and let $|u''(z)| \leq k$ for $|z| \leq \rho$. Let $s_j = \rho \exp(2\pi i j/p)$, $j = 0, \ldots, p-1$. If $|u(s_j)| \leq \delta$ for $j = 0, \ldots, p-1$, then

$$\max_{|z|=\rho} |u(z)| \leq \delta \sec \frac{\pi}{2p} + 4k\rho^2 \sin^2 \frac{\pi}{2p} \left(1 + 2\rho \sin \frac{\pi}{2p}\right) .$$

Proof. Let z_0 lie on $|z| = \rho$ between s_j and s_{j+1}. Then,

$$\begin{cases} u(z_0) = u(s_j) + (z_0 - s_j)u'(s_j) + \xi_1 k|z_0 - s_j|^2/2 , \\ u(z_0) = u(s_{j+1}) + (z_0 - s_{j+1})u'(s_j) + \xi_2 k[|z_0 - s_{j+1}||s_{j+1} - s_j| \\ \qquad + |z_0 - s_{j+1}|^2/2] , \end{cases}$$

where $|\xi_i| \leq 1$. Then,

$$u(z_0) = \frac{s_{j+1} - z_0}{s_{j+1} - s_j} u(s_j) + \frac{z_0 - s_j}{s_{j+1} - s_j} u(s_{j+1})$$

$$+ \xi k \left[\frac{|z_0 - s_j|^2 |z_0 - s_{j+1}|}{2|s_{j+1} - s_j|} + |z_0 - s_{j+1}||z_0 - s_j| \right.$$

$$\left. + \frac{|z_0 - s_j||z_0 - s_{j+1}|^2}{2|s_{j+1} - s_j|} \right] .$$

Hence,

$$|u(z_0)| \leq \left[\frac{|s_{j+1} - z_0| + |z_0 - s_j|}{|s_{j+1} - s_j|} \right] \delta$$

$$+ k|z_0 - s_{j+1}||z_0 - s_j| \left[1 + \tfrac{1}{2}(|z_0 - s_{j+1}| + |z_0 - s_j|)\right] .$$

Clearly, both terms are maximized by taking $z_0 = \rho \exp(2\pi i(j+\frac{1}{2})/p)$. Then,

$$\begin{cases} |s_{j+1} - z_0| = |z_0 - s_j| = \rho\sqrt{2 - 2\cos \pi/p} = 2\rho \sin \dfrac{\pi}{2p} . \\ |s_{j+1} - s_j| = 2\rho \sin \pi/p . \end{cases}$$

Consequently,

$$|u(z_0)| \le \frac{\delta}{\cos\frac{\pi}{2p}} + 4k\,\rho^2 \sin^2 \frac{\pi}{2p}\,(1 + 2\rho \sin\frac{\pi}{2p}) \quad .$$

Next, we shall need to estimate the error involved in using a Riemann sum instead of an integral.

Lemma 2.5. Let $h(z)$ be analytic in $|z| \le R$, and let $|h'(z)| \le b_1$ and $|h''(z)| \le b_2$ in $|z| \le R$. Let $s_j = R \exp(2\pi i j/p)$ and $\Delta s_j = s_{j+\frac{1}{2}} - s_{j-\frac{1}{2}}$. Then,

$$\left| \frac{1}{2\pi i} \oint_{|z|=R} h(z)dz - \frac{1}{2\pi i} \sum_{j=0}^{p-1} h(s_j)\,\Delta s_j \right| \le \frac{\pi^2}{2p^2}(R^2 b_1 + R^3 b_2) \quad .$$

Proof. First,

$$\int_{s_{j-\frac{1}{2}}}^{s_{j+\frac{1}{2}}} h(z)dz = h(s_j)\,\Delta s_j + \tfrac{1}{2}h'(s_j)(z-s_j)^2 \Big|_{s_{j-\frac{1}{2}}}^{s_{j+\frac{1}{2}}}$$

$$+ \tfrac{1}{2}\,\xi_2 b_2\, |s_{j+\frac{1}{2}} - s_j|^2 \cdot \frac{2\pi}{p} R \;,$$

where $|\xi_2| \le 1$. As

$$|(s_{j+\frac{1}{2}} - s_j)^2 - (s_{j-\frac{1}{2}} - s_j)^2| = 8R^2 \sin^2 \frac{\pi}{2p} \sin\frac{\pi}{p}$$

and

$$|s_{j+\frac{1}{2}} - s_j|^2 = 4R^2 \sin^2 \frac{\pi}{2p} \;,$$

$$\int_{s_{j-\frac{1}{2}}}^{s_{j+\frac{1}{2}}} h(z)dz = h(s_j)\,\Delta s_j + 4\,\xi_1 b_1 R^2 \sin^2\frac{\pi}{2p} \sin\frac{\pi}{p} + 4\pi\,\xi_2 b_2 R^3 \frac{\sin^2 \frac{\pi}{2p}}{p} \quad .$$

Thus,

$$\oint h(z)dz = \sum_{j=0}^{p-1} h(s_j)\,\Delta s_j + 4\,\xi_3 b_1 R^2 p \sin^2\frac{\pi}{2p} \sin\frac{\pi}{p} + 4\pi\,\xi_4 b_2 R^2 \sin^2\frac{\pi}{2p}$$

$$= \sum_{j=0}^{p-1} h(s_j)\,\Delta s_j + \xi\,\frac{\pi^3}{p^2}(R^2 b_1 + R^3 b_2) \quad .$$

Let us apply this to the Cauchy integral for $f(z)$.

Lemma 2.6. If $f(z)$ is analytic in $|z| \leq 1$ and if $|f(z)| \leq m_0$, $|f'(z)| \leq m_1$, and $|f''(z)| \leq m_2$ in $|z| \leq 1$, then

$$\left| f(z) - \frac{1}{2\pi i} \sum_{k=0}^{n-1} \frac{f(t_k)\,\Delta t_k}{t_k - z} \right| \leq \frac{\pi^2}{2n^2}(b_1 + b_2), \quad |z| \leq \rho < 1 ,$$

where

$$b_1 = \frac{m_1}{1-\rho} + \frac{m_0}{(1-\rho)^2} ,$$

$$b_2 = \frac{m_2}{\cos\frac{\pi}{n} - \rho} + \frac{2m_1}{(\cos\frac{\pi}{n} - \rho)^2} + \frac{2m_0}{(\cos\frac{\pi}{n} - \rho)^3} .$$

Proof. Let $h(t) = f(t)/(t-z)$. Then,

$$h'(t) = \frac{f'(t)}{t-z} - \frac{f(t)}{(t-z)^2} ,$$

$$h''(t) = \frac{f'(t)}{t-z} - \frac{2f'(t)}{(t-z)^2} + \frac{2f(t)}{(t-z)^3} .$$

Now, $h'(t)$ is evaluated on the circle $|z| = 1$. Thus,

$$|h'(t)| \leq \frac{m_1}{1-\rho} + \frac{m_0}{(1-\rho)^2} = b_1 , \quad |z| \leq \rho .$$

However, $h''(t)$ is evaluated in the annulus $\cos\frac{\pi}{n} \leq |z| \leq 1$. Hence, $|t-z| \geq \cos\frac{\pi}{n} - \rho$, and

$$|h''(t)| \leq \frac{m_2}{\cos\frac{\pi}{n} - \rho} + \frac{2m_1}{(\cos\frac{\pi}{n} - \rho)^2} + \frac{2m_0}{(\cos\frac{\pi}{n} - \rho)^3} = b_2 .$$

Then, by lemma 2.5,

$$\left| f(z) - \frac{1}{2\pi i} \sum_{k=0}^{n-1} \frac{f(t_k)\,\Delta t_k}{t_k - z} \right| \leq \frac{\pi^2}{2n^2}(b_1 + b_2) .$$

This completes the preliminary lemmas.

§3. A Priori Estimate of Error

Using the Hadamard three circle theorem, the lemmas of the previous section, and the general line of argument of [2], we shall derive an a priori estimate of the error at a point z , $\rho < |z| = R < 1$, in terms of ϵ , p , and n . Let

$$
(3.1)\quad \begin{cases} s_j = \rho \exp\{2\pi ij/p\} \ , \ j = 0,\ldots, p-1 \ , \\ t_k = \exp\{2\pi ik/n\} \ , \quad k = 0,\ldots, n-1 \ , \\ |g_\epsilon(s_j) - f(s_j)| \le \epsilon \ , \ j = 0,\ldots, n-1 \ , \\ A = \dfrac{\pi^2}{2}\left[\dfrac{m_1 + m_2}{\cos\frac{\pi}{n} - \rho} + \dfrac{m_0 + 2m_1}{(\cos\frac{\pi}{n} - \rho)^2} + \dfrac{2m_0}{(\cos\frac{\pi}{n} - \rho)^3}\right] . \end{cases}
$$

Then, by lemma 2.6,

$$
(3.2)\quad \left| f(s_j) - \frac{1}{2\pi i} \sum_{k=0}^{n-1} \frac{f(t_k)\,\Delta t_k}{t_k - s_j} \right| \le \frac{A}{n^2} \ , \ j = 0,\ldots, p-1 \ .
$$

Thus,

$$
(3.3)\quad \left| g_\epsilon(s_j) - \frac{1}{2\pi i} \sum_{k=0}^{n-1} \frac{f(t_k)\,\Delta t_k}{t_k - s_j} \right| \le \frac{A}{n^2} + \epsilon \ , \ j = 0,\ldots, p-1 \ .
$$

Since $\{f(t_k)\}$ is an admissable choice of $\{a_k\}$ in the minimization problem,

$$
(3.4)\quad |g_\epsilon(s_j) - F(s_j, n, p, \epsilon)| \le \frac{A}{n^2} + \epsilon \ , \quad j = 0,\ldots, p-1 \ .
$$

Consequently,

$$
(3.5)\quad |f(s_j) - F(s_j, n, p, \epsilon)| \le \frac{A}{n^2} + 2\epsilon \ , \ j = 0,\ldots, p-1 \ .
$$

We are ready to use lemma 2.4 to bound $f(z) - F(z, n, p, \epsilon)$ on the entire circle $|z| = \rho$. First, if

$$
u(z) = f(z) - F(z, n, p, \epsilon) \ ,
$$

then

$$
|u''(z)| \le m_2 + \frac{2m_0}{(1-\rho)^3}
$$

on $|z| \le \rho$, by assumption and lemma 2.1. Thus, by lemma 2.4,

$$\gamma = \max_{|z|=\rho} |f(z) - F(z,n,p,\epsilon)| \le \left(\frac{A}{n^2} + 2\epsilon\right) \sec \frac{\pi}{2p}$$

$$(3.6) \qquad + 4\left(m_2 + \frac{2m_0}{(1-\rho)^3}\right)\rho^2 \sin^2 \frac{\pi}{2p}\left(1 + 2\rho \sin \frac{\pi}{2p}\right),$$

$$\le \left(\frac{A}{n^2} + 2\epsilon\right) \sec \frac{\pi}{2p} + \frac{\pi^2\rho^2}{p^2}\left(m_2 + \frac{2m_0}{(1-\rho)^3}\right)\left(1 + \frac{\pi\rho}{p}\right) .$$

Thus, the maximum error on $|z| = \rho$ tends to zero as ϵ goes to zero and n and p go to infinity. As $f(z)$ and $F(z,n,p,\epsilon)$ are bounded in $|z| \le 1-\delta$, $\delta > 0$, $F(z,n,p,\epsilon)$ converges to $f(z)$ in $|z| < 1$; we shall use the three circle theorem [1] to estimate the rate of convergence. By lemma 2.3,

$$(3.7) \qquad M_\delta = \max_{|z|=1-\delta} |f(z)-F(z,n,p,\epsilon)| \le m_0 + H(\rho)$$

$$\le m_0 + \frac{2m_0}{n\delta} + G(1-\delta, 1) .$$

Then

$$\log \max_{|z|=R} |f(z)-F(z,n,p,\epsilon)| \le (\log\gamma) \frac{\log \frac{1-\delta}{R}}{\log \frac{1-\delta}{\rho}} + (\log M_\delta) \frac{\log \frac{R}{\rho}}{\log \frac{1-\delta}{\rho}} .$$

Let

$$(3.9) \qquad \begin{cases} a(R,\delta) = \dfrac{\log \frac{1-\delta}{R}}{\log \frac{1-\delta}{\rho}}, \\[2ex] b(R,\delta,n) = M_\delta^{(\log R/\rho)/(\log \frac{1-\delta}{\rho})} . \end{cases}$$

Then,

$$(3.10) \qquad \max_{|z|=R} |f(z)-F(z,n,p,\epsilon)| \le b(R,\delta,n)\gamma^{a(R,\delta)} .$$

<u>Theorem</u>. For $0 < \delta < 1-\rho$,

$$\max_{|z|=R} |f(z)-F(z,n,p,\epsilon)|$$
$$\le b(R,\delta,n) \left[\left(\frac{A}{n^2} + 2\epsilon\right)\sec \frac{\pi}{2p} + \frac{\pi^2\rho^2}{p^2}\left(m_2 + \frac{2m_0}{(1-\rho)^3}\right)\left(1+\frac{\pi\rho}{p}\right)\right]^{a(R,\delta)}$$

where A is defined by (3.1) and $a(R,\delta)$ and $b(R,\delta,n)$ by (3.9).

The best choice of δ is clearly not simply made. As δ tends to zero, the exponent $a(R, \delta)$ increases, but the coefficient $b(R, \delta, n)$ also increases unboundedly, as M_δ tends to infinity.

§4. Linear Programming Problem

Since the numerical solution of a linear programming problem is a relatively easy computation [3], we can assume the analytic continuation problem to be solved if the continuation problem can be reduced to a linear programming problem. This may be done by a trivial modification of the procedure outlined above.

First, change the restraints on $\{a_k\}$ to

$$(4.1) \quad \begin{cases} |\mathrm{Re}(a_k)| \leq m_0 , \\ |\mathrm{Im}(a_k)| \leq m_0 , \quad k = 0, \dots, n-1 . \end{cases}$$

Add the conditions

$$(4.2) \quad \begin{cases} \left| \mathrm{Re} \left[g_\epsilon(s_j) - \frac{1}{2\pi i} \sum_{k=0}^{n-1} \frac{a_k \Delta t_k}{t_k - s_j} \right] \right| \leq \eta , \\ \left| \mathrm{Im} \left[g(s_j) - \frac{1}{2\pi i} \sum_{k=0}^{n-1} \frac{a_k \Delta t_k}{t_k - s_j} \right] \right| \leq \eta, j=0, \dots, p-1, \\ \eta \geq 0 . \end{cases}$$

Then, the linear programming problem is the minimization of the linear functional

$$(4.3) \qquad L(\{a_k\} , \eta) = \eta$$

subject to the $4(n + p) + 1$ linear inequalities defined by (4.1) and (4.2).

This minor alteration of the original procedure affects the a priori bound for the error in the continuation given in the theorem of the last section only by introducing factors of $\sqrt{2}$ into bounds for $F(z, n, p, \epsilon)$ and its derivatives and onto the $(A/n^2 + 2\epsilon)$ term.

§5. A Posteriori Estimates

An improvement in the estimate of the error at z, $|z| = R$, can be obtained from the results of the linear programming problem. Equation (3.4) can be replaced by

$$(5.1) \quad |g_\epsilon(s_j) - F(s_j, n, p, \epsilon)| \leq \sqrt{2}\, \eta , \quad j = 1, \dots, p-1 ,$$

where η is the value of the linear functional at its constrained minimum. Then, (3.5) becomes

$$(5.2) \qquad |f(s_j) - F(s_j, n, p, \epsilon)| \leq \sqrt{2}\,\eta + \epsilon \ , \quad j = 1, \ldots, p-1 \ .$$

Consequently, the $A/n^2 + 2\epsilon$ term in the a priori bound (3.11) can be changed to $\sqrt{2}\,\eta + \epsilon$. As the A/n^2 is likely to be as large as 2ϵ for reasonable n, the a posteriori estimate may be considerably better than the a priori estimate.

§6. Interior results

All of the results above have been for the annulus between the data circle $|z| = \rho$ and $|z| = 1$. Obviously, $f(z)$ may also be approximated by $F(z, n, p, \epsilon)$ inside $|z| = \rho$. The a priori inequality (3.6) applies in the disk $|z| \leq \rho$, by the maximum principle; an a posteriori inequality is simply obtained.

REFERENCES

1. Bieberbach, L., Lehrbuch der Funktionentheorie, II, Leipzig, 1931.
2. Douglas, J., Jr., and T. M. Gallie, Jr., An Improper Boundary Problem, Duke Mathematical Journal, 1959.
3. Koopmans, T., Activity Analysis of Production and Allocation, Chapter 21, New York, 1951.
4. Pucci, C., Discussione del problema di Cauchy per le equazione di tipo ellittico, Annali di matematica pura ed applicata, series 4, vol. 66 (1958), pp. 131-154.

W. T. KOITER

Stress Distribution in an Infinite Elastic Sheet with a Doubly-Periodic Set of Equal Holes

Summary

The doubly-periodic stress distribution in an infinite elastic sheet with a doubly-periodic set of equal holes of arbitrary shape is investigated. The doubly-periodic character of the sheet region and of the solution are exploited by a suitable modification of Muskhelishvili's method of Cauchy-integrals. The required properties of these modified Cauchy-integrals and a general theorem on boundary values of a quasi-periodic or doubly-periodic function were developed in an earlier paper [12]. The resulting functional equation for one of the two complex stress functions is reduced to an ordinary Fredholm integral equation of the second kind, and the existence of the essentially unique solution of the problem is proved.

§1. Introduction

The problem of generalized plane stress in a perforated sheet with a doubly-periodic set of holes is of considerable importance to engineering. Nevertheless the available information on the stress distribution in such perforated plates is rather scarce. A recent survey by Dally and Durelli [1] mentions only the results of some approximate calculations by Horvay [2, 3] and fairly extensive experimental results by Siebel and Kopf. Natanson's theoretical investigation of the plate with circular holes [4], based on the complex stress functions of Kolosov and Muskhelishvili, is not mentioned by Dally and Durelli [1], possibly because Natanson did not evaluate his theory numerically.

Recently, Saito [5] attacked the problem anew and obtained some numerical results for a plate with circular holes whose centers are at the intersections of a square mesh. However, Saito's approach to the problem seems rather crude because it does not fully exploit the doubly-periodic character of the solution; moreover, parts of his analysis are open to the criticism that certain operations carried out on his infinite series are not justified. Nevertheless his numerical results may be correct; it often happens in theoretical investigations that unjustified operations on series expansions yield a correct final result.

However, Natanson's earlier, subtler and more careful approach is to be preferred above Saito's method. Natanson employs series expansions of both complex functions with respect to elliptic and associated functions and obtains the expansion coefficients from a doubly-infinite system of equations. Although no numerical results are obtained, it is shown that the series converge and satisfy all conditions of the problem.

Both Natanson's and Saito's investigations suffer from the drawback that series expansions have to be assumed for <u>both</u> complex functions of Kolosov and Muskhelishvili. The complex coefficients of these series have to be solved from a doubly-infinite system of complex equations. It need not be argued that the actual solution of these equations involves heavy numerical work.

The present investigation has two aims in view, viz. a more general theory of the problem, valid for an infinite plate with a doubly-periodic set of <u>holes of arbitrary shape</u> (all holes being of course congruent), and a more convenient approach to the actual numerical solution in the case of circular holes; this first report deals only with the general theory. Both objects are achieved by the development of a theory, based on the properties of modified Cauchy-integrals (to be defined below) and on some general theorems on the boundary values of a holomorphic doubly-periodic or quasi-periodic function. The author has been led to this approach by Muskhelishvili's stimulating book [6], which gives a vivid account of the successful approach, by means of Cauchy-integrals, to the fundamental problems of the two-dimensional theory of elasticity for regions with a <u>finite</u> number of holes [6, Part V].

The modified Cauchy-integral is defined by the replacement of the singular kernel $(t-z)^{-1}$ in the ordinary Cauchy-integral [6, Part IV] by the Weierstrasz zêta function $\zeta(t-z)$ [8]; the modified Cauchy-integral is taken along a single contour, the boundary of the fundamental hole. Rather to the author's surprise no reference to such modified Cauchy-integrals has been found in the literature. The text books on doubly-periodic and quasi-periodic functions [e.g. 8, 9, 10] deal exclusively with elliptic or quasi-elliptic functions, i.e. meromorphic doubly-periodic and quasi-periodic functions. Only one paper has been found [11] which deals with isolated essential singularities in doubly-periodic functions. In the present problem, however, an even more general approach is needed because nothing whatever is known a priori about the singularities of the functions concerned inside the boundaries of the holes. It might even happen that these functions, although holomorphic in the plate region, do not admit an analytic continuation through the hole boundaries! The required properties of modified Cauchy-integrals, and the necessary theorems on boundary values of arbitrary doubly-periodic and quasi-periodic functions, holomorphic in the plate region, have been developed in a separate paper [12], together with a theorem on the expansion in series of elliptic functions in the case of circular hole boundaries. *

A brief review of the basic equations and stress functions of Kolosov and Muskhelishvili [6] is given in par. 2. A discussion of the requirements on the stress functions, in order that the stress distribution be doubly-periodic, is given in par. 3. The essential uniqueness of the solution, i.e. uniqueness but for a rigid body displacement, is proved in par. 4. In par. 5 elimination of one of the stress functions is achieved by means of our general theorem [12] on the boundary value of a quasi-periodic function, holomorphic outside the hole boundaries. The resulting functional equation for the remaining stress function is reduced to an ordinary Fredholm integral equation of the second kind in par. 6. The proof of existence of a solution in par. 7 completes the general theory.

§2. The basic equations of Kolosov-Muskhelishvili

The average displacements u, v in the problem of generalized plane stress in a plate, i.e. the mean values of the displacements over the plate thickness, can always be expressed by means of two functions $\phi(z)$, $\psi(z)$ of the complex variable $z = x + iy$, which are analytic in the plate region [6, par. 32]

$$2G(u + iv) = \kappa\phi(z) - \overline{z\phi'(z)} - \overline{\psi(z)} \quad . \tag{2.1}$$

A dash indicates a differentiation with respect to z, and a bar denotes that the conjugate value of the barred function is to be taken. The number κ is given by §

$$\kappa = \frac{3-\nu}{1+\nu} \quad , \tag{2.2}$$

where ν is Poisson's ratio; finally, G denotes the shear modulus.

The average stresses, again defined as mean values over the plate thickness, are expressed by means of derivatives of $\phi(z)$ and $\psi(z)$ [6, par. 32]

$$\sigma_x + \sigma_y = 2[\phi'(z) + \overline{\phi'(z)}] \quad , \tag{2.3}$$

$$\sigma_y - \sigma_x + 2i\tau_{xy} = 2[\bar{z}\phi''(z) + \psi'(z)] \ . \tag{2.4}$$

The (average) tractions transmitted through an arc (by the material to the right of this arc on the material to the left of this arc, cf. fig. 1) are given by [6, par. 32]

$$X_n + iY_n = -i\frac{d}{ds}[\phi(z) + \overline{z\phi'(z)} + \overline{\psi(z)}] \ , \tag{2.5}$$

where the tangential derivative is taken in the positive direction along the arc, defined in fig. 1.

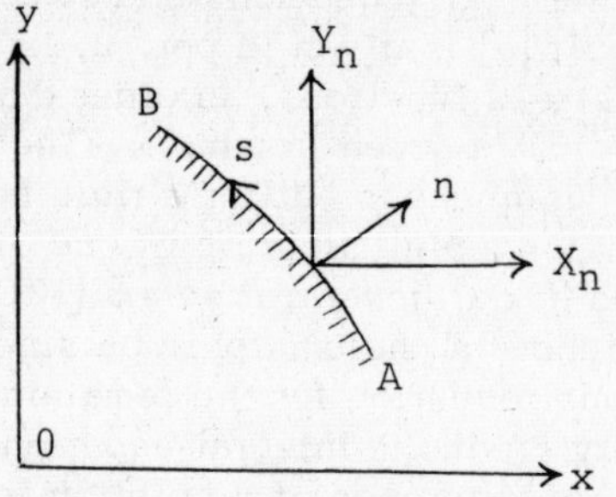

Fig. 1
Tractions along an arc.

The resulting force of the tractions along arc AB is given by

$$(X + iY)_{AB} = \int_A^B (X_n + iY_n)ds = -i[\phi(z) + \overline{z\phi'(z)} + \overline{\psi(z)}]_A^B \ , \tag{2.6}$$

and the resulting moment of these tractions, referred to the origin is given by [6, par. 33][#]

$$M_{AB} = \int_A^B (xY_n - yX_n)ds = \mathrm{Re}\left\{\int_A^B \psi(z)dz - [z\psi(z) + z\bar{z}\phi'(z)]_A^B\right\} \tag{2.7}$$

The complex stress functions $\phi(z)$ and $\psi(z)$ need not always be single-valued in a multiply-connected plate, although of course both the stresses and displacements are single-valued. However, if the resulting force of the tractions along every hole boundary vanishes, both $\phi(z)$ and $\psi(z)$ are also single-valued, and hence holomorphic, in the plate region.

Finally, it should be mentioned that the stress distribution is not affected by addition to $\phi(z)$ of a linear function $Ciz + \delta$, and addition to $\psi(z)$ of a constant ϵ , where C is real and δ and ϵ may be complex [6, par. 34]. This addition only superimposes a rigid body displacement on (2. 1).

§3. Doubly-periodic stress distribution in a sheet with a doubly-periodic set of holes

Consider a plate with a doubly-periodic set of holes with fundamental periods $2\omega_1$, $2\omega_2$ and $\mathrm{Im}(\omega_2/\omega_1) > 0$. It will be assumed that the hole boundaries are simple, closed, smooth and non-intersecting contours $L \equiv L_0 \pmod{2\omega_1, 2\omega_2}$. The origin will be chosen inside the fundamental contour L_0 . The fundamental (if necessary curvilinear) period-parallelogram will be assumed to surround the contour L_0 , and the positive direction on L_0 will be chosen such that the plate region is on the left of L_0 (fig. 2). The plate region is the region outside all holes (the shaded region in fig. 2 and all its congruent regions) and will be denoted by S_+ . The region inside L_0 is the fundamental hole region and will be denoted by S_{0-} . The aggregate of all regions inside a contour $L \equiv L_0 \pmod{2\omega_1, 2\omega_2}$ is the region of all holes and will be denoted by S_- .

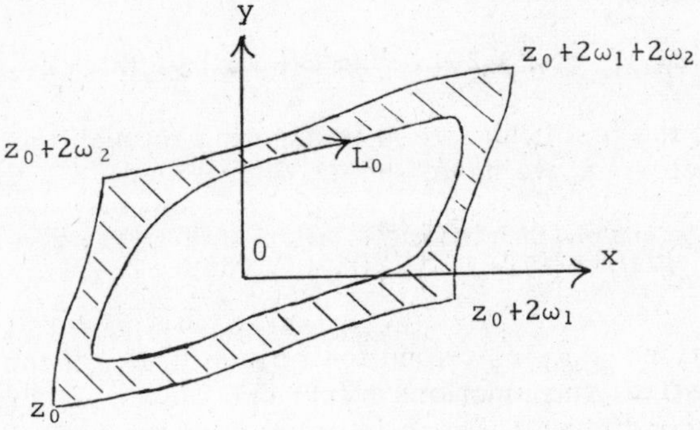

Fig. 2

Fundamental (curvilinear) period-parallelogram.

The investigation will be restricted to doubly-periodic stress distributions in the plate. The specified tractions $X_n = p_x$, $Y_n = p_y$ along the hole boundaries must now of course be equal in congruent points, and the resulting force of these tractions along each hole boundary must vanish.[±] Hence $\phi(z)$ and $\psi(z)$ are holomorphic in the entire plate region S_+ . From (2.3) it now follows immediately that $\phi'(z)$ must have a doubly-periodic real part, and hence it must be a doubly-periodic function, i.e.

$$\left.\begin{aligned}\phi'(z + 2\omega_1) - \phi'(z) &= 0 \ ,\\ \phi'(z + 2\omega_2) - \phi'(z) &= 0 \ .\end{aligned}\right\} \tag{3.1}$$

Integration of (3. 1) in the plate region results in

$$\left.\begin{aligned}\phi(z + 2\omega_1) - \phi(z) &= 2a_1 \ ,\\ \phi(z + 2\omega_2) - \phi(z) &= 2a_2 \ ,\end{aligned}\right\} \tag{3.2}$$

with constants of integration $2a_1$, $2a_2$. This result expresses the fact that $\phi(z)$ is a quasi-periodic function with cyclic increments $2a_1$, $2a_2$.

Next, it follows from the doubly-periodic character of the tractions across congruent arcs that the non-analytic expression in S_+

$$\overline{\phi(z)} + \bar{z}\phi'(z) + \psi(z) = g(z) \ , \tag{3.3}$$

the conjugate of the expression between brackets in (2. 6), must also be quasi-periodic. Its cyclic increments $2\gamma_1$, $2\gamma_2$, defined by

$$g(z + 2\omega_1) - g(z) = 2\gamma_1 \ , \quad g(z + 2\omega_2) - g(z) = 2\gamma_2 \ , \tag{3.4}$$

are related to the resulting forces transmitted through the sides of a period-parallelogram; we have from (2. 6)

$$\int_z^{z+2\omega_1} (X_n + iY_n)ds = -2i\bar{\gamma}_1 \ , \quad \int_z^{z+2\omega_2} (X_n + iY_n)ds = -2i\bar{\gamma}_2 \ . \tag{3.5}$$

If the tractions p_x , p_y along the boundary L_0 of the fundamental hole are specified, the functions $\phi(z)$ and $\psi(z)$ must finally satisfy the boundary condition at a generic point t of the fundamental contour L_0 , obtained from (2. 6) ,

$$\overline{\phi(t)} + \bar{t}\phi'(t) + \psi(t) = h(t) \ , \tag{3.6}$$

where $h(t)$ is a given function of position on L_0

$$h(t) = -\int_{t_0}^{t} (p_y + ip_x)ds \ , \tag{3.7}$$

and the integral in (3. 7) is taken along L_0 from a fixed point t_0 to the running point t . The constant of integration may be omitted since the addition of a constant to $\phi(z)$ or $\psi(z)$ is immaterial. It should be observed that $h(t)$ is a single-valued (non-analytic) function of position on L_0 since the resulting force of the tractions along the hole boundary vanishes

$$\int_{L_0} (p_y + ip_x) ds = 0 \ . \qquad (3.8)$$

The boundary value problem may now be formulated in the following form: It is required to obtain two functions $\phi(z)$ and $\psi(z)$, holomorphic in S_+ , in such a way that expression (3.3) is quasi-periodic with specified cyclic increments $2\gamma_1$, $2\gamma_2$ and subject to the boundary conditions (3.6); moreover, the function $\phi(z)$ itself must be quasi-periodic.

It should be noted that the cyclic increments $2\gamma_1$, $2\gamma_2$ cannot be specified entirely arbitrarily. In fact, the resulting moment of the tractions transmitted along a closed curve in S_+ , surrounding the fundamental hole, must be in equilibrium with the resulting moment of the boundary tractions p_x, p_y along L_0 . The moment of all tractions along a closed curve is obtained from (2.7)

$$M = \text{Re} \oint \psi(z) dz = \text{Re} \oint [\psi(z) + \bar{z}\phi'(z) + \overline{\phi(z)}] dz - \text{Re} \oint [\bar{z}\phi'(z) + \overline{\phi(z)}] dz \ . \qquad (3.9)$$

The second integral is zero, as may be shown by integration by parts

$$\text{Re} \oint [\bar{z}\phi'(z) + \overline{\phi(z)}] dz = \text{Re} \oint [\overline{\phi(z)}\, dz - \phi(z)\, d\bar{z}] = 0 \ . \qquad (3.10)$$

Hence we obtain for the moment of the boundary tractions p_x, p_y along L_0

$$M_1 = \text{Re} \int_{L_0} h(t) dt \ . \qquad (3.11)$$

On the other hand, the moment of all tractions, transmitted on the interior of the fundamental period-parallelogram is given by (3.9) and the quasi-periodic properties of (3.3)

$$M_2 = 4\text{Re}(\gamma_1\omega_2 - \gamma_2\omega_1) \ . \qquad (3.12)$$

Equilibrium of moments now requires $M_1 + M_2 = 0$, or

$$4\text{Re}(\gamma_1\omega_2 - \gamma_2\omega_1) + \text{Re} \int_{L_0} h(t) dt = 0 \ . \qquad (3.13)$$

For practical applications the most important case is that in which the resulting moment of the boundary tractions along L_0 is zero. Condition (3.13) is then simplified into

$$\text{Re}(\gamma_1\omega_2 - \gamma_2\omega_1) = 0 \ , \qquad (3.14)$$

expressing a linear relation between the four real constants in γ_1 and γ_2 . The general solution of (3.14) may be written in the form

$$\left.\begin{aligned} 2\gamma_1 &= (S_x + S_y)\,\overline{\omega}_1 + (S_y - S_x + 2iT_{xy})\omega_1 \;, \\ 2\gamma_2 &= (S_x + S_y)\,\overline{\omega}_2 + (S_y - S_x + 2iT_{xy})\omega_2 \;, \end{aligned}\right\} \tag{3.15}$$

where S_x, S_y and T_{xy} are three independent real constants, which may be interpreted as average stresses in the perforated plate. These average stresses play a similar role as the uniform stresses at infinity in an infinite sheet with a finite number of holes or a row of holes.

§4. Uniqueness of solution

We shall now prove that the solution of the boundary value problem, defined in par. 3, is essentially unique, i.e. unique but for a rigid-body-displacement. To this end it is observed that the difference $\phi_1(z) - \phi_2(z)$, $\psi_1(z) - \psi_2(z)$ of two distinct solutions defines a doubly-periodic stress distribution for unloaded holes and zero resulting forces transmitted through the sides of a period-parallelogram. The corresponding strain energy in the period parallelogram is given by

$$\tfrac{1}{2}\oint [(X_{n1} - X_{n2})(u_1 - u_2) + (Y_{n1} - Y_{n2})(v_1 - v_2)]ds \;, \tag{4.1}$$

where the integral is taken along the fundamental period-parallelogram. On account of the doubly-periodic properties of $X_{n1} - X_{n2}$ and $Y_{n1} - Y_{n2}$, and of the quasi-periodic properties of $u_1 - u_2$ and $v_1 - v_2$, described by

$$\left.\begin{aligned} u_1(z+2\omega_1) - u_2(z+2\omega_1) - [u_1(z) - u_2(z)] &= 2c_1 \;, \\ u_1(z+2\omega_2) - u_2(z+2\omega_2) - [u_1(z) - u_2(z)] &= 2c_2 \;, \\ v_1(z+2\omega_1) - v_2(z+2\omega_1) - [v_1(z) - v_2(z)] &= 2d_1 \;, \\ v_1(z+2\omega_2) - v_2(z+2\omega_2) - [v_1(z) - v_2(z)] &= 2d_2 \;, \end{aligned}\right\} \tag{4.2}$$

where c_1, c_2, d_1, d_2 are real constants, expression (4.1) may be reduced to

$$\begin{aligned} &-\int_{z_0}^{z_0+2\omega_1} [(X_{n1} - X_{n2})\,c_2 + (Y_{n1} - Y_{n2})d_2]ds \;+ \\ &+\int_{z_0}^{z_0+2\omega_2} [(X_{n1} - X_{n2})\,c_1 + (Y_{n1} - Y_{n2})d_1]ds = 0 \;, \end{aligned} \tag{4.3}$$

because the resulting force transmitted through a side of the period-parallelogram is zero.

It follows that the strain energy in the plate with a stress distribution described by $\phi_1(z) - \phi_2(z)$, $\psi_1(z) - \psi_2(z)$ is zero. Hence all stresses are zero, and the difference between two solutions must have the form [6, par. 34]

$$\phi_1(z) - \phi_2(z) = Ciz + \delta \ , \quad \psi_1(z) - \psi_2(z) = \epsilon \ , \tag{4.4}$$

where C is an arbitrary real constant, and δ and ϵ are arbitrary complex constants, representing a rigid-body-displacement.

§5. Reduction to a functional equation

The boundary problem, defined in par. 3, requires the determination of two functions $\phi(z)$ and $\psi(z)$, holomorphic in the plate region S_+, subject to the boundary condition (3.6) on L_0, to the prescribed cyclic increments $2\gamma_1$ and $2\gamma_2$ of expression (3.3), and to the condition of quasi-periodicity for $\phi(z)$. The function $\psi(z)$ will now be eliminated by observing that its boundary value, as expressed by means of (3.6) in the specified non-analytic function $h(t)$, and in $\phi(t)$ and its derivative, must satisfy the conditions for the boundary values of a holomorphic function in S_+. However, these conditions have been derived in [12] only for quasi-periodic functions, whereas it is obvious from the quasi-periodic properties of expression (3.3) and of $\phi(z)$ that $\psi(z)$ is itself not a quasi-periodic function.

In order to overcome this difficulty an auxiliary stress function $\Omega(z)$ is introduced, defined by

$$\Omega(z) = \psi(z) - \chi(z)\phi'(z) \ , \tag{5.1}$$

where $\chi(z)$ is a quasi-periodic function, holomorphic in the closed region S_+(i.e. including the boundaries $L \equiv L_0$ (mod. $2\omega_1$, $2\omega_2$)), and with cyclic increments $-2\overline{\omega}_1$, $-2\overline{\omega}_2$, i.e.

$$\chi(z+2\omega_1) - \chi(z) = -2\overline{\omega}_1 \ , \ \chi(z+2\omega_2) - \chi(z) = -2\overline{\omega}_2 \ . \tag{5.2}$$

Apart from these requirements the function $\chi(z)$ is arbitrary, and it will be shown later that the solution for $\phi(z)$ and $\psi(z)$ is not affected by the particular choice of the function $\chi(z)$, and the corresponding function $\Omega(z)$, defined by (5.1).**

It is now easily seen by substitution into (3.3) of $\psi(z)$, expressed in $\Omega(z)$ by means of (5.1), that $\Omega(z)$ is indeed not only holomorphic in S_+, but also quasi-periodic with cyclic increments $2(\gamma_1 - \overline{a}_1)$, $2(\gamma_2 - \overline{a}_2)$, where $2a_1$, $2a_2$ are the (as yet unknown) cyclic increments of $\phi(z)$. Introducing the abbreviation $m(z)$ for the non-analytic doubly-periodic expression

$$\overline{z} + \chi(z) = m(z) \ , \tag{5.3}$$

the boundary value of $\Omega(z)$ is given by (3.6) in the form

$$\Omega(t) = -\overline{\phi(t)} - m(t)\phi'(t) + h(t) \ . \tag{5.4}$$

The conditions that (5.4) represents the boundary values on L_0 of a quasi-periodic function with cyclic increments $2(\gamma_1 - \bar{a}_1), 2(\gamma_2 - \bar{a}_2)$, holomorphic in S_+, are now expressed by the functional equation [12]

$$\frac{1}{2\pi i}\int_{L_0}[-\overline{\phi(t)} - m(t)\phi'(t) + h(t)][\zeta(t-z)-\zeta(t)]dt = \frac{2}{\pi i}[(\gamma_1-\bar{a}_1)\eta_2-(\gamma_2-\bar{a}_2)\eta_1]z, \tag{5.5}$$

holding for all z in S_{0-}, i.e. for all z inside the fundamental hole boundary L_0, where $\zeta(z)$ is the quasi-periodic Weierstrasz zêta function and $2\eta_1$, $2\eta_2$ are its cyclic increments, and by the auxiliary condition

$$\frac{1}{2\pi i}\int_{L_0}[-\overline{\phi(t)} - m(t)\phi'(t) + h(t)]dt = -\frac{2}{\pi i}[(\gamma_1-\bar{a}_1)\omega_2-(\gamma_2-\bar{a}_2)\omega_1] \ . \tag{5.6}$$

Since the cyclic increments of the function $\phi(z)$ are expressed in its boundary values by means of the equations [12]

$$\left.\begin{aligned} 2\pi i a_1 &= \omega_1\int_{L_0}\phi(t)\zeta'(t)dt - \eta_1\int_{L_0}\phi(t)dt \ , \\ 2\pi i a_2 &= \omega_2\int_{L_0}\phi(t)\zeta'(t)dt - \eta_2\int_{L_0}\phi(t)dt \ , \end{aligned}\right\} \tag{5.7}$$

the functional equation (5.5) and the auxiliary condition (5.6) contain as their single unknown quantity the boundary value of $\phi(z)$ on L_0.

Once a function $\phi(t)$ has been obtained which satisfies the functional equation (5.5) and the auxiliary condition (5.6), the corresponding stress functions $\Omega(z)$ and $\psi(z)$ for all z in S_+ are obtained immediately from the formula [12]

$$\begin{aligned} \psi(z) - \chi(z)\phi'(z) &= \Omega(z) = \\ &= \frac{1}{2\pi i}\int_{L_0}[-\overline{\phi(t)} - m(t)\phi'(t) + h(t)][\zeta(t-z) - \zeta(t)]dt + \\ &\quad - \frac{2}{\pi i}[(\gamma_1-\bar{a}_1)\eta_2 - (\gamma_2-\bar{a}_2)\eta_1]z \ . \end{aligned} \tag{5.8}$$

Since (5.5) and (5.6) are both necessary and sufficient conditions for the existence of the quasi-periodic function (5.8) with boundary values (5.4), it follows that the solution of the boundary problem has then been completed. On the other hand, it is far from obvious that a solution $\phi(t)$ of the functional equation (5.5) and auxiliary condition (5.6) exists, and even if it exists, it remains to be proved that this solution $\phi(t)$ is indeed the boundary value on L_0 of a quasi-periodic function

$\phi(z)$, holomorphic in S_+ . We shall return to this rather complicated existence problem in par. 7.

It is now appropriate to examine our earlier statement that the particular choice of $\chi(z)$, holomorphic in the closed region S_+ and subject to conditions (5.2) concerning its quasi-periodicity, does not affect the solutions for $\phi(z)$ and $\psi(z)$. In fact, the difference $\chi_2(z) - \chi_1(z)$ of two such functions is a doubly-periodic function, holomorphic in S_+ . Assuming that $\phi'(z)$, doubly-periodic and holomorphic in S_+ , is continuous up to and including L_0 , the product

$$[m_2(z) - m_1(z)]\phi'(z) = [\chi_2(z) - \chi_1(z)]\phi'(z) \tag{5.9}$$

is also doubly-periodic and holomorphic in S_+ , and continuous up to and including L_0 . It now follows from our general theorem [12] that

$$\frac{1}{2\pi i}\int_{L_0} [\chi_2(t) - \chi_1(t)]\phi'(t)[\zeta(t-z) - \zeta(t)]dt = \begin{cases} 0 & \text{for } z \text{ in } S_{0-} \\ [\chi_2(z)-\chi_1(z)]\phi'(z) & \text{for } z \text{ in } S_+ ; \end{cases} \tag{5.10}$$

$$\frac{1}{2\pi i}\int_{L_0} [\chi_2(t) - \chi_1(t)]\phi'(t)dt = 0 \ . \tag{5.11}$$

Hence a solution $\phi(t)$ of the functional equation (5.5) and auxiliary condition (5.6), obtained by means of the function $\chi_1(z)$, is also a solution of the similar equations on the basis of $\chi_2(z)$, and the corresponding functions $\psi(z)$, obtained from (5.8), are identical.

§6. Reduction to a Fredholm integral equation

As in Muskhelishvili's theory for a region with a finite number of holes [6, ch. 17], the functional equation (5.5) may be reduced to an integral equation of Fredholm of the second kind. Such a reduction is needed in order to obtain a convenient approach to numerical evaluation of the theory for holes of arbitrary shape; §§ modern digital computers are especially adapted to solve such integral equations for nonsingular kernels. Moreover, the well-known existence theorems for Fredholm equations allow a complete discussion of the existence of a solution of our problem (cf. par. 7).

Let the point z inside L_0 , for which (5.5) holds, approach a point t_0 on L_0 . If it is assumed that the expression

$$\overline{-\phi(t)} - m(t)\phi'(t) + h(t) \tag{6.1}$$

satisfies a Hölder-condition on L_0 [12], the modified Cauchy-integral in (5.5) may be evaluated by the analogue to Plemelj's formula [12], and (5.5) may be rewritten in the form

$$\tfrac{1}{2}\,\overline{\phi(t_0)} + \tfrac{1}{2}m(t_0)\overline{\phi'(t_0)} - \tfrac{1}{2}h(t_0) +$$

$$+\frac{1}{2\pi i}\int_{L_0}[-\overline{\phi(t)} - m(t)\overline{\phi'(t)} + h(t)][\zeta(t-t_0) - \zeta(t)]dt = \tag{6.2}$$

$$= \frac{2}{\pi i}[(\gamma_1 - \overline{a}_1)\eta_2 - (\gamma_2 - \overline{a}_2)\eta_1]t_0 ,$$

where Cauchy's principal value of the singular integral should be taken.

The requirement that $\phi(z)$ and $\phi'(z)$ must be quasi-periodic and doubly-periodic functions, holomorphic in S_+ and continuous up to and including L_0, is expressed by the equations

$$\frac{1}{2\pi i}\int_{L_0}\phi(t)[\zeta(t-z) - \zeta(t)]dt = \frac{2}{\pi i}(a_1\eta_2 - a_2\eta_1)z , \tag{6.3}$$

$$\frac{1}{2\pi i}\int_{L_0}\phi'(t)[\zeta(t-z) - \zeta(t)]dt = 0 , \tag{6.4}$$

holding for all z in S_{0-}. Let now z approach a point t_0 on L_0. If it is also assumed that $h(t)$ and $\phi'(t)$ each satisfy a Hölder-condition on L_0, these equations become

$$-\tfrac{1}{2}\phi(t_0) + \frac{1}{2\pi i}\int_{L_0}\phi(t)[\zeta(t-t_0) - \zeta(t)]dt = \frac{2}{\pi i}(a_1\eta_2 - a_2\eta_1)t_0 , \tag{6.5}$$

$$-\tfrac{1}{2}\phi'(t_0) + \frac{1}{2\pi i}\int_{L_0}\phi'(t)[\zeta(t-t_0) - \zeta(t)]dt = 0 ; \tag{6.6}$$

taking conjugate values in (6.5), we have

$$-\tfrac{1}{2}\,\overline{\phi(t_0)} - \frac{1}{2\pi i}\int_{L_0}\overline{\phi(t)}[\overline{\zeta(t-t_0)} - \overline{\zeta(t)}]d\overline{t} = -\frac{2}{\pi i}(\overline{a}_1\overline{\eta}_2 - \overline{a}_2\overline{\eta}_1)\overline{t}_0 . \tag{6.7}$$

We now subtract (6.7) from (6.2), and we add (6.6) after multiplication by $m(t_0)$; the resulting equation reads

$$\overline{\phi(t_0)} - \frac{1}{2\pi i}\int_{L_0}\overline{\phi(t)}\{[\zeta(t-t_0) - \zeta(t)]dt - [\overline{\zeta(t-t_0) - \zeta(t)}]d\overline{t}\} +$$

$$-\frac{1}{2\pi i}\int_{L_0}\phi'(t)[m(t) - m(t_0)][\zeta(t-t_0) - \zeta(t)]dt = \tag{6.8}$$

$$= -H_-(t_0) + \frac{2}{\pi i}[(\gamma_1 - \overline{a}_1)\eta_2 - (\gamma_2 - \overline{a}_2)\eta_1]t_0 + \frac{2}{\pi i}(\overline{a}_1\overline{\eta}_2 - \overline{a}_2\overline{\eta}_1)\overline{t}_0 ,$$

where $H_-(t_0)$ is given by

$$H_-(t_0) = -\tfrac{1}{2}h(t_0) + \frac{1}{2\pi i}\int_{L_0} h(t)\,[\zeta(t-t_0) - \zeta(t)]dt \ . \tag{6.9}$$

The main purpose in the foregoing reduction of (6.2) to (6.8) is the removal of the singularity in the kernel of (6.2). Indeed, if ds is the arc element of L_0, the cofactor of ds in the expression

$$\begin{aligned}&[\zeta(t-t_0) - \zeta(t)]dt - [\overline{\zeta(t-t_0)} - \overline{\zeta(t)}]d\bar{t} = \\ &= \{[\zeta(t-t_0) - \zeta(t)]\frac{dt}{ds} - [\overline{\zeta(t-t_0)} - \overline{\zeta(t)}]\frac{d\bar{t}}{ds}\}ds\end{aligned} \tag{6.10}$$

is continuous on a smooth contour L_0 because

$$\frac{1}{t-t_0}\frac{dt}{ds} - \frac{1}{\bar{t}-\bar{t}_0}\frac{d\bar{t}}{ds} \tag{6.11}$$

is continuous on L_0 ; similarly, the expression

$$[m(t) - m(t_0)]\,\zeta(t-t_0) \tag{6.12}$$

is also continuous on L_0 . Moreover, the integral involving $\phi'(t)$ may be integrated by parts, and we obtain a Fredholm equation, the analogue of Muskhelishvili's equation [6, (98.9)] for a simply-connected region

$$\begin{aligned}&\overline{\phi(t_0)} - \frac{1}{2\pi i}\int_{L_0} \overline{\phi(t)}\{[\zeta(t-t_0) - \zeta(t)]dt - [\overline{\zeta(t-t_0)} - \overline{\zeta(t)}]d\bar{t}\} + \\ &+ \frac{1}{2\pi i}\int_{L_0} \phi(t)d\{[m(t) - m(t_0)][\zeta(t-t_0) - \zeta(t)]\} = \\ &= -H_-(t_0) + \frac{2}{\pi i}[(\gamma_1 - \bar{a}_1)\eta_2 - (\gamma_2 - \bar{a}_2)\eta_1]t_0 + \frac{2}{\pi i}(\bar{a}_1\bar{\eta}_2 - \bar{a}_2\bar{\eta}_1)\,\bar{t}_0 \ .\end{aligned} \tag{6.13}$$

The boundary values $\phi(t)$ of the function $\phi(z)$ have to satisfy both the integral equation (6.13), where the cyclic increments $2a_1$, $2a_2$ of $\phi(z)$ are expressed in the boundary values by means of (5.7), and the auxiliary condition (5.6). It is now convenient to modify the integral equation by adding the auxiliary condition; it will be shown in par. 7 that any solution of the modified equation simultaneously satisfies both the original integral equation (6.13) and the auxiliary condition (5.6). We first write the auxiliary condition (5.6) in the form

$$\theta = 0 \ , \tag{6.14}$$

where θ is the expression, defined by

$$\theta = \frac{1}{2\pi i}\int_{L_0}[-\overline{\phi(t)}\,dt + \phi(t)dm(t) + h(t)dt] + \frac{2}{\pi i}[(\gamma_1-\overline{a}_1)\omega_2-(\gamma_2-\overline{a}_2)\omega_1]. \quad (6.15)$$

which is independent of t_0, and the modified integral equation then takes the form

$$\theta + \overline{\phi(t_0)} - \frac{1}{2\pi i}\int_{L_0}\overline{\phi(t)}\{[\zeta(t-t_0)-\zeta(t)]dt - [\overline{\zeta(t-t_0)}-\overline{\zeta(t)}]d\overline{t}\} +$$

$$+ \frac{1}{2\pi i}\int_{L_0}\phi(t)d\{[m(t) - m(t_0)][\zeta(t-t_0) - \zeta(t)]\} = \quad (6.16)$$

$$= -H_-(t_0) + \frac{2}{\pi i}[(\gamma_1-\overline{a}_1)\eta_2 - (\gamma_2-\overline{a}_2)\eta_1]t_0 + \frac{2}{\pi i}(\overline{a}_1\overline{\eta}_2 - \overline{a}_2\overline{\eta}_1)\overline{t}_0 .$$

§7. Existence of a solution

7.1 The proof of existence of a solution of the boundary value problem, defined in par. 3, will be given on the basis of two additional assumptions: it will be assumed that both the curvature of L_0 and the boundary tractions p_x, p_y along L_0 satisfy Hölder-conditions. It is easily verified that any solution of (6.16) then has a tangential derivative along L_0 which also satisfies a Hölder-condition.##

It may be helpful to give first a preliminary sketch of the proof to be given. It will be shown that the homogeneous modified integral equation, i.e. the equation obtained from (6.16) by putting γ_1, γ_2 and $h(t)$ all zero, has three linearly independent solutions $\phi_0(t)$, all of which also satisfy the homogeneous auxiliary condition $\theta_0 = 0$, where θ_0 is obtained from (6.15) by putting again γ_1, γ_2 and $h(t)$ zero (par. 7.2). The non-homogeneous modified integral equation (6.16) then admits a solution if, and only if the specified data γ_1, γ_2 and $h(t)$ satisfy three linearly independent conditions. On the assumption that these three conditions are indeed satisfied, it will then be shown that the solution $\phi(t)$ of (6.16) also satisfies the auxiliary condition $\theta = 0$, and that it is the boundary value of a quasi-periodic function $\Phi(z) \equiv \phi(z)$ holomorphic in S_+, which constitutes, together with the function $\Psi(z) \equiv \psi(z)$ given by (5.8), the solution of the boundary problem (par. 7.3). Finally, it will be observed that the three linearly independent conditions (3.8) and (3.13), which have so far not been considered in the existence proof, must also be satisfied, since no solution to the problem can exist if these conditions are violated. Hence the three independent requirements (3.8) and (3.13) on the data of the problem must be implied by the three linearly independent conditions which have to be imposed on these data in order that a solution of the non-homogeneous equation (6.16) exists. Conversely, the latter three conditions must be implied by the three linearly independent requirements (3.8) and (3.13), and the proof of existence of a solution will have been completed (par. 7.4).

7.2 In order to prove existence of solutions of the homogeneous modified equation, it will first be assumed that such a solution $\phi_0(t)$ exists; this solution and its tangential derivative along L_0 obviously satisfy Hölder-conditions. It will be shown that any solution of the homogeneous modified equation must necessarily have the form

$$\phi_0(t) = C_0 it + \delta_0 , \tag{7.1}$$

where C_0 is a real and δ_0 is a complex constant. It is then easily verified that (7.1) indeed satisfies both the homogeneous modified equation and the homogeneous auxiliary condition.

It is convenient to write the homogeneous modified equation in the form

$$\begin{aligned} \theta_0 + \overline{\phi_0(t_0)} - \frac{1}{2\pi i}\int_{L_0} \overline{\phi_0(t)}\{[\zeta(t-t_0)-\zeta(t)]dt - [\overline{\zeta(t-t_0)} - \overline{\zeta(t)}]d\bar{t}\} + \\ - \frac{1}{2\pi i}\int_{L_0} \phi_0'(t)[m(t)-m(t_0)][\zeta(t-t_0)-\zeta(t)]dt + \\ + \frac{2}{\pi i}(\bar{a}_{10}\eta_2 - \bar{a}_{20}\eta_1)t_0 - \frac{2}{\pi i}(\bar{a}_{10}\bar{\eta}_2 - \bar{a}_{20}\bar{\eta}_1)\bar{t}_0 = 0 , \end{aligned} \tag{7.2}$$

where a_{10} and a_{20} are defined by (cf. (5.7))

$$\left.\begin{aligned} 2\pi i a_{10} &= \omega_1 \int_{L_0} \phi_0(t)\, \zeta'(t)dt - \eta_1 \int_{L_0} \phi_0(t)dt , \\ 2\pi i a_{20} &= \omega_2 \int_{L_0} \phi_0(t)\, \zeta'(t)dt - \eta_2 \int_{L_0} \phi_0(t)dt , \end{aligned}\right\} \tag{7.3}$$

and θ_0 represents the left-hand member of the homogeneous auxiliary condition $\theta_0 = 0$

$$\theta_0 = -\frac{1}{2\pi i}\int_{L_0} [\overline{\phi_0(t)} + m(t)\phi_0'(t)]dt - \frac{2}{\pi i}(\bar{a}_{10}\omega_2 - \bar{a}_{20}\omega_1) . \tag{7.4}$$

By means of the solution $\phi_0(t)$ of (7.2) we define the functions $\Phi_0(z)$ and $\Psi_0(z)$, holomorphic in S_+, and the functions $i\Phi_0^*(z)$ and $i\Psi_0^*(z)$, holomorphic in S_{0-}, by the modified Cauchy-integrals

$$-\frac{1}{2\pi i}\int_{L_0} \phi_0(t)[\zeta(t-z)-\zeta(t)]dt - \frac{2}{\pi i}(a_{10}\eta_2 - a_{20}\eta_1)z = \begin{cases} \Phi_0(z) & \text{for } z \text{ in } S_+ , \\ i\Phi_0^*(z) & \text{for } z \text{ in } S_{0-} ; \end{cases} \tag{7.5}$$

$$-\frac{1}{2\pi i}\int_{L_0}[\overline{\phi_0(t)}+m(t)\phi_0'(t)][\zeta(t-z)-\zeta(t)]dt+\frac{2}{\pi i}(\overline{a}_{10}\eta_2-\overline{a}_{20}\eta_1)z=$$

$$=\begin{cases}\Psi_0(z)-\chi(z)\Phi_0'(z) & \text{for } z \text{ in } S_+\\ i\Psi_0^*(z)-i\chi(z)\Phi_0^{*\prime}(z) & \text{for } z \text{ in } S_{0-}\ .\end{cases} \tag{7.6}$$

Differentiating (7.5) with respect to z, and applying the formula

$$\frac{1}{2\pi i}\int_{L_0}\phi_0'(t)\zeta(t)dt=-\frac{1}{2\pi i}\int_{L_0}\phi_0(t)\zeta'(t)dt=\frac{2}{\pi i}(a_{10}\eta_2-a_{20}\eta_1), \tag{7.7}$$

obtained from (7.3) and the well-known formula [8]

$$\eta_1\omega_2-\eta_2\omega_1=\tfrac{1}{2}\pi i\ , \tag{7.8}$$

we obtain

$$\frac{1}{2\pi i}\int_{L_0}\phi_0'(t)[\zeta(t-z)-\zeta(t)]dt=\begin{cases}\Phi_0'(z) & \text{for } z \text{ in } S_+\ ,\\ i\Phi_0^{*\prime}(z) & \text{for } z \text{ in } S_{0-}\ .\end{cases} \tag{7.9}$$

We now evaluate with these definitions in S_{0-} the boundary value of the expression

$$i[\Psi_0^*(z)+\overline{z}\Phi_0^{*\prime}(z)+\overline{\Phi_0^*(z)}\,]=i\Psi_0^*(z)+i\overline{z}\Phi_0^{*\prime}(z)-[\,\overline{i\Phi_0^*(z)}\,]\ , \tag{7.10}$$

if z in S_{0-} approaches a point t_0 on L_0, by application of the theorem on boundary values of modified Cauchy-integrals [12]. Making appropriate use of the fact that $\phi_0(t)$ satisfies (7.2), the result is after some straight-forward algebra

$$\Psi_0^*(t_0)+\overline{t}_0\Phi_0^{*\prime}(t_0)+\overline{\Phi_0^*(t_0)}=i\theta_0\ . \tag{7.11}$$

We now remember that θ_0 is independent of t_0; the expression

$$\Psi_0^*(z)+\overline{z}\Phi_0^{*\prime}(z)+\overline{\Phi_0^*(z)}\ , \tag{7.12}$$

defined in S_{0-}, therefore has a <u>constant</u> boundary value (7.11). The functions $\Phi_0^*(z)$, $\Psi_0^*(z)$, holomorphic in S_{0-} are therefore the <u>solution to the first fundamental problem</u> (prescribed boundary tractions) <u>for the simply-connected region</u> S_{0-} <u>for zero boundary tractions</u> on the boundary L_0 of S_{0-} [6, par. 41]. The general form of this stress-free solution is

$$\Phi_0^*(z)=C_0^*iz+\delta_0^*\ ,\qquad \Psi_0^*(z)=\epsilon_0^*\ , \tag{7.13}$$

where C_0^* is a real constant, and δ_0^*, ϵ_0^* are complex constants.

By substituting (7.13) into the right-hand members of (7.5), (7.6) and (7.9) it follows immediately by the validity of these relations for $z = 0$ that all constants C_0^*, δ_0^* and ϵ_0^* must be zero. Hence (7.13) may be replaced by

$$\Phi_0^*(z) = 0 \ , \quad \Psi_0^*(z) = 0 \ , \tag{7.14}$$

and $\theta_0 = 0$ now follows from (7.11). The solution $\phi_0(t)$ of the homogeneous modified equation (7.2) therefore satisfies also the homogeneous auxiliary condition.

We now infer from (7.5) by our general theorem [12] on boundary values of a quasi-periodic function, holomorphic in S_+, that $\phi_0(t)$ is the boundary value of the quasi-periodic function $\Phi_0(z)$, holomorphic in S_+ and with cyclic increments $2a_{10}$, $2a_{20}$. It also follows from (7.9) that $\phi_0'(t)$ is the boundary value of $\Phi_0'(z)$ and from (7.6) that $\Psi_0(z) - \chi(z)\Phi_0'(z)$, holomorphic in S_+, is quasi-periodic with cyclic increments $-2\overline{a}_{10}$, $-2\overline{a}_{20}$.

Hence the expression

$$\Psi_0(z) + \overline{z}\Phi_0'(z) + \overline{\Phi_0(z)} \tag{7.15}$$

is doubly-periodic because its cyclic increments are zero. The boundary values of expression (7.15) are again evaluated by the analogue of Plemelj's formulae for modified Cauchy-integrals [12], making appropriate use of the fact that $\phi_0(t)$ satisfies (7.2), where now θ_0 is zero. The result is after some straight-forward algebra

$$\Psi_0(t_0) + \overline{t}_0\Phi_0'(t_0) + \overline{\Phi_0(t_0)} = 0 \ . \tag{7.16}$$

It is now evident that $\Phi_0(z)$, $\Psi_0(z)$ represent the solution of the problem of a doubly-periodic stress distribution for vanishing tractions along a hole boundary and vanishing resulting forces transmitted through the sides of a period-parallelogram. This solution is stress-free (par. 4), and it is therefore given by

$$\Phi_0(z) = C_0 iz + \delta_0 \ , \qquad \Psi_0(z) = \epsilon_0 \ , \tag{7.17}$$

where C_0 is a real constant, and δ_0 and ϵ_0 are complex constants. Since $\phi_0(t)$ is the boundary value of $\Phi_0(z)$, this result is expressed by the statement that any solution of the homogeneous modified equation (7.2) must necessarily have the form (7.1); it has already been noted that this solution also satisfies the homogeneous auxiliary condition $\theta_0 = 0$.

It now only remains to be verified whether (7.1) indeed satisfies the homogeneous modified equation (7.2), since it will be remembered that the form (7.1) of the solution has been found on the assumption that a solution exists. This verification is performed most conveniently by returning from (7.2) to the corresponding homogeneous functional equation, the homogeneous counterpart of (5.5)

$$\frac{1}{2\pi i}\int_{L_0}[\overline{\phi_0(t)}+m(t)\phi_0'(t)][\zeta(t-z)-\zeta(t)]dt = \frac{2}{\pi i}(\overline{a}_{10}\eta_2-\overline{a}_{20}\eta_1)z\ , \qquad (7.18)$$

holding for all z in S_{0-}, where a_{10} and a_{20} are given by (7.3). This return is justified because (7.1) satisfies all assumptions made in the transformation of (5.5) into (6.16). Remembering that $\chi(z)$ is a quasi-periodic function, holomorphic in S_+, and with cyclic increments $-2\overline{\omega}_1$, $-2\overline{\omega}_2$, we apply our general theorem [12] to the left-hand member of (7.18) in the form

$$\frac{1}{2\pi i}\int_{L_0} C_0 i\chi(t)[\zeta(t-z)-\zeta(t)]dt = -\frac{2C_0}{\pi}(\overline{\omega}_1\eta_2-\overline{\omega}_2\eta_1)z\ , \qquad (7.19)$$

and the verification of (7.18) is obvious from $a_{10} = C_0 i\omega_1$, $a_{20} = C_0 i\omega_2$. Likewise, the auxiliary condition $\theta_0 = 0$ is also satisfied on account of the relation[±±]

$$\frac{1}{2\pi i}\int_{L_0}\chi(t)dt = \frac{2}{\pi i}(\overline{\omega}_1\omega_2-\overline{\omega}_2\omega_1)\ . \qquad (7.20)$$

7.3 It should be noted that the general solution (7.1) of the homogeneous modified equation (7.2) represents three linearly independent solutions, the complex constant δ_0 counting for two. By a general theorem on Fredholm equations the inhomogeneous modified integral equation (6.16) now has a solution --determinate but for an additional linear function (7.1) -- if and only if the specified data in (6.16), viz. γ_1, γ_2 and $h(t)$, satisfy three linearly independent conditions. The explicit form of these conditions will not be needed; it is sufficient to note that they are conditions to be imposed on the prescribed boundary tractions p_x, p_y along L_0 and on the cyclic increments $2\gamma_1$, $2\gamma_2$. For the time being it will be assumed that these three conditions are satisfied. A solution $\phi(t)$ of the modified integral equation (6.16) then does exist, and it has a tangential derivative $\phi'(t)$ along L_0, satisfying a Hölder-condition since it has been assumed that p_x, p_y and the curvature satisfy such a condition.

By means of the solution $\phi(t)$ of the modified integral equation we now define functions $\Phi(z)$, $\Psi(z)$, holomorphic in S_+, and functions $i\Phi^*(z)$, $i\Psi^*(z)$, holomorphic in S_{0-}, by modified Cauchy-integrals, similar to (7.5) and (7.6)

$$\frac{1}{2\pi i}\int_{L_0}\phi(t)[\zeta(t-z)-\zeta(t)]dt-\frac{2}{\pi i}(a_1\eta_2-a_2\eta_1) = \begin{cases}\Phi(z) & \text{for } z \text{ in } S_+\ ,\\ i\Phi^*(z) & \text{for } z \text{ in } S_{0-}\ ;\end{cases} \qquad (7.21)$$

$$-\frac{1}{2\pi i}\int_{L_0}[\overline{\phi(t)}+m(t)\phi'(t)-h(t)][\zeta(t-z)-\zeta(t)]dt-\frac{2}{\pi i}[(\gamma_1-\overline{\alpha}_1)\eta_2-(\gamma_2-\overline{\alpha}_2)\eta_1]z=$$

$$=\begin{cases}\Psi(z)-\chi(z)\,\Phi'(z) & \text{for } z \text{ in } S_+ ,\\ i\Psi^*(z)-i\chi(z)\,\Phi^{*\prime}(z) & \text{for } z \text{ in } S_{0-},\end{cases} \tag{7.22}$$

where α_1 and α_2 are given by (5.7). By differentiating (7.21) we obtain an equation similar to (7.9)

$$\frac{1}{2\pi i}\int_{L_0}\phi'(t)[\zeta(t-z)-\zeta(t)]dt=\begin{cases}\Phi'(z) & \text{for } z \text{ in } S_+ ,\\ i\Phi^{*\prime}(z) & \text{for } z \text{ in } S_{0-} .\end{cases} \tag{7.23}$$

The analysis now follows the same lines as in the discussion of the solution of the homogeneous equation, and the details may safely be left to the reader. First it is shown that the boundary value of the expression

$$i[\Psi^*(z)+\overline{z}\Phi^{*\prime}(z)+\overline{\Phi^*(z)}] \tag{7.24}$$

has a constant value $-\theta$ on account of the modified integral equation (6.16), where θ is given by (6.15). It follows that the functions $\Phi^*(z)$, $\Psi^*(z)$ solve the first fundamental problem for the simply-connected region S_{0-} for vanishing boundary tractions, i.e.

$$\Phi^*(z)=C^*iz+\delta^* , \qquad \Psi^*(z)=\epsilon^* , \tag{7.25}$$

where C^* is a real constant, and δ^* and ϵ^* are complex constants. Taking $z=0$ in (7.21), (7.22) and (7.23), it is then easily seen that all constants are zero, i.e.

$$\Phi^*(z)=0 , \qquad \Psi^*(z)=0 . \tag{7.26}$$

Hence the constant θ is also zero, and the auxiliary condition (6.14) is therefore satisfied by the solution of (6.16). From (7.21) and (7.26) it now follows that $\phi(t)$ is the boundary value of the function $\Phi(z)$, holomorphic in S_+ and with cyclic increments $2\alpha_1$, $2\alpha_2$. Next, (7.22) and the auxiliary condition (6.14), which was already seen to be satisfied, express that $\Psi(z)-\chi(z)\Phi'(z)$ is indeed quasi-periodic with the required cyclic increments (cf. par. 5) $2(\gamma_1-\overline{\alpha}_1)$, $2(\gamma_2-\overline{\alpha}_2)$. Hence the expression

$$\Psi(z)+\overline{z}\Phi'(z)+\overline{\Phi(z)} \tag{7.27}$$

has indeed the specified cyclic increments $2\gamma_1, 2\gamma_2$. Finally, the boundary value of (7.27) for z in S_+ approaching a point t_0 on L_0

may again be evaluated by means of the analogue to Plemelj's formulae [12] and appropriate use of the modified integral equation. The result is

$$\Psi(t_0) + \overline{t}_0 \Phi'(t_0) + \overline{\Phi(t_0)} = h(t_0) \ . \tag{7.28}$$

The functions $\Phi(z) \equiv \phi(z)$ and $\Psi(z) \equiv \psi(z)$, defined by (7.21) and (7.22), where $\phi(t)$ is a solution of (6.16) and at the same time the boundary value of $\phi(z)$, therefore represent the (essentially unique) solution of the boundary problem, defined in par. 3.

7.4 Our discussion of the inhomogeneous equation was based on the assumption that the three linearly independent conditions on the boundary tractions p_x, p_y and on the cyclic increments $2\gamma_1$, $2\gamma_2$, necessary in order to ensure the existence of a solution of (6.16), are always satisfied. We verify this assumption now by observing that a solution does indeed exist, once this assumption is made, even although the necessary conditions (3.8) and (3.13) for the existence of a doubly-periodic stress distribution have so far been entirely disregarded in our discussion of existence. It follows that the conditions (3.8) and (3.13) must be implied by the three linearly independent conditions referred to above. On the other hand, the conditions (3.8) and (3.13) are also three linearly independent conditions on the boundary tractions p_x, p_y and on the cyclic increments $2\gamma_1$, $2\gamma_2$. Hence the two triples of linearly independent conditions on the data of the problem must be equivalent, and the proof of existence of the (essentially unique) solution of our boundary value problem has been completed.

Our final argument may also be clad in a more physical (although mathematically less conclusive) form by observing that the solution (7.1) of the homogeneous modified integral equation represents a rigid-body-displacement. In the absence of appropriate supports to prevent such a displacement, the external loads must be self-equilibrating, and this requirement is in fact expressed by (3.8) and (3.13).

7.5 In our proof of existence we have introduced the additional assumption of Hölder-conditions, satisfied by the specified boundary tractions along L_0 and by the curvature of L_0. In particular, the assumption on the curvature may exclude practically important hole contours, e.g. rectangular hole boundaries. Fortunately our assumption may be relaxed by allowing a finite number of corners on our contours. Although special care must then be taken with respect to the integration by parts in the transformation of (6.8) into (6.13), which transformation requires a slight modification by the occurrence of some additional terms in (6.13) due to the corners, it appears that the analysis does not require any essential modification.

§8. Concluding remarks

Our theory for an infinite sheet with a doubly-periodic set of equal holes includes as a special case the problem of a sheet with a single row of holes. The latter problem is obtained in the limit if the modulus of one of the fundamental periods, e.g. $2\omega_2$ tends to infinity. The Weierstrasz zêta function then degenerates into the function [8]

$$\lim_{|\omega_2| \to \infty} \zeta(z; 2\omega_1, 2\omega_2) = \frac{\pi}{2\omega_1}\left(\frac{\pi z}{6\omega_1} + \cot\frac{\pi z}{2\omega_1}\right) . \tag{8.1}$$

Special care will be necessary in the application of our general theory because the cyclic increment $2\eta_2$ now has an infinite modulus. Nevertheless it may be worthwhile to investigate this limiting case in some more detail, and to compare the results with Savin's special theory for the case of a single row of holes [14, 15], based on a conformal mapping on a region with a single hole. It is hoped to return to this aspect at a later time, in particular with respect to the important case of a row of rectangular holes.

NOTES

*At the time of writing of [12] the author was unaware of an earlier paper by Woods [13]; in which a function, analytic in a rectangular region, is expressed in its boundary values by means of integrals involving theta functions (the author is indebted to Professor Hirsh Cohen for this reference in aerodynamic theory). The relations between Woods' theorem and our theorems in [12] have not yet been fully investigated, but it seems obvious that Woods' representation would require considerable modifications for application to our problem.

§Eq. (2.1) also holds for plane strain if κ is replaced by $\kappa^*=3-4\nu$.

#It should be noted that a misprint occurs in the sign of the last term in eq. (33.3) of [6].

±It should be noted that the resulting moment of these boundary tractions along a hole boundary need not vanish; this resulting moment must of course have the same value for all hole boundaries.

**The existence of functions $\chi(z)$ with the required properties is easily verified by constructing such a function as a linear combination of z and $\zeta(z)$, the Weierstrasz zêta function [8]; this special function $\chi(z)$ may also be most suitable in applications of the theory.

§§In the case of circular holes it would seem more convenient to expand the function $\phi(z)$ in a series of derivatives of the zêta function [cf. 12], and to apply the functional equation (5.5) directly; this numerical approach is now under investigation in the author's laboratory.

##See [6, par. 98] for a similar argument in the case of a simply-connected region.

±±This verification is already implied by the foregoing analysis (see the discussion following (7.14)).

REFERENCES

1. J. W. Dally and A. J. Durelli, Stresses in perforated panels, Product Engineering, March 1956, p. 188.

2. G. Horvay, Thermal stresses in perforated plates, Proc. First U. S. National Congress of Applied Mechanics (1951), p. 247.

3. G. Horvay, The plane-stress problem of perforated plates, Journ. Appl. Mech., vol. 19, (1952), p. 355.

4. W. J. Natanson, Uber die Spannungen in einer auf Zug beanspruchten Platte, die durch Schachbrettförmig verteilte untereinander gleiche Löcher geschwächt ist. Rec. math. Moscow 42 (1935), S. 617 (in Russian).

5. H. Saito, Stress in a plate containing infinite parallel rows of holes, Zeitschr. Angew. Math. und Mech., Bd. 37 (1957), p. 111.

6. N. I. Muskhelishvili, Some basic problems of the mathematical theory of elasticity, Translated from the 3rd Russian edition by J. R. M. Radok, Groningen (1953).

7. N. I. Muskhelishvili, Singular integral equations, Translated from the second Russian edition by J. R. M. Radok, Groningen (1953).

8. E. T. Whittaker and G. N. Watson, Modern Analysis, 4th Ed., Cambridge (1927), ch. 20.

9. J. Tannery et J. Molk, Fonctions elliptiques, Paris, I (1893), II(1896), III(1898), IV(1902).

10. A. Hurwitz und R. Courant, Allgemeine Funktionentheorie und Elliptische Funktionen, Berlin (1922).

11. C. Guichard, Théorie des points singuliers essentiels, Ann. Sci. de l'École Normale Supérieure, 2me série, t. 12 (1883), p. 301.

12. W. T. Koiter, Some general theorems on doubly-periodic and quasi-periodic functions, Proc. Kon. Ned. Ak. Wet., Amsterdam, A, Vol. LXII, 2, (1959), p. 120-128.

13. L. C. Woods, Subsonic plane flow in an annulus or a channel with spacewise periodic boundary conditions, Proc. Roy. Soc., London A 228 (1955), p. 63.

14. G. N. Savin, Tensions dans un plan élastique avec une série infinie de coupures égales, Comptes rendus de l'académie des sciences de l'U.R.S.S. 23 (1939), p. 515.

15. S. G. Mikhlin, Integral equations, Translated from the second Russian edition by A. H. Armstrong, London (1957).

HANS F. BUECKNER

Some Stress Singularities and Their Computation by Means of Integral Equations

§1. Introduction

With respect to a Cartesian coordinate system with axes x, y, z we consider an elastically deformed cylindrical body with generators parallel to the z-axis. A state of plane strain is assumed, i.e., strains do not depend on z ; moreover, there shall be no displacement in z-direction.

Stresses and strains shall be related to one another by Hooke's law. They depend on x and y only. In the sequel we will be mostly concerned with the stresses σ_x, σ_y, τ_{xy} and with the displacements u, v in x- and y-direction respectively.

Our interest centers on two bodies, namely the rotor of Fig. 1 and the slab of Fig. 2. The rotor has a borehole with radius a ; the outer radius is b . The only load on the rotor shall be the centrifugal forces of rotation. The slab's cross-section is a strip bounded by the y-axis and the line $x = d = \text{const.}$ The slab is bent by two moments of magnitude M (per unit length) acting at $y = \pm\infty$ in opposite directions.

Both rotor and slab are sharply notched, the notch extending along the x-axis. In the case of the rotor, the notch shall be defined by

$$a \le x \le c < b\,; \quad y = 0\,; \tag{1.1}$$

as to the slab we prescribe

$$0 \le x \le c < d\,; \quad y = 0 \tag{1.2}$$

as the location of the notch.

A stress-concentration at the root of the notch will appear. It implies the singular behavior

$$\sigma_y \cdot \sqrt{2(x-c)} \to K \quad \text{when } x \to c+0 \text{ on } y=0 \tag{1.3}$$

$$\frac{|v|}{\sqrt{2(c-x)}} \to \frac{2(1-\nu^2)\cdot K}{E} \quad \text{when } x \to c-0 \text{ on } y=0\,. \tag{1.4}$$

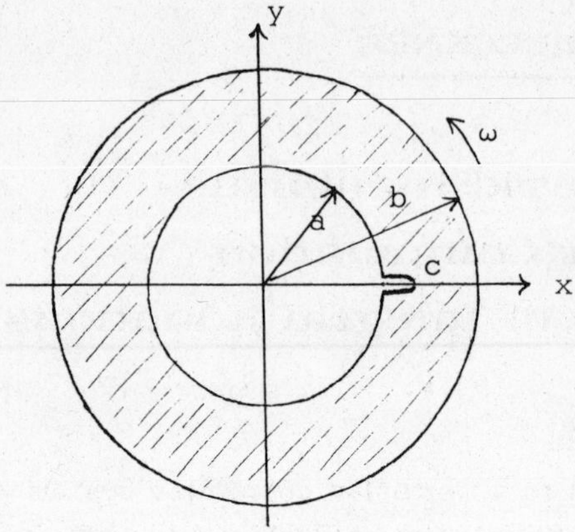

Fig. 1

Here K is a certain quantity depending on the shape of the notched body and on its external load; E is Young's modulus, ν is Poisson's parameter.

The stress-concentrations factor $K > 0$ was introduced by Irwin [1]. Our principal objective is the computation of K.

Relation (1.3) means that we will find a stress-field with unbounded stresses. Such fields do not occur in nature; instead plastic deformation will appear near the root of the notch. Yet the knowledge of K is valuable; its magnitude will give some information about the extent of plastic deformation. There is also a concept of brittle fracture which relates the onset of fracture to a critical value of K[2, 3]. The two bodies of Fig. 1 and Fig. 2 were chosen for the purpose of a check on the latter concept. For details the reader is referred to [1].

It is useful to modify the problems for rotor and slab. We note that the problems of determining displacements and stresses are elementary if no notches exist. Let us subtract the stress-field of the unnotched specimen from the stress-field of the notched one under the same external loading. The difference field can be interpreted as the response to the following external load:

(1.5) $\sigma_y = -p(x)\ ;\ \tau_{xy} = 0$ along the notch;

there are no other loads; in particular the rotor is no longer subjected to centrifugal forces and the slab no longer to bending moments at $|y| = \infty$. The cylindrical boundaries of the rotor as well as the boundaries $x = 0$, $x = d$ of the slab are free from tractions.

The function $p(x)$ is the stress σ_y of the unnotched body at the notch-interval. We have for the rotor

$$(1.6) \qquad p(x) = \frac{\rho\omega^2(1-2\nu)(3-2\nu)(1+\nu)}{8E(1-\nu)}\left[a^2 + b^2 + \frac{a^2b^2}{r^2} - \frac{1+2\nu}{3-2\nu}r^2\right]$$

$$\rho = \text{mass density;} \quad \omega = \text{angular velocity}$$

and for the slab

$$(1.6') \qquad p(x) = 6M(1 - 2x/d)/d^2 \quad .$$

The field of the unnotched specimen is regular at the root of the notch. Hence the difference field exhibits the behavior (1. 3), (1. 4) with the quantity K of the original problem.

From here on we will consider the problem (1. 5) only.

§2. Muskhelishvili's formulas

The load (1. 5) being self-equilibrated, we shall derive displacements and stresses from two analytic functions $\phi(z)$, $\psi(z)$; $z = x + iy$, which are holomorphic inside the cross-sections shown in Fig. 1 and Fig. 2 respectively. Following Muskhelishvili [4], we write

$$(2.1) \qquad \mu = \frac{E}{2(1+\nu)} \ , \quad \kappa = 3 - 4\nu$$

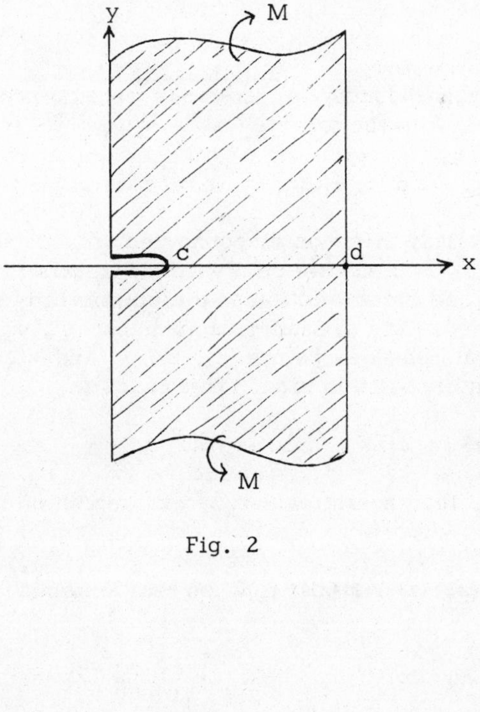

Fig. 2

and

(2.2) $$2\mu(u + iv) = \kappa\phi(z) - z \cdot \overline{\phi'(z)} - \overline{\psi(z)}$$

(2.3) $$\sigma_x = \mathrm{Re}[\,\phi'(z) + \overline{\phi'(z)} - z \cdot \overline{\phi''(z)} - \overline{\psi'(z)}\,]$$

(2.4) $$\sigma_y = \mathrm{Re}[\,\phi'(z) + \overline{\phi'(z)} + z \cdot \overline{\phi''(z)} + \overline{\psi'(z)}]$$

(2.5) $$\tau_{xy} = -\mathrm{Im}[z \cdot \overline{\phi''(z)} + \overline{\psi'(z)}] \ .$$

The components X in x-direction, Y in y-direction of the traction which attacks the elastic material situated on the left-hand side of an oriented arc element ds are given by the differential relation

(2.6) $$i(X + iY)ds = d[\phi(z) + z\overline{\phi'(z)} + \overline{\psi(z)}\,] \ : \ \text{(Fig. 3)}$$

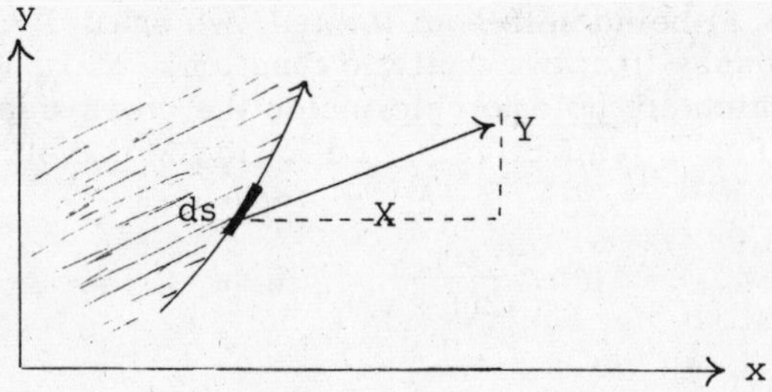

Fig. 3

Where an arc of the boundary of the cross-section is free from traction we can apply (2.6) in the form

(2.6') $$\overline{\phi(z)} + \bar{z}\,\phi'(z) + \psi(z) = A = \text{const.}$$

The constant A may differ on disconnected arcs.

In the special problems we deal with, the x-axis is an axis of symmetry so far as the cross-section of the elastic body and its loading are concerned. The symmetry implies that u, σ_x, σ_y are the same at conjugate complex points z, $\bar{z}$; v and τ_{xy} are the same in modulous but opposite in sign. This leads to

(2.7) $$\overline{\phi(z)} = \phi(\bar{z}) \ , \ \overline{\psi(z)} = \psi(\bar{z}) \ .$$

Furthermore, the shearstress τ_{xy} will vanish on the real axis. Hence

(2.8) $$\mathrm{Im}(z\phi''(z) + \psi'(z)) = 0 \ \text{on real axis.}$$

Formulas (2.7), (2.8) indicate that $z\phi'' + \psi'$ is a holomorphic function in the unnotched cross-section. We therefore introduce

$$\omega(z) = \psi - \phi + z\phi' \quad \text{with} \quad \omega' = \psi' + z\phi'' ;$$

and substitute ψ by ϕ and ω correspondingly. This gives

$$(2.2') \qquad 2\mu(u + iv) = \kappa\phi - \bar{\phi} + (\bar{z} - z)\bar{\phi}' - \bar{\omega}$$

$$(2.3') \qquad \sigma_x = \mathrm{Re}[\phi' + \bar{\phi}' - (z - \bar{z})\bar{\phi}'' - \bar{\omega}']$$

$$(2.4') \qquad \sigma_y = \mathrm{Re}[\phi' + \bar{\phi}' + (z - \bar{z})\bar{\phi}'' + \bar{\omega}']$$

$$(2.5') \qquad \tau_{xy} = -\mathrm{Im}[(z - \bar{z})\bar{\phi}'' + \bar{\omega}']$$

We shall consider $\omega(z)$ as a function which is holomorphic inside the <u>unnotched</u> cross-section. Since (2.7), (2.9) require

$$(2.7') \qquad \overline{\omega(z)} = \omega(\bar{z})$$

the function ω will be real on the real axis.

The calculation of displacements and stresses for both slab and rotor requires to find functions ϕ and ω in accordance with (2.7), (2.7'). They have to satisfy certain boundary conditions. With the possible exception of endpoints of the notch-segments we will require that ϕ, ϕ', ω, ω' are continuous in the domain of the cross-section with the boundary included, that furthermore

$$(2.9) \qquad \mathrm{Re}(2\phi' + \omega') = -p(x) \quad \text{along the notch}$$

and finally

$$(2.6'') \qquad \phi + \bar{\phi} + (\bar{z} - z)\phi' + \omega = \text{const.} \quad \text{on the other parts of the boundary.}$$

Our regularity conditions on ϕ and ω imply that $\lim_{y\to 0} \mathrm{Im}(\bar{z} - z)\phi''(z) = 0$ where x is a point inside the notch interval. We do not go into the proof. The preceding limit relation makes it superfluous to formulate a special boundary condition for $\tau_{xy} = 0$ along the notch.

§3. <u>The auxiliary problem of a given notch-displacement v</u>

Let t be a point inside the notch interval. The approach $z \to t$ furnishes, due to (2.2'),

(3.1) $$2\mu v(t \pm 0.i) = (\kappa+1)\mathrm{Im}\,\phi(t \pm 0.i) = \pm(\kappa+1)\mathrm{Im}\,\phi(t + 0.i) .$$

Instead of (2.9), let us prescribe the upper notch displacement in the form

(3.2) $$q(t) = \frac{2\mu}{\pi(\kappa+1)} v(t + 0.i)$$

along the notch $c' \leq t \leq c$, where $c' = a$ for the rotor and $c' = 0$ for the slab. The function $q(t)$ shall be restricted to the class of f functions

(3.3) $$q(t) = f(t)\sqrt{c-t} ,$$

where $f(t)$ admits a derivative $f'(t)$ that satisfies a Hoelder-condition

(3.3') $$|f'(t) - f'(t')| \leq C \cdot |t-t'|^{\lambda} \quad ; \quad 0 < \lambda \leq 1 .$$

The Cauchy integral

(3.4) $$\phi_0(z) = \int_{c'}^{c} \frac{q(t)dt}{t-z} \quad ; \quad z \text{ not on notch}$$

defines a holomorphic function in the z-plane, cut along the interval $c' \leq t \leq c$; ϕ_0 and ϕ_0' satisfy the requirements of the preceding section. The Plemelj formulas furnish

(3.5) $$\phi_0(\tau \pm 0.i) = \pm i q(\tau)\pi + \int_{c'}^{c} \frac{q(t)dt}{t-\tau} \quad ; \quad c' < \tau < c ;$$

the integral being in the sense of the Cauchy principal value.

The pair of functions $\phi = \phi_0$, $\omega = \omega_0 \equiv 0$ gives rise to displacements and stresses in the notched elastic body. They give a vanishing shear-stress along the notch and also by comparison of (3.2), (3.5) the required notch displacement. Along the notch a certain stress $\sigma_y = -p_0(x)$ will be induced. The other boundaries will not be free from tractions, and one will find

(3.6) $$\phi_0(\zeta) + \phi_0(\bar{\zeta}) + (\bar{\zeta} - \zeta)\phi'_0(\zeta) = T(\zeta) \neq \text{const.}$$

Thus the condition (2.6") is not satisfied. Our next step is to relieve the boundary stresses due to (3.6). To this end we need two functions $\phi_1(z)$, $\omega_1(z)$ both holomorphic inside the unnotched cross-section, such that

(3.7) $$\phi_1(\zeta) + \phi_1(\bar{\zeta}) + (\bar{\zeta} - \zeta)\phi_1'(\zeta) + \omega_1(\zeta) = -T(\zeta) + \text{const.}$$

on the boundaries. This problem, although not readily solved, involves less difficulties than a problem for a notched specimen. We write $\phi = \phi_0 + \phi_1$, $\omega = \omega_0 + \omega_1$ and

(3.8) $\mathrm{Re}(2\phi'_1 + \omega'_1) = -p_1(x)$ along notch.

The functions ϕ, ω do not create boundary stresses outside the notch. On the notch itself they create no shear and they furnish the required notch-displacement v ; furthermore

(3.9) $\sigma_y = -p_0(x) - p_1(x)$ on the notch.

Let us write briefly

(3.10) $$+ p_0(x) + p_1(x) = \frac{d}{dx}(Lq)$$

where L stands for a linear operator. It will turn out later that L represents a singular integral operator,

(3.11) $$Lq = \int_{c'}^{c} L(x,t)q(t)dt \ .$$

Now we return to the original problem (2.9). Its solution will go with a certain notch-displacement $q(t)$; we can reduce the problem (2.9) by solving

(3.12) $$\frac{d}{dx} Lq = p$$

for q and by using the solution of the auxiliary problem. So far as the stress-concentration factor K is concerned, we need not go beyond the solution of (3.12). The solution will be of the form (3.3) and the factor K is

(3.13) $$K = \frac{1}{4}\sqrt{2} \cdot \frac{E f(c)}{1-\nu^2} \ .$$

Thus the following steps will be directed toward

1. Finding the operator L ;
2. Solving (3.12) for q .

In the second step a way of solving (3.12) approximately will be described.

§4. The operator L of a special rotor problem and the approximate solution of an integral equation*

We specialize the rotor problem by setting $b = \infty$ and $a = 1$. It is required to find $\phi_1(z)$, $\omega_1(z)$ holomorphic for $|z| > 1$ such that

(4.1) $$\phi_0(z) + \phi_0(\bar{z}) + (\bar{z} - z)\phi'_0(z)$$
$$+ \phi_1(z) + \phi_1(\bar{z}) + (\bar{z} - z)\phi'_1(z) + \omega_1(z) = \text{const. on } |z| = 1 \ .$$

But $\overline{z} = \frac{1}{z}$ on $|z| = 1$; hence

$$\phi_0(z) + \phi_0(\tfrac{1}{z}) + (\tfrac{1}{z} - z)\phi'_0(z) + \phi_1(z) + \phi_1(\tfrac{1}{z}) + (\tfrac{1}{z} - z)\phi'_1(z) + \omega_1(z) = \text{const.}, \tag{4.2}$$

and this will be considered as a functional equation for both ϕ_1 and ω_1 wherever these functions can be defined. Since $\phi_0(1/z)$ is holomorphic for $|z| > 1$ we set

$$\phi_1(z) = -\phi_0(\tfrac{1}{z}) - (z - \tfrac{1}{z})\phi'_0(\tfrac{1}{z}) + z\phi'_0(0) \tag{4.3}$$

$$\omega_1(z) = (z - \tfrac{1}{z})[\phi'_0(\tfrac{1}{z}) + \phi'_1(z)] - (z + \tfrac{1}{z})\phi'_0(0) \tag{4.4}$$

and (4.2) is satisfied.§ We find

$$2\phi + \omega = 2\phi_0(z) - 2\phi_0(\tfrac{1}{z}) + \frac{z^2-1}{z^2}\frac{d}{dz}[(z^2-1)z^2\frac{d}{dz}\phi_0(\tfrac{1}{z})] + \frac{2(z^2-1)}{z}\phi'_0(0) \; ; \tag{4.5}$$

by comparison with (2.9), (3.9) the integral operator L turns out to be

$$L(x,t) = -\frac{2}{t-x} + \frac{2x}{tx-1} - \frac{x^2-1}{x}\frac{d}{dx}[x^2(x^2-1)\frac{d}{dx}(\frac{x}{tx-1})] - \frac{2(x^2-1)}{xt^2} \; . \tag{4.6}$$

Here the first term on the right-hand side represents a singular operator; the integral pertaining to it is to be taken as the Cauchy principal value.

Additive real constants disregarded, it can be shown that ϕ_1, ω_1 are uniquely determined by (4.2). The additive constants give rise to rigid body motion in the direction of the real axis. Our choice of ϕ_1, ω_1 implies

$$Lq = \int_1^x p(s)ds = P(x) \; . \tag{4.7}$$

The transformation

$$x = \frac{1+\gamma\xi}{1-\gamma\xi} \; , \; t = \frac{1+\gamma\tau}{1-\gamma\tau} \; ; \; \gamma = \frac{c-1}{c+1} < 1 \tag{4.8}$$

$$q(t) = q^*(\tau) \; ; \; P(x) = P^*(\xi) \tag{4.9}$$

results in

(4.10) $$\int_0^1 L^*(x,\tau)q^*(\tau)d\tau = P^*(\xi) \quad \text{with}$$

(4.11) $$L^* = L_1 + L_2$$

(4.12) $$L_1 = L_1(\xi,\tau) = \frac{2}{\tau+\xi} - \frac{2}{\tau-\xi}$$

(4.13) $$L_2(\xi,\tau) = -\frac{8\xi^2}{(\tau+\xi)^3} + \frac{4\xi}{(\tau+\xi)^2} + \frac{16\gamma\xi(\xi-\gamma\tau^2)}{(1+\gamma\xi)(1+\gamma\tau)(\tau+\xi)^2} .$$

The limit case $\gamma = 0$ gives the relations of the notched half-space (Fig. 4), which we rewrite in the form

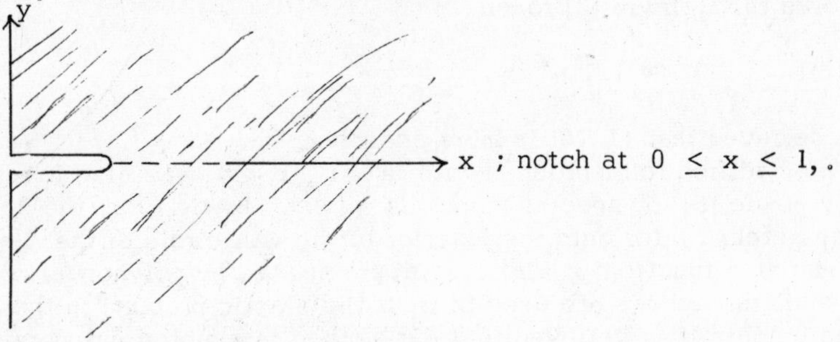

Fig. 4

(4.14) $$p(x) = \frac{d}{dx}\int_0^1 L(x,t)q(t)dt \; ; \; L = -\frac{2}{t-x} + \frac{2}{t+x} + \frac{4x}{(t+x)^2} - \frac{8x^2}{(t+x)^3}$$

The integral equation (4.10) can be transformed to the Fredholm type by using the well-known inversion formula for the operator L_1. However this does not seem to be useful for numerical computations. Therefore a procedure for treating (4.10) directly was adopted. The functions

(4.15) $$q^*_n(\tau) = \tau^n \cdot \sqrt{1-\tau}$$

have stress responses $p^*_n(\xi)$ which can be represented in closed form. A linear combination

(4.16) $$\mathfrak{p}(\xi) = \sum_{\kappa=0}^{m} a_\kappa p^*_\kappa(\xi)$$

can be taken to match the prescribed function $p^*(\xi)$. This involves the determination of the coefficients a_κ in accordance with a prescribed principle of best approximation. Here the method of least squares is one possibility. Another one is collocation. It was decided to use the latter principle and to require $\mathfrak{p}(\xi) = p^*(\xi)$ at $(n+1)$ equidistant abscissas ξ. The numerical experience was good. For the integral equation (4.14) and for $p^*(\xi) \equiv 1$ only four terms $(n = 3)$ were needed in order to match $p^*(\xi)$ with an error of not more than 3%. The approximate value of f(c) in (3.13) is the sum of the coefficients a_κ for the case (4.14) and

$$f(c) \approx \sqrt{\frac{2}{c^2 - 1}} \cdot \sum_{\kappa=0}^{n} a_\kappa \tag{4.17}$$

in general. The case $p^* = \text{const.}$ for the notched half-space leads to

$$K \approx 1.13\, p^* \sqrt{h} \quad ; \quad h = \text{length of notch.} \tag{4.18}$$

By using a set of dual integral equations and an iterative technique to solve them, Irwin [2] found

$$K \approx 1.1\, p^* \sqrt{h} \; . \tag{4.18'}$$

It is believed that (4.18) is more accurate.

The modified rotor problem with $a = 1$, $b = \infty$ was also investigated by Bowie [5] for special functions $p(x)$. Bowie maps the domain of the notched rotor onto the exterior of the unit circle of the ζ-plane. The mapping function $z = z(\zeta)$ is approximated by polynomials; Muskhelishvili's methods are used to treat the elastic problem in the image plane. Again it is believed that our method is simpler and more accurate.

§5. The half-plane with a periodic set of collinear cracks

As a preparation to the slab problem we shall consider the elastic z-plane with a periodic set of cracks on the x-axis (Fig. 5). The period shall be 2π ; one of the cracks shall occupy the interval $-c \leq x \leq c$. As before symmetric deformation due to (2.7) is considered, and again, the function $q(t)$ on the cracks is prescribed; we require $q(t + 2\pi) = q(t)$ and

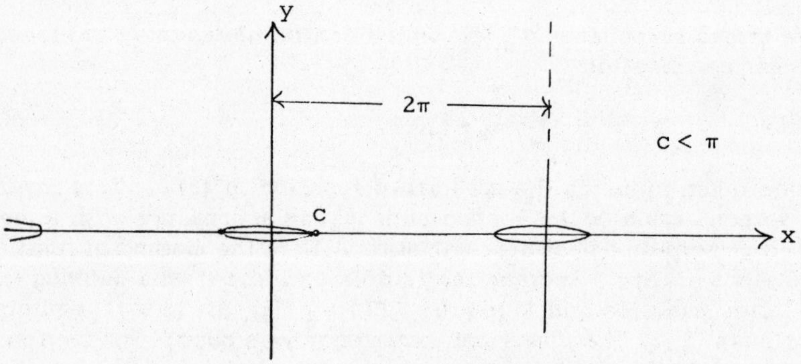

Fig. 5

(5.1) $q(t) = \sqrt{c^2-t^2}\, f(t)$; $-c \leq t \leq c$

where $f'(t)$ satisfies a Hoelder-condition in $<-c, c>$. We introduce

(5.2) $$2\phi_0(z) = \int_{-c}^{c} q(t)\operatorname{ctg}\left(\frac{t-z}{2}\right)dt ,$$

and $\omega_0 \equiv 0$. These two functions solve the displacement problem under conditions (2.7). This follows from the Plemelj formulas. There is no shear stress along the x-axis. One finds

(5.3) $$-p(x) = +\sigma_y = 2R\phi'_0 = \frac{d}{dx}\int_{-c}^{c} q(t)\operatorname{ctg}\left(\frac{t-x}{2}\right)dt : -c < x < c ; y = 0 .$$

If vice versa $p(x)$ is prescribed periodically and if $p(x)$ satisfies a Hoelder-condition for $-c \leq x \leq c$ then $\phi'_0(z)$ is the Cauchy integral

(5.4) $$-\phi'_0(z) = \frac{1}{2\pi i Y(z)} \cdot \int_{-c}^{c} \frac{p(t) \cdot Y(t)dt}{2 \sin \frac{t-z}{2}}$$

with

(5.5) $$Y(z) = \sqrt{\sin^2 \frac{z}{2} - \sin^2 \frac{c}{2}} ;$$

$Y(z)$ is so determined that it has a positive imaginary part on the "upper" side $(y = +0)$ of the crack to which (5.4) refers. The integration in (5.4) pertains to the "upper" side.

$Y(z)$ is holomorphic in the z-plane cut along the crackintervals. It has period 4π . The product $Y(z) \sin \left(\frac{t-z}{2}\right)$ has period 2π and so has the function $\phi'_0(z)$ defined by (5.4). The integral over $\phi'_0(z)$ on any closed curve not intersecting with the cracks gives zero. It is sufficient to prove this for the rectangle defined by the lines $x = \alpha$, $x = \alpha + 2\pi$, $y = \beta$, $y = -\beta$, where $< \alpha, \alpha + 2\pi >$ contains one crack. Due to periodicity the integral has contributions from segments of $y = \beta$, $y = -\beta$ only. But it is obvious that $\phi'_0(z) \to 0$ as $\beta \to \infty$. Therefore the integral vanishes as asserted. Consequently the indefinite integral $\phi_0(z)$ of $\phi'_0(z)$ is holomorphic in the "cracked" plane. Finally we note that $-p(x) = 2\text{Re}\, \phi'_0$ on $-c < x < c$ follows from an application of the Plemelj formulas to (5.4).

In the special case

(5.6) $q(t) = q(-t)$

our formulas become

(5.2') $$\phi_0(z) = \sin z \int_0^c \frac{q(t)dt}{\cos z - \cos t}$$

(5.3') $$-p(x) = 2\frac{d}{dx} \sin x \int_0^c \frac{q(t)dt}{\cos x - \cos t}$$

(5.4') $$-\phi'_0(z) = \frac{\sin {}^z\!/_2}{i\pi Y(z)} \int_0^c \frac{p(t)Y(t)\cos {}^t\!/_2 \cdot dt}{\cos z - \cos t} .$$

Formulas (5.2'), (5.3') stay valid for the case of a function $f(t)$ in (5.1) which has a derivative $f'(t)$ with a jump-discontinuity at $t = 0$.# Formulas (5.4), (5.4') have been added for the sake of completeness. They will not be used later.

For very short cracks $c \ll 2\pi$ formula (5.3') changes approximately into

(5.3") $$-p(x) = 4\frac{d}{dx}\, x\int_0^c \frac{q(t)dt}{t^2 - x^2} = -\frac{d}{dx}\int_0^c L_1(x,t)q(t)dt$$

with the operator L_1 of (4.12); this relation is correct for a single crack $-c \le x \le c$, a case which is well known from the literature.

The symmetry (5.6) implies that $\tau_{xy} = 0$ on the lines $x = 0$ and $x = \pi$. This follows immediately from (2.5') and $\mathrm{Re}\,\phi_0 = 0$ on these lines.

As for the stress σ_x relation (2.3') furnishes

(5.7) $$\sigma_x = 2\phi'_0 + 2z\phi''_0 = 2(z\phi'_0)' \quad \text{on } x = 0$$

(5.7') $$\sigma_x = 2\phi'_0 + 2(z-\pi)\phi''_0 = 2((z-\pi)\phi'_0)' \quad \text{on } x = \pi .$$

Use has been made of the fact that ϕ'_0 is real and ϕ''_0 is imaginary on those lines.

For later application we need the Fourier-transforms

(5.8) $$\nu_i(\lambda) = -\int_0^\infty \sigma_x \cos \lambda y\, dy\ ;\ i = 1 \text{ for } x = \pi\ ,\ i = 2 \text{ for } x = 0 .$$

It is easily seen that $\sigma_x = O(ye^{-y})$ for large $y > 0$; we add without proof that $\sigma_x = O(\log\frac{1}{y})$ on $x = 0$ for small $y > 0$. The transforms (5.8) can be rewritten as

(5.9) $$\nu_2(\lambda) = -2\,\mathrm{Im}\int_0^{i\infty} (z\phi'_0)'e^{\lambda z}dz = 2\lambda\frac{d}{d\lambda}\,\mathrm{Im}\int_0^{i\infty} \phi'_0(z)e^{\lambda z}dz$$

(5.10) $$\nu_1(\lambda) = 2\lambda\frac{d}{d\lambda}\,\mathrm{Im}\int_\pi^{\pi+i\infty} \phi'_0(z)e^{\lambda(z-\pi)}dz .$$

Using Cauchy's integral theorem and the periodicity of $\phi'_0(z)$ one arrives at

(5.11) $\rho(\lambda) = \int_{a}^{a+i\infty} \phi'_0(z)e^{\lambda z}dz = \int_{a+2\pi}^{a+2\pi+i\infty} \phi'_0(z)e^{\lambda z}dz + \int_{a}^{a+2\pi} \phi'_0(z)e^{\lambda z}dz \ : \mathrm{Im}\, a = +0$

and

(5.12) $\rho(\lambda)(1 - e^{2\pi\lambda}) = \int_{a}^{a+2\pi} \phi'_0(z)e^{\lambda z}dz \ ;$

(5.12') $(1 - e^{2\pi\lambda})\mathrm{Im}\,\rho(\lambda) = \mathrm{Im}\int^{*} \phi'_0(z)e^{\lambda z}dz$

where $\int^{*}$ refers to the upper crack segments which are in the interval $\langle a, a+2\pi \rangle$. Outside of these segments we have $\mathrm{Im}\,\phi'_0 = 0$. Inside the segments we have $\mathrm{Im}\,\phi'_0(z) = \pi q$, where q refers to the displacement at point z . With the aid of (5.12') the functions $\nu_i(\lambda)$ can be given the following form

(5.13) $\nu_1(\lambda) = -2\lambda\pi \frac{d}{d\lambda}\left[\frac{1}{\sinh \lambda\pi}\int_0^c q'(t)\sinh \lambda t \, dt\right]$

(5.14) $\nu_2(\lambda) = -2\lambda\pi \frac{d}{d\lambda}\left[\frac{1}{\sinh \lambda\pi}\int_0^c q'(t)\sinh \lambda(t-\pi)dt\right]$.

§6. The slab

We consider the unnotched slab of width $d = \pi$ subjected to the normal stresses σ_x as given by formulas (5.7), (5.7').

The stress-field in the slab can be determined by the method of Fourier-transforms. The result is well-known [6], and in particular the stress σ_y on the x-axis is given by

(6.1) $$\frac{\pi^2}{2}\sigma_y = \frac{\partial}{\partial\eta}\int_0^\infty \frac{H_1(\eta)[\nu_1(\frac{2\lambda}{\pi}) + \nu_2(\frac{2\lambda}{\pi})]d\lambda}{\sin 2\lambda + 2\lambda} + \frac{\partial}{\partial\eta}\int_0^\infty \frac{H_2(\eta)[\nu_1(\frac{2\lambda}{\pi}) - \nu_2(\frac{2\lambda}{\pi})]d\lambda}{\sin 2\lambda - 2\lambda}$$

with $\eta = \frac{2x}{\pi} - 1$ and

(6.2) $H_1(\eta) = (1-\eta)\sinh \lambda(1+\eta) - (1+\eta)\sinh \lambda(1-\eta)$

(6.3) $H_2(\eta) = (1-\eta)\sinh \lambda(1+\eta) + (1+\eta)\sinh \lambda(1-\eta)$.

Calculations of an elementary nature furnish

$$(6.4)\quad \sigma_y = \frac{d}{dx}\int_0^c K(\xi,\eta)q'(t)dt \;;\; \xi = \frac{2t}{\pi} - 1 \;;$$

with

$$(6.5)\quad K(\xi,\eta) = \int_0^\infty \left[\frac{\lambda H_1(\xi)H_1(\eta)}{\sinh^2\lambda(\sinh 2\lambda + 2\lambda)} + \frac{\lambda H_2(\xi)H_2(\eta)}{\cosh^2\lambda(\sinh 2\lambda - 2\lambda)}\right]d\lambda .$$

With the aid of the integral

$$(6.6)\quad 4F(s) = \int_0^\infty \left[\frac{\cosh\lambda s - 1}{\sinh^2\lambda(\sinh 2\lambda + 2\lambda)} + \frac{\cosh\lambda s - 1}{\cosh^2\lambda(\sinh 2\lambda - 2\lambda)}\right]\lambda d\lambda$$

one may write

$$\begin{aligned}(6.7)\quad K(\xi,\eta) = {} & 2(1-\xi)(1-\eta)[F(2+\xi+\eta) - F(\xi-\eta)] \\ & + 2(1+\xi)(1+\eta)[F(2-\xi-\eta) - F(\xi-\eta)] \\ & - 2(1-\xi)(1+\eta)[F(2+\xi-\eta) - F(\xi+\eta)] \\ & - 2(1+\xi)(1-\eta)[F(2-\xi+\eta) - F(\xi+\eta)] \quad .\end{aligned}$$

We need $F(s)$ for $-4 < s < 4$; $F(s)$ is holomorphic in the strip $-4 < \mathrm{Re}\, s < 4$ but it has poles at $s = \pm 4$. Indeed the behavior near $s = \pm 4$ is represented by

$$\begin{aligned}(6.8)\quad F^*(s) &= 4\int_0^\infty \lambda(\cosh\lambda s - 1)e^{-4\lambda}d\lambda \\ &= \frac{2}{(s-4)^2} + \frac{2}{(s+4)^2} - \frac{1}{4} \;;\end{aligned}$$

the integral $F - F^*$ is regular beyond $|\mathrm{Re}\, s| = 4$. By virtue of (6.7) the function F^* gives rise to the kernel

$$(6.9)\quad K^*(\xi,\eta) = \frac{2(1+\xi)(1+\eta)}{(2+\xi+\eta)^2} = \frac{4xt}{(x+t)^2} \;;$$

the kernel $M = K - K^*$ is analytic in x, t for $0 \le x, t \le \pi$. This kernel was computed for $0 \le x, t \le \frac{\pi}{2}$. It turned out that M is very close to a degenerate kernel. Approximately

$$(6.10)\quad M(\xi,\eta) \simeq \frac{M(\xi,0)M(\eta,0)}{M(0,0)} + 0.21\,\xi\eta(1+\xi)(1+\eta);\; -1 \le \xi,\eta \le 0 \;.$$

holds; the absolute error is less than 0.001. $M(\xi,\eta)$ vanishes for $\eta = -1$, i.e. $t = 0$.

We write $M(\xi, \eta) = \widetilde{M}(x, t)$ and as our final result

$$(6.11) \quad \sigma_y = 4\frac{d}{dx}\int_0^c \frac{xt}{(x+t)^2}\, q'(t)dt + \frac{d}{dx}\int_0^c \widetilde{M}(x,t)q'(t)dt$$

$$= +\frac{d}{dx}\int_0^c L_2(x,t)q(t)dt - \frac{d}{dx}\int_0^c \frac{\partial \widetilde{M}}{\partial t}\cdot q(t)dt \ .$$

The operator L_2 is identical with the sum of the third and fourth term in (4.14).

We are now prepared to accomplish the procedure of section 3 for the notched slab. For simplicity we set $d = \pi$. The formulas (5.2') and (5.3') serve our purpose; we have to find p_1 ; but this quantity is identical with σ_y in (6.11). Hence

$$(6.12) \qquad L(x,t) = -\frac{2 \sin x}{\cos x - \cos t} + L_2(x,t) - \frac{\partial}{\partial t}\widetilde{M}(x,t) \ .$$

This is the operator of (3.10) for the notched slab. It would have been possible to obtain L in another way, namely by using the response to q(t) for the notched half-space and by relieving normal and shear stresses on the boundary $x = d$ of the unnotched slab.

The integral equation with (6.12) as kernel can be and was treated numerically in the way which was pointed out in connection with the rotor problem. As for the stress-concentration factor K the following numerical results may be given:

$$(6.13) \qquad K = \frac{6M}{d^2}\sqrt{\frac{2}{\pi}d\cdot h\left(\frac{c}{d}\right)}$$

and some values of the function h are:

c/d	0.1	0.2	0.5
h(c/d)	0.17	0.35	2.10

§7. Acknowledgment and Conclusions

The preceding remarks represent a condensed version of several technical reports which this author wrote for the Large Steam Turbine and Generator Department of the General Electric Company in Schenectady between three and two years ago. Mr. Ivar Giaever shares the work on the rotor problem. The author wishes to thank the General Electric Company for their permission to represent this work at the Symposium on Boundary Problems.

The emphasis of this paper is on practical application of singular integral equations to actual problems of mechanical engineering. It is believed that the numerical evaluation of stress-fields near the root of notches or cracks finds one of its most adequate tools in the method of integral equations.

NOTES

* The work on the rotor problem was done jointly by Ivar Giaever, presently with General Electric Company, Knoll's Research Laboratory, Schenectady, New York, and by this author. A joint publication is intended. For this reason the following description will be in the nature of a short preview.

§ The terms with $\phi_0'(0)$ are necessary in order to make ϕ, ω holomorphic at infinity.

#In this case we request $f'(t)$ to satisfy a Hoelder-condition for $0 < t \leq c$.

REFERENCES

1. G. R. Irwin, J. A. Kies and H. L. Smith, Fracture strengths relative to onset and arrest of crack propagation, a paper presented at the Sixty-first Annual Meeting of the American Society for Testing Materials, Boston, Mass., June 22-27, 1958.

2. G. R. Irwin, The crack extension-force for a crack at a free surface boundary, Naval Research Laboratory, Washington, D.C., NRL Report 5120, 1958.

3. H. Bueckner, The propagation of cracks and the energy of elastic deformation, ASME Paper No. 57-A-189.

4. N. I. Muskhelishvili, Some Basic Problems of the Mathematical Theory of Elasticity, P. Noordhoff, Ltd., Groningen, Holland, 1953.

5. O. L. Bowie, Analysis of an infinite plate containing radial cracks originating at the boundary of an internal circular hole, Journal of Mathematics and Physics, Vol. 25, 1956, p. 60-71.

6. I. N. Sneddon, Fourier Transforms, McGraw-Hill Book Company, Inc., 1951, p. 412, 413.

IAN N. SNEDDON

Boundary Value Problems in Thermoelasticity

§1. Introduction

The theory of thermoelasticity is concerned with the effect of the thermal state of an elastic solid upon the distribution of stress, and also with the complementary problem of determining the influence of the stresses in an elastic body on the conduction of heat through it. The subject, which is obviously of some technical interest, goes back to 1838 when Duhamel first formulated the stress-strain relation for an elastic body in which the temperature varied from point to point, but it is only recently that much work has been done on the resolution of boundary value problems. Recent mathematical interest in thermoelasticity has been along two main lines. In the first, revived by a paper of Biot (1) the emphasis has been on dynamical problems. Biot's study of the thermodynamics of an elastic solid led to an equation for the conduction of heat in the solid which differed from the classical equation in that it contained a term depending upon the rate of change of the dilatation of the body. These developments have recently been reviewed by Chadwick (2). The effect of this work is that in time-dependent problems the stress distribution and the temperature distribution cannot be treated separately, but are governed by a set of cross-linked equations. The solution of these equations is a matter of some difficulty but a few attempts have been made to solve boundary value problems for these equations (3).

There has also been a recent revival of interest in the calculation of steady thermal stresses in elastic bodies (see, for example, (4) and (5)). This is a much simpler problem altogether and, since it is of the form of a time-derivative, the additional term due to Biot is zero in this case.

It is this second class of boundary value problem which we consider here. We assume that the thermal gradients within the elastic body do not vary with the time and also that the strains are infinitessimal so that we employ the differential equations of the classical theory of elasticity. To simplify the analysis we shall consider here only problems in which there is axial symmetry. This is not a necessary restriction; the analysis can easily be extended to the non-symmetric case either by the method of Muki (6) or by the method used in (8). The assumption of axial symmetry enables us to solve the relevant partial differential equations by means of the theory of Hankel transforms. The boundary conditions in the simple cases we consider then lead either to a simple integral equation which can be solved by a straightforward application of the Hankel inversion theorem, or to a pair of dual integral equations. In one of the problems we shall discuss this pair of dual integral equations is capable of exact analytical solution in closed form (see §5 below), but in another, (§8 below) the equations appear to be too complicated to permit this. This suggests a fruitful problem for the numerical analyst to consider--the numerical solution of a pair of dual integral equations of the type

$$\int_0^\infty K(\xi)\psi(\xi)L(\xi,\rho)d\xi = f(\rho) , \quad \rho \in S$$

$$\int_0^\infty \psi(\xi)L(\xi,\rho)d\xi = g(\rho) , \quad \rho \in \complement S ,$$

in which the weight function $K(\xi)$ and the kernel $L(\xi, \rho)$ have explicit forms, the functions $f(\rho)$ and $g(\rho)$ are given either in closed form or by a set of numerical values, and it is desired to find the function $\psi(\xi)$. S denotes a segment of finite length of the real axis $-\infty < \rho < +\infty$, and $\complement S$ its complement. This is a problem which arises frequently in the analysis of mixed boundary value problems in mathematical physics, and which, for that reason, would be worthy of the attention of mathematicians interested in numerical analysis.

§2. The Equations of Equilibrium

We consider an elastic body whose boundaries are parallel to the plane $z = 0$, and in which is established a temperature field $T\{1 + \theta(x, y, z)\}$, where T is the temperature of the solid in a state of zero stress and strain. We assume that there are no body forces acting within the solid, and also that no heat sources are present. To simplify the analysis, we restrict our attention to those problems which exhibit symmetry about the z-axis. To formulate such problems we introduce a set of cylindrical coordinates $r = \rho\ell$, ϕ , $z = \zeta\ell$, where ℓ is some length characteristic of the problem being discussed. If we take ℓ as our unit of length, the reference temperature T as the unit of temperature, and the rigidity modulus μ as unit of stress, we find (7) that the equations of equilibrium take the dimensionless forms

$$\left(\frac{\partial^2 u}{\partial \rho^2} + \frac{1}{\rho}\frac{\partial u}{\partial \rho} - \frac{u}{\rho^2}\right) + \frac{\partial^2 u}{\partial \zeta^2} + (\beta^2 - 1)\frac{\partial^2 w}{\partial \rho \partial \zeta} = b\frac{\partial \theta}{\partial \rho} \qquad (1)$$

$$\frac{\partial^2 w}{\partial \rho^2} + \frac{1}{\rho}\frac{\partial w}{\partial \rho} + \beta^2\frac{\partial^2 w}{\partial \zeta^2} + (\beta^2 - 1)\frac{\partial}{\partial \zeta}\left(\frac{\partial u}{\partial \rho} + \frac{u}{\rho}\right) = b\frac{\partial \theta}{\partial \zeta} \qquad (2)$$

where, in terms of Poisson's ratio ν and the coefficient of linear expansion α ,

$$\beta^2 = \frac{2(1-\nu)}{1-2\nu} \qquad b = \frac{2(1+\nu)}{1-2\nu} \alpha T .$$

In these equations $u\ell$ is the displacement in the r-direction and $w\ell$ is the component of the displacement in the z-direction. The variation of θ throughout the elastic solid is governed by Laplace's equation

$$\frac{\partial^2 \theta}{\partial \rho^2} + \frac{1}{\rho}\frac{\partial \theta}{\partial \rho} + \frac{\partial^2 \theta}{\partial \zeta^2} = 0 . \tag{3}$$

To solve the equations (1), (2) and (3) for the class of problem in which we are interested, we introduce the Hankel transforms

$$\overline{u}(\xi,\zeta) = \int_0^\infty \rho u J_1(\xi\rho)d\rho , \quad \overline{w}(\xi,\zeta) = \int_0^\infty \rho w J_0(\xi\rho)d\rho , \quad \overline{\theta}(\xi,\zeta) = \int_0^\infty \rho\theta J_0(\xi\rho)d\rho . \tag{4}$$

Using the properties of Hankel transforms we can then show that these partial differential equations are equivalent to the set of simultaneous ordinary differential equations

$$\left.\begin{aligned} (D^2 - \beta^2\xi^2)\overline{u} - (\beta^2-1)\xi D\overline{w} &= -b\xi\overline{\theta} \\ (\beta^2-1)\xi D\overline{u} + (\beta^2 D^2 - \xi^2)\overline{w} &= bD\overline{\theta} \\ (D^2-\xi^2)\overline{\theta} &= 0 \end{aligned}\right\} \tag{5}$$

where D denotes the operator $d/d\zeta$.

§3. <u>Solution for a Semi-infinite Solid</u>

If we are interested in the stress and temperature fields in the semi-infinite solid $z \geq 0$, then, on the assumption that the disturbances from the reference state tend to zero at great distances from the origin of coordinates, we take the solutions of the equations (5) to be

$$\overline{\theta} = \xi f e^{-\xi\zeta} , \quad \overline{u} = b(f_1 + g_1\xi\zeta)e^{-\xi\zeta} , \quad \overline{w} = b(f_2 + g_1\xi\zeta)e^{-\xi\zeta} \tag{6}$$

where f , f_1 , f_2 and g_1 are functions of the variable ξ and are connected by the equation

$$(\beta^2-1)f_1 - (\beta^2-1)f_2 + (\beta^2+1)g_1 = f . \tag{7}$$

From the stress-strain relations we know that the Hankel transform of order 1 of the shearing stress τ_{rz} is, in our units, given by the equation

$$\bar{\tau}_{rz} = D\bar{u} - \xi\bar{w} = -b\xi(f_1 + f_2 - g_1 + 2g_1\xi\zeta)e^{-\xi\zeta} \quad . \tag{8}$$

Hence, if we assume that the bounding plane $z = 0$ is free from shearing stress we find that

$$f_1 + f_2 = g_1 \quad . \tag{9}$$

We can write the solution of the pair of equations (7) and (9) in the form

$$f_1 = \frac{1}{2\beta^2}\{f(\xi) - \frac{2}{\xi}\psi(\xi)\}, \; f_2 = \frac{1}{\xi}\psi(\xi) \; , \; g_1(\xi) = \frac{1}{2\beta^2}\{f(\xi) + \frac{2(\beta^2-1)}{\xi}\psi(\xi)\} \tag{10}$$

where the functions $f(\xi)$ and $\psi(\xi)$ are, as yet, undetermined.

From these expressions we can easily show that, on the boundary plane $z = 0$,

$$w = b\int_0^\infty \psi(\xi)\, J_0(\rho\xi)d\xi \tag{11}$$

$$\sigma_z = -\frac{b}{\beta^2}\int_0^\infty [\xi^2 f(\xi) + 2(\beta^2-1)\xi\psi(\xi)]J_0(\rho\xi)d\xi \tag{12}$$

$$\tau_{rz} = 0 \quad , \tag{13}$$

$$\theta = \int_0^\infty \xi^2 f(\xi)\, J_0(\rho\xi)d\xi \tag{14}$$

§4. The Sternberg-McDowell Problem

In a recent paper (5), Sternberg and McDowell have discussed the determination of the steady-state thermal stresses and displacements in a semi-infinite elastic solid when the boundary surface is free from stress and the stress distribution arises from an arbitrary temperature distribution on the surface of the solid. Recently (8), Sneddon and Lockett have discussed the same general problem and verified the general result of Sternberg and McDowell that the stress field due to an arbitrary (but steady) distribution of surface temperature is plane and parallel to the boundary. The methods employed in both these papers are applicable to distributions of temperature which are not axially symmetrical, but it is easy to treat the symmetrical case by the use of the solution we have derived above, and, here, we shall restrict ourselves to that case.

If $\sigma_z = \tau_{rz} = 0$ on the plane $z = 0$, then it follows from equation (12) that

$$\psi(\xi) = -\frac{1}{2(\beta^2-1)}\xi f(\xi) \; , \; f_1(\xi) = \frac{1}{2(\beta^2-1)}f(\xi), \; f_2(\xi) = -\frac{1}{2(\beta^2-1)}f(\xi), \; g_1(\xi) = 0, \tag{15}$$

so that we obtain the expressions

$$w(\rho, \zeta) = -\frac{b}{2(\beta^2-1)} \int_0^\infty \xi f(\xi) e^{-\xi\zeta} J_0(\rho\xi) d\xi \, , \quad u(\rho,\zeta) = \frac{b}{2(\beta^2-1)} \int_0^\infty \xi f(\xi) e^{-\xi\zeta} J_1(\xi\rho) d\xi \tag{16}$$

for the non-vanishing components of the displacement vector. Since the temperature field is determined by means of the equation

$$\theta(\rho, \zeta) = \int_0^\infty \xi^2 f(\xi) J_0(\rho\xi) d\xi \tag{17}$$

we see that we may write the equations (16) in the form

$$u(\rho, \xi) = -\frac{b}{2(\beta^2-1)} \frac{1}{\rho} \int_\rho^\infty p\theta(p, \zeta) dp \, , \quad w(\rho, \zeta) = -\frac{b}{2(\beta^2-1)} \int_\zeta^\infty \theta(\rho, q) dq \, . \tag{18}$$

For these forms of the components of the displacement vector, it is readily shown that $\sigma_z = \tau_{rz} = 0$, and that the non-vanishing components of the stress tensor may be determined by means of the equations

$$\sigma_r - \sigma_\phi = \frac{b}{\beta^2-1} \{\theta(\rho, \zeta) + \frac{2}{\rho^2} \int_\rho^\infty p\theta(p, \zeta) dp\} \tag{19}$$

$$\sigma_r + \sigma_\phi = -\frac{b}{\beta^2-1} \theta(\rho, \zeta) \, . \tag{20}$$

By means of equation (19) it is a simple matter to calculate the surfaces of equal maximum shearing stress in the interior of the elastic body; for an example of this see (8).

§5. Semi-infinite Solid with a Rigid Boundary

If, instead of making the assumption that the normal component of stress vanishes on the surface $z = 0$, we assume that the normal component of the displacement vanishes, i.e. if we take $\tau_{rz} = w = 0$ on $z = 0$, then $\psi(\xi) = 0$, and

$$f_1 = g_1 = \frac{1}{2\beta^2} f(\xi) \, , \quad f_2 = 0 \, .$$

It follows immediately that for a temperature field of the type

$$\theta(\rho, \zeta) = \int_0^\infty \xi^2 f(\xi) e^{-\xi\zeta} J_0(\rho\xi) d\xi \tag{21}$$

the corresponding components of the displacement vector are given by the equations

$$u(\rho, \zeta) = \frac{b}{2\beta^2} \int_0^\infty \xi(1+\xi\zeta) f(\xi) e^{-\xi\zeta} J_1(\rho\xi) d\xi \, , \quad w(\rho,\zeta) = \frac{b\zeta}{2\beta^2} \int_0^\infty \xi^2 f(\xi) e^{-\xi\zeta} J_0(\rho\xi) d\xi . \tag{22}$$

For this displacement vector, we have the following equations by means of which we can determine the distribution of stress in the body:

$$\tau_{rz} = -\frac{b\zeta}{\beta^2}\int_0^\infty \xi^3 f(\xi)e^{-\xi\zeta}J_1(\rho\xi)d\xi \tag{23}$$

$$\sigma_z = -\frac{b}{\beta^2}\int_0^\infty \xi^2(1+\xi\zeta)f(\xi)e^{-\xi\zeta}J_0(\rho\xi)d\xi \tag{24}$$

$$\sigma_r - \sigma_\phi = \frac{b}{\beta^2}\int_0^\infty \xi^2(1+\xi\zeta)f(\xi)e^{-\xi\zeta}[J_0(\rho\xi) - \frac{2}{\rho\xi}J_1(\rho\xi)]d\xi \tag{25}$$

$$\sigma_r + \sigma_\phi + \sigma_z = -\frac{4b}{\beta^2}\int_0^\infty \xi^2 f(\xi)e^{-\xi\zeta}J_0(\rho\xi)d\xi \tag{26}$$

The problem is therefore reduced to a series of simple integrations.

It will be observed that it is no longer true that the stress components σ_z and τ_{rz} are zero at every point of the solid, so that the Sternberg-McDowell result appears as a direct consequence of the imposed boundary conditions.

§6. Distribution of Stress in the Neighborhood of a Crack

If we consider the distribution of stress in the neighborhood of a penny-shaped crack lying in the plane $z = 0$ with its center at the origin, and deformed by the application of identical temperature distributions to its upper and lower surfaces, then, because of the symmetry of the problem, we can reduce the problem to one about a semi-infinite medium. If we take the radius of the crack to be ℓ, and if we assume that the surfaces of the crack are free from stress, we find that the distribution of stress in the vicinity of the crack can be deduced from that in the semi-infinite solid $z \geq 0$, when the boundary $z = 0$ is subjected to the conditions

$$\sigma_z = 0, \qquad 0 < \rho < 1,$$

$$w = 0, \qquad \rho > 1,$$

$$\tau_{rz} = 0, \qquad \rho > 0,$$

$$\frac{\partial\theta}{\partial z} = 0, \qquad \rho > 1.$$

If we substitute these conditions into equations (11) through (14) we see that the function $\psi(\xi)$ is a solution of the dual integral equations

$$\left.\begin{aligned}&\int_0^\infty \xi\psi(\xi)\,J_0(\xi)d\xi = \chi(\rho)\,, \qquad 0<\rho<1\,,\\&\int_0^\infty \psi(\xi)\,J_0(\xi\rho)d\xi = 0\,, \qquad \rho>1\end{aligned}\right\} \tag{27}$$

where the function $\chi(\rho)$ can be calculated from the heat conduction problem by means of the equation

$$\chi(\rho) = -\frac{1}{2(\beta^2-1)}\int_0^\infty \xi^2 f(\xi)\,J_0(\rho\xi)d\xi = -\frac{\theta(\rho,0)}{2(\beta^2-1)}\,. \tag{28}$$

The general case in which there is pressure as well as heat generated at the crack surfaces can be obtained by adding to the present solution the known solution for a crack deformed by internal pressure (9).

The solution of equations (28) is a simple matter and it is possible to describe the stress distributions arising from various thermal conditions at the crack surfaces. This has been done by Sneddon and Olesiak in a recent paper (10).

§7. Solution for a Thick Plate

As an example of the derivation of a solution for a thick plate let us consider a plate whose thickness ℓ is taken to be the unit of length. If both surfaces of the plate are free from stress then we have the conditions $\sigma_z = \tau_{rz} = 0$ on $\zeta = \pm 1$. For definiteness we shall assume that the stresses are produced by the temperature distribution $\theta=\phi(\rho)$ on the surface $\zeta = +1$, the surface $\zeta = -1$ being maintained at zero temperature. The equation (3) is then seen to have the solution

$$\theta(\rho,\zeta) = \int_0^\infty \xi\overline{\phi}(\xi)\,\frac{\sinh\xi(\zeta+1)}{\sinh 2\xi}\,J_0(\xi\rho)d\xi \tag{29}$$

where $\overline{\phi}(\xi)$ denotes the zero-order Hankel transform of the prescribed function $\phi(\rho)$. The corresponding expressions for the components of the displacement are

$$u = \frac{b}{2(\beta^2-1)}\int_0^\infty \overline{\phi}(\xi)\frac{\sinh\xi(\zeta+1)}{\sinh 2\xi}J_1(\xi\rho)d\xi\,,\quad w = \frac{b}{2(\beta^2-1)}\int_0^\infty \overline{\phi}(\xi)\frac{\cosh\xi(\zeta+1)}{\sinh 2\xi}J_0(\xi\rho)d\xi \tag{30}$$

In general, i.e. for $-1 \le \zeta \le +1$,

$$\sigma_z = \tau_{rz} = 0\,, \tag{31}$$

showing that the Sternberg-McDowell result holds also for a thick plate provided that both plane surfaces are free from applied stress. We have proved the result here for the case in which the distorting temperature distribution is axially symmetrical about an axis normal to the plate but in the paper (8) it is shown to be true in the unsymmetrical case also.

An inspection of equations (30) makes it obvious that, for general forms of the function $\phi(\rho)$, the evaluation of the relevant integrals will be quite a difficult problem. However it is possible to choose a surface temperature which looks physically possible and yet which yields closed forms for these integrals. For example, Sneddon and Lockett have discussed the case in which

$$\phi(\rho) = \frac{(k^2-4)^2\theta_0}{8k}\left\{\frac{k-2}{[\rho^2+(k-2)^2]^{3/2}} - \frac{k+2}{[\rho^2+(k+2)^2]^{3/2}}\right\} \tag{32}$$

for which

$$\overline{\phi}(\xi) = \frac{(k^2-4)^2\theta_0}{4k}\, e^{-k\xi} \sinh 2\xi \quad . \tag{33}$$

For this surface distribution it is found that the maximum shearing stress is by the equation

$$\sigma_\rho - \sigma_\phi = \frac{(k^2-4)^2 b\theta_0}{8k(\beta^2-1)}\left\{\frac{k-1-\zeta}{[\rho^2+(k-1-\zeta)^2]^{3/2}} - \frac{k+1+\zeta}{[\rho^2+(k+1+\zeta)^2]^{3/2}}\right.$$
$$\left. + \frac{2(k-1-\zeta)}{\rho^2[\rho^2+(k-1-\zeta)^2]^{1/2}} - \frac{2(k+1+\zeta)}{\rho^2[\rho^2+(k+1+\zeta)^2]^{1/2}}\right\} . \tag{34}$$

By means of this simple result it is an easy matter to plot out the surfaces of equal maximum shearing stress within the plate.

§8. Elastic Strip Resting on a Rigid Foundation

If we have an elastic strip of width $d = \delta\ell$, then we can choose the top surface of the strip to be the plane $\zeta = 0$, and the lower surface (i.e. the one in contact with the rigid body) to be the plane $\zeta = \delta$. There are two main cases to be considered.

Case (a): The upper surface $\zeta = 0$ is supposed to be free from applied stress so that $\sigma_z = \tau_{rz} = 0$, and the lower surface is supposed to be rigid and impervious to heat so that $w = \tau_{rz} = \partial\theta/\partial z = 0$ on $\zeta = \delta$. In this case the temperature field is given by the equation

$$\theta = \int_0^\infty \xi^2 f(\xi)\cosh \xi(\delta-\zeta) J_2(\xi\rho)d\xi \tag{35}$$

and the displacement field by the equations

$$u = \frac{b}{2(\beta^2-1)} \int_0^\infty \xi f(\xi) \cosh \xi(\delta-\zeta) J_1(\xi\rho) d\xi \tag{36}$$

$$w = \frac{-b}{2(\beta^2-1)} \int_0^\infty \xi f(\xi) \sinh \xi(\delta-\zeta) J_0(\xi\rho) d\xi \quad . \tag{37}$$

When either the temperature or the heat flux is prescribed on the surface $\zeta = 0$, the function $f(\xi)$ occurring in these equations can be calculated by means of the Hankel inversion theorem.

Case (b): In the second case we suppose the upper surface to be attached to a rigid surface so that the boundary conditions may be represented by the equations $w = \tau_{rz} = 0$, $\theta = \phi(\rho)$ on $\zeta = 0$, and $w = \tau_{rz} = \partial\theta/\partial z = 0$ on $\zeta = \delta$. It is easily shown that, in this case the temperature field is given by the equation

$$\theta = \int_0^\infty \xi \bar{\phi}(\xi) \frac{\cosh \xi(\delta-\zeta)}{\cosh \xi\delta} J_0(\xi\rho) d\xi \tag{38}$$

while the components of the displacement vector are given by the equations

$$u = \frac{b}{2\beta^2} \int_0^\infty \frac{\xi\bar{\phi}(\xi)}{\cosh \xi\delta} \{(1+\xi\delta \coth \xi\delta) \cosh \xi(\delta-\zeta) + \xi^2 \delta(\delta-\zeta) \coth \xi\delta \sinh \xi(\delta-\zeta)\} J_1(\xi\rho) d\xi \tag{39}$$

$$w = \frac{b}{2\beta^2} \int_0^\infty \frac{\xi\bar{\phi}(\xi)}{\cosh \xi\delta} \{\xi(\delta-\zeta) \cosh \xi(\delta-\zeta) - \xi\delta \coth \xi\delta \sinh \xi(\delta-\zeta)\} J_0(\xi\rho) d\xi \tag{40}$$

§9. Crack in a Thick Plate

Suppose we consider a penny-shaped crack of radius equal to the unit of length ℓ situated in the center of a thick plate of thickness $2\delta\ell$, the crack lying with its center at the origin of coordinates and parallel to the surfaces of the plate. On the surfaces of the plate, suppose that the boundary conditions are identical and that

$$\tau_{rz} = w = \frac{\partial\theta}{\partial z} = 0 \ , \qquad \zeta = \pm \delta \ .$$

In the plane of the crack, the boundary conditions will be that $\sigma_z = 0$, when $0 < \rho < 1$, and (because of the symmetry of the problem) $w = \partial\theta/\partial z = 0$, $\rho > 1$, while the shearing stress τ_{rz} is zero for all values of ρ. In the lower half $(0 \leq \zeta \leq \delta)$ of the plate we can readily show that the distribution of temperature is given by the equation

$$\theta = \int_0^\infty \xi^2 f(\xi) \cosh \xi(\delta-\zeta) J_0(\xi\rho) d\xi \tag{41}$$

while the normal stress σ_z and the normal component of displacement w are given by the equations

$$\sigma_z = 2b \int_0^\infty \frac{\xi\delta + \sinh \xi\delta}{\sinh \xi\delta} f_2(\xi)\xi J_0(\xi\rho)d\xi \tag{42}$$

$$w = -\frac{b}{2(\beta^2-1)} \int_0^\infty [f + 2\beta^2 f_2]\xi \sinh(\xi\delta)J_0(\xi\rho)d\xi \tag{43}$$

where, if we write

$$\Psi(\xi) = \xi f_2(\xi)\sinh \xi\delta \quad , \quad K(\xi) = (\xi\delta + \sinh \xi\delta)/\sinh^2 \xi\delta \quad ,$$

we find that $\Psi(\xi)$ is a solution of the pair of dual integral equations

$$\left.\begin{aligned} &\int_0^\infty K(\xi)\Psi(\xi)J_0(\xi\rho)d\xi = 0 \quad , \qquad 0 < \rho < 1 \quad , \\ &\int_0^\infty \Psi(\xi)J_0(\xi\rho)d\xi = -\chi(\rho) \quad , \qquad \rho > 1 \quad , \end{aligned}\right\} \tag{44}$$

with

$$\chi(\rho) = \frac{1}{2\beta^2} \int_0^\infty \xi f(\xi)\sinh \xi\delta\, J_0(\xi\rho)d\xi \quad . \tag{45}$$

Various procedures exist by means of which a pair of dual integral equations of this type may be reduced to a single integral equation (11), which can then be solved numerically (12).

REFERENCES

1. M. A. Biot, Thermoelasticity and Irreversible Thermodynamics, J. Appl. Phys., 27, (1956), p. 240.

2. P. Chadwick, Thermoelasticity: the Dynamical Theory, Progress in Solid Mechanics, vol. 1 (North Holland Publishing Co., 1959).

3. I. N. Sneddon, Proracun dinamickih termickih napona, (The calculation of dynamical thermal stresses), Tehnika, (Beograd), 14, (1959), p. 173.

G. Paria, Coupling of Elastic and Thermal Deformations, Appl. Sci. Res., A., 7, (1958), p. 463.

I. N. Sneddon, The Propagation of Thermal Stresses in Thin Metallic Rods, Proc. Roy. Soc. Edin. A., 65, (1959), p. 121.

I. N. Sneddon, and G. Eason, The Stresses induced in an Elastic Body due to Uneven Heating, Proc. Roy. Soc. Edin. A., 65, (1959), p. 143.

4. W. Nowacki, Two steady-state thermoelastic problems, Arch. Mech. Stos. 9, (1947), p. 579. (See also the papers referred to here.)

5. E. Sternberg and E. L. McDowell, On the Steady-state Thermoelastic Problem for the Half-Space, Quart. Appl. Math., 14, (1957), p. 381.

6. R. Muki, Thermal Stress in a Semi-infinite Solid and a Thick Plate under Steady Distribution of Temperature, Proc. Fac. Engrg. Keio Univ. 9, (1956), p. 42.

7. I. N. Sneddon and D. S. Berry, The Classical Theory of Elasticity, Handbuch der Physik, 6, (1958), pp. 1-126, Section F.

8. I. N. Sneddon and F. J. Lockett, On the Steady-state Thermoelastic Problem for the Half-space and the Thick Plate, AFOSR, Tech. Note 59-301, (1959).

9. I. N. Sneddon, The Distribution of Stress in the Neighborhood of a Crack in an Elastic Solid, Proc. Roy. Soc., A., 187, (1946), p. 229.

10. I. N. Sneddon and Z. Olesiak, The Opening of Cracks in an Elastic Solid by Thermal Means, (in course of publication).

11. B. Noble, Certain Dual Integral Equations, Journ. Math. Phys., 37, (1958), p. 128.

N. N. Lebedev and Ya. C. Ufliand, Osesimmetrichnaya Kontaktnaya Zadacha Dlya Uprugogo Sloya, (The axially symmetrical contact problem for the elastic layer), Prik. Math. i. Mek., 22, (1958), p. 346.

12. L. Fox and E. T. Goodwin, The Numerical Solution of Non-singular Linear Integral Equations, Phil. Trans. A., 245, (1953), p. 501.

LESLIE FOX

Some Numerical Experiments with Eigenvalue Problems in Ordinary Differential Equations

§1. Introduction

1. In many problems in theoretical physics involving eigenvalues and eigenfunctions of ordinary differential equations, it happens not uncommonly that particular solutions are required for which reasonable approximations are already known, at least for the eigenvalue and perhaps for the rough shape of the function. The methods described here are intended for use in these circumstances, though they may be valuable in other contexts also.

The method described is not new: it was suggested for example, by Garwick (1955), Fox (1957), Hartree (1957), and probably other workers in this field, and the main purpose of this paper is to describe some applications to fairly difficult problems, with a view to testing the possible limits of success of the method.

2. The basic idea is to solve the differential equation for guessed values of the eigenvalue and any other quantities, and to determine subsequent appropriate changes in the guessed values so that boundary conditions or continuity conditions are ultimately satisfied. In general, we need to determine parameters $\lambda, \alpha, \beta, \ldots$ so that various functions $f_1(\lambda, \alpha, \beta \ldots)$, $f_2(\lambda, \alpha, \beta, \ldots)$ shall vanish, and use for this purpose the Newton process, which gives simultaneous equations

$$\left.\begin{aligned} \delta\lambda \frac{\partial f_1}{\partial \lambda} + \delta\alpha \frac{\partial f_1}{\partial \alpha} + \delta\beta \frac{\partial f_1}{\partial \beta} + \ldots &= -f_1 \\ \delta\lambda \frac{\partial f_2}{\partial \lambda} + \delta\alpha \frac{\partial f_2}{\partial \alpha} + \delta\beta \frac{\partial f_2}{\partial \beta} + \ldots &= -f_2 \end{aligned}\right\} \quad (1)$$

for the calculation of corrections $\delta\lambda$, $\delta\alpha$, $\delta\beta$, ... The right-hand sides are obtained from solutions of the original equations, and the coefficients $\partial f/\partial\lambda$, ... , from solutions of "variational equations" derived from the original.

3. The paper discusses techniques for solving a single second-order equation, a single fourth-order equation, and up to three simultaneous second-order equations. Particular difficulties in the determination of the eigenfunction arise in the common case of one boundary at infinity,

with the function tending asymptotically to zero, and the chosen examples of simultaneous equations are of this kind.

4. A single second-order equation: For experiment we take one of the problems of Wittmeyer (1958), representing the torsional vibration of a beam clamped at one end and free at the other, with varying stiffness and inertia. The governing equations are given by

$$\frac{d}{dx}\left(K\frac{dy}{dx}\right) + \lambda My = 0 \ , \ \text{with} \ \ y(0) = y'(1) = 0 \ , \tag{2}$$

and we consider one of his most difficult cases, for which

$$K = (1 - 0.9x)^4 \ , \quad M = (1 - 0.9x)^4 \ . \tag{3}$$

Since the equation is homogeneous we can fix arbitrarily the value of y at any non-nodal point. In particular we could take $y(h) = 1$, where h is the constant interval between selected pivotal points in our numerical method, and this fixes the "size" of the solution. An alternative normalization is to choose $y'(0) = 1$, the particular selection depending on the method of solution.

With such a start, together with the given $y(0) = 0$, we carry out a step-by-step integration with a guessed value of λ, and evaluate $y'(1)$ at the other end of the range. This quantity is clearly a function of λ, and we seek that λ for which it vanishes.

5. We could find zeros of this function by evaluating it for various values of λ, and performing a process of inverse interpolation, but if an approximation to a required root is known we can take advantage of the quadratic convergence of Newton's process to obtain the result with a minimum of effort.

In this case a correction $\delta\lambda$ to a starting λ comes from the equation

$$y'(1) + \delta\lambda \frac{dy'}{d\lambda}(1) = 0 \ , \tag{4}$$

which requires a knowledge of the derivative of y' with respect to λ, evaluated at $x = 1$. We can find a differential equation for $dy/d\lambda = z$, say, by differentiating the original equation (2) with respect to λ, so that

$$\frac{d}{dx}\left(K\frac{dz}{dx}\right) + \lambda Mz + My = 0 \ . \tag{5}$$

The initial conditions $y(0) = 0$ and $y(h) = 1$ or $y'(0) = 1$ are independent of λ, so that the starting conditions for z are given by

$$z(0) = 0 \ , \ z(h) = 0 \ \text{ or } \ z'(0) = 0 \ . \tag{6}$$

The step-by-step solution of (5) and (6) gives $z(x)$ and hence finally

$z'(1)$, and hence also $\delta\lambda = -y'(1)/z'(1)$. Repetitions of the process with the new λ and successively corrected values converges, if at all, very rapidly to the required result, and both eigenvalue and eigenvector are produced simultaneously.

6. The numerical solutions of (2) and (5) will produce, at a finite interval h , approximations to the true solutions, but can be corrected by any standard method such as repetition at different intervals and the application of the "deferred approach to the limit". Indeed it may be advantageous first to find solutions at relatively large intervals involving few steps in the integration, so that the starting value of λ at the smaller intervals can be as good as possible. The largest interval, however, must be such that the eigenfunction can be adequately represented. For example, it would be useless to start with only one intermediate point in the range 0 to 1 for the calculation of say the third eigenvalue of the equation $y'' + \lambda y = 0$, with $y(0) = y(1) = 0$.

7. Using the Runge-Kutta method for step-by-step integration, for which we replace each of (2) and (5) by two simultaneous first-order equations, we find, at interval $h = 0.1$, the following successive six-figure approximations to the smallest eigenvalue λ :

8.0(start), 13.3866, 15.8458, 16.3475, 16.3668 .

Convergence is rapid and ultimately of second order. Changing the interval to 0.05 , and starting with the final λ obtained at $h = 0.1$, we find that only two iterations are needed, with the successive values 16.3668 and 16.3580 for λ .

The order of extrapolation with this method is h^4 , (for both eigenvalue and function) so that we take for our final value $\lambda = 16.3574$, which is certainly correct within one unit in the last figure.

8. In this problem there is no difficulty in finding the eigenfunction. Rounding errors in the step-by-step process do not accumulate to any substantial degree, and with a λ obtained to four decimals the boundary condition at $x = 1$ is satisfied accurately with y and y' calculated to four figures, y having its maximum value at $x = 1$.

We can reverse the process, starting at $x = 1$ and adjusting λ to satisfy the condition at the origin, and it is interesting to find that, with the same starting λ , the successive corrections are identical with those of the previous "outward" integration. This result can be proved analytically, and its numerical verification shows that rounding errors are insignificant.

9. A single fourth-order equation: We take next the fourth-order equation

$$\frac{d^2}{dx^2}\left(K\frac{d^2y}{dx^2}\right) - \lambda My = 0 \text{ , with } y(0) = y'(0) = 0, y''(1) = y'''(1) = 0, \quad (7)$$

and

$$K = (1 - 0.9x)^4 \ , \ M = (1 - 0.9x)^2 \ . \tag{8}$$

For a fourth-order equation the step-by-step process requires four initial conditions, in addition to a starting λ . Two of the initial conditions are already given, and we can take $y''(0) = 1$ to fix the "size" of the solution as a third. The fourth condition cannot be stated arbitrarily, so that, if we take $y'''(0) = p$, say, then a correct p must be computed, together with a correct λ , so that the other boundary conditions $y''(1) = y'''(1) = 0$ are both satisfied. To this end we make corrections $\delta\lambda$, δp , so that, at any stage,

$$\left.\begin{aligned} \delta\lambda \frac{\partial y''}{\partial \lambda}(1) + \delta p \frac{\partial y''}{\partial p}(1) + y''(1) = 0 \\ \delta\lambda \frac{\partial y'''}{\partial \lambda}(1) + \delta p \frac{\partial y'''}{\partial p}(1) + y'''(1) = 0 \ , \end{aligned}\right\} \tag{9}$$

and start again with the new λ and p .

For the coefficients in (9), we must solve, as before, a variational equation for λ , given by

$$\frac{d^2}{dx^2}\left(K\frac{d^2 z}{dx^2}\right) - \lambda M z = My \ , \tag{10}$$

where $z = \partial y/\partial\lambda$ and has starting conditions $z(0) = z'(0) = z''(0) = z'''(0) = 0$. In addition we use a variational equation for $q = \partial y/\partial p$ obtained by differentiating (7) with respect to p , and given by

$$\frac{d^2}{dx^2}\left(K\frac{d^2 q}{dx^2}\right) - \lambda M q = 0 \ , \tag{11}$$

with starting conditions $q(0) = q'(0) = q''(0) = 0$, $q'''(0) = 1$.

These equations and conditions relate to the Runge-Kutta method which solves twelve first-order equations in each run, four for each of equations (7), (10) and (11). If we used finite-difference equations we could replace (7) by a five-term formula of the form

$$a_r y_{r-2} + b_r y_{r-1} + c_r y_r + d_r y_{r+1} + e_r y_{r+2} = 0 \ , \tag{12}$$

in which the coefficients are functions of x , and c_r also contains λ . For initial conditions we could take $y(0) = y_0 = 0$ to satisfy exactly the first given condition , $y_{-1} = y_1$, or some more accurate formula, to satisfy approximately the second given condition $y'(0) = 0$, and something like $y_{-1} - 2y_0 + y_1 = h^2$ to satisfy approximately the imposed condition $y''(0) = 1$. These formulae would produce starting values for y_{-1} , y_0 and y_1 , and the extra condition $y'''(0) = p$ would provide y_2 as a function of p . The variational equations follow as before.

10. Convergence for both λ and p is again very rapid for the solution corresponding to the smallest eigenvalue. With the interval $h = 0.05$, and starting with $\lambda = 1$, $p = 0$, we obtain the following results:

λ	1.0	15.9536	47.8562	52.1230	51.9123	51.9127
p	0.0	-1.4149	-1.7138	-1.7250	-1.7228	-1.7228

Again there was no difficulty associated with rounding error in producing the corresponding solutions y and y', say, to four figures with a maximum value of unity.

11. Similar rapid convergence was obtained in the inadvertent solution, through a programming error, of equation (7) with $M = (1-0.9x)^8$. At the same interval $h = 0.05$ we obtained as successive approximations the following values of λ and p:

λ	1.0	1455.4592	2916.4734	2997.7747	2996.6453	2996.6454
p	0.0	-3.1680	-3.7481	-3.7451	-3.7446	-3.7446

12. Experiments with a finite-difference method for the original equation produced the following results, each iteration stopping when corrections to λ and p are less than 0.0001:

h = 0.5	λ	1.0	59.4582	91.7600	96.2106	96.2984
	p	0.0	-1.5621	-1.8674	-1.9095	-1.9103
h = 0.25	λ	96.2984	58.9615	60.2974	60.2841	
	p	-1.9103	-1.7482	-1.7461	-1.7459	
h = 0.125	λ	60.2841	54.1993	53.9322	53.9329	
	p	-1.7459	-1.7309	-1.7281	-1.7281	
h = 0.0625	λ	53.9329	52.4354	52.4122		
	p	-1.7281	-1.7244	-1.7241		

This process clearly reduces the amount of work involved, and would be particularly valuable in the Runge-Kutta method, for which the deferred approach to the limit has h^4 extrapolation, compared with extrapolation of order h^2 in the particular finite-difference method used here. Even here, however, extrapolation from the last three results produces $\lambda = 51.9113$, incorrect by at most one unit in the fifth significant figure.

13. Simultaneous second-order equations: For experiment in this class we take a problem, suggested by Mr. M. Cohen, relating to the solution of the Schrodinger equation for the hydrogen-molecule ion with fixed nuclei. Solution of the partial differential equation can be obtained from that of an infinite set of ordinary differential equations of the form

$$H_{2s} f_{2s}(x) + \sum_{r=0}^{\infty} g_{r,s}(x) f_{2r}(x) = 0 , \quad s = 0, 1, \ldots , \tag{13}$$

where

$$H_{2s} = \frac{d^2}{dx^2} + 2E - \frac{2s(2s+1)}{x^2} , \tag{14}$$

and the $g_{r,s}(x)$ are known functions with a discontinuous derivative at $x = 1$. The problem is to calculate one or more eigenvalues E and the corresponding eigenfunctions of the system, starting with a single equation involving f_0, assuming f_2, f_4, ... to be negligible, repeating with two equations, three equations, etc., and stopping when the interesting eigenvalues show no further change to a given precision.

Specifically, the first three equations, with f_6, f_8, ... assumed negligible, are

$$\left.\begin{aligned}
&\left(\frac{d^2}{dx^2} + 2E\right)f_0 + 4E_0 f_0 + \frac{4}{5} E_2 f_2 + \frac{4}{9} E_4 f_4 = 0 \\
&\left(\frac{d^2}{dx^2} + 2E - \frac{6}{x^2}\right)f_2 + 4E_2 f_0 + \left(4E_0 + \frac{8}{7} E_2 + \frac{8}{7} E_4\right)f_2 \\
&\qquad + \left(\frac{8}{7} E_2 + \frac{400}{693} E_4 + \frac{100}{143} E_6\right)f_4 = 0 \\
&\left(\frac{d^2}{dx^2} + 2E - \frac{20}{x^2}\right)f_4 + 4E_4 f_0 + \left(\frac{72}{35} E_2 + \frac{80}{77} E_4 + \frac{180}{143} E_6\right)f_2 \\
&\qquad + \left(4E_0 + \frac{80}{77} E_2 + \frac{648}{1001} E_4 + \frac{80}{143} E_6 + \frac{1960}{2431} E_8\right)f_4 = 0
\end{aligned}\right\} , \tag{15}$$

where $E_s = x^s$ for $x \le 1$, $E_s = x^{-(s+1)}$ for $x \ge 1$. All the functions required vanish at $x = 0$ and as $x \to \infty$.

14. Determination of eigenvalues: Step-by-step integration, in either direction, will fail to produce an accurate function throughout the whole range, but the eigenvalues may still be determined by methods similar to those already described.

For example, assuming f_2 and f_4 to be negligible in (15), we have the single equation, for $u = f_0$, given by

$$u'' + (2E + 4E_0)u = 0 , \quad \text{with } u(0) = u(\infty) = 0 . \tag{16}$$

We represent infinity by a suitably large value X of x, integrate from $x = 0$ to X for both u and $U = du/dE$, and correct an approximate E from the formula

$$\delta E U(X) + u(X) = 0 \quad . \tag{17}$$

Using the simplest finite-difference representations of (16) and the derived equation, the step-by-step formulae are given by

$$\left.\begin{aligned} u_{r+1} &= \{2 - h^2(2E + 4E_0)\}\ u_r - u_{r-1} \\ U_{r+1} &= \{2 - h^2(2E + 4E_0)\}\ U_r - U_{r-1} - 2h^2 u_r \end{aligned}\right\} \tag{18}$$

and we can take $u(0) = u_0 = 0$, $u_1 = 1$, $U_0 = 0$, $U_1 = 0$, as fixed starting conditions, only E requiring any change.

The process is repeated, with E corrected each time from (17), until the next correction is less than a specified amount. The corresponding value of $u(X)$ may not vanish to the same precision, and the values of u in the later part of the range may be almost meaningless.

15. If f_2 is also included we have the equations, with $u = f_0$, $v = f_2$ given by

$$\left.\begin{aligned} & u'' + (2E + 4E_0)u + \frac{4}{5} E_2 v = 0 \\ & v'' + (2E - \frac{6}{x^2} + 4E_0 + \frac{8}{7}E_2 + \frac{8}{7} E_4)v + 4E_2 u = 0 \end{aligned}\right\} \tag{19}$$

with $u(0) = v(0) = u(\infty) = v(\infty) = 0$. The finite-difference equations corresponding to (19) are here

$$\left.\begin{aligned} u_{r+1} &= \{2 - h^2(2E + 4E_0)\}u_r - u_{r-1} - \frac{4}{5}h^2 E_2 v_r \\ v_{r+1} &= \{2 - h^2(2E - \frac{6}{x^2} + 4E_0 + \frac{8}{7} E_2 + \frac{8}{7}E_4)\}\ v_r - v_{r-1} - 4h^2 E_2 u_r \end{aligned}\right\} \tag{20}$$

and we can fix $u(0) = u_0 = 0$, $u_1 = 1$, $v_0 = 0$. The other required starting value v_1 is not arbitrary, and we must adjust its value, say p, together with that of E, so that both u and v vanish at large $x = X$. If $\partial u/\partial E = U$, $\partial v/\partial E = V$, $\partial u/\partial p = L$, $\partial v/\partial p = M$, we have for corrections to E and p the equations

$$\left.\begin{aligned} & \delta E\ U(X) + \delta p L(X) + u(X) = 0 \\ & \delta E\ V(X) + \delta p M(X) + v(X) = 0 \ . \end{aligned}\right\} \tag{21}$$

The recurrence equations for the functions $U(x)$ and $V(x)$ are obtained by differentiating (20) with respect to E, so that their form is that of

(20) with the respective extra terms $-2h^2u_r$, $-2h^2v_r$ on their right-hand sides, and their starting values are $U_0 = U_1 = V_0 = V_1 = 0$.

Equations for L and M are obtained by differentiating (20) with respect to p , so that their form is identical with (20), and their starting values are $L_0 = 0$, $L_1 = 0$, $M_0 = 0$, $M_1 = 1$.

Again we make successive corrections, from (21), until δE and δp become negligible to the required precision, and the eigenvalue is determined quite accurately even though the later values of u and v are meaningless.

16. Similarly, for the three equations (15), the limit used in this investigation, we solve the step-by-step equations for u , v and w , representing f_0 , f_2 and f_4 , with starting values $u_0 = 0$, $u_1 = 1$, $v_0 = 0$, $v_1 = p$, $w_0 = 0$, $w_1 = q$, and p , q and E are chosen so that all three functions vanish at X . To correct initial values of these unknowns we use the Newton equations

$$\left.\begin{aligned} \delta E\, U(X) + \delta p\, L(X) + \delta q\, R(X) + u(X) &= 0 \\ \delta E\, V(X) + \delta p\, M(X) + \delta q\, S(X) + v(X) &= 0 \\ \delta E\, W(X) + \delta p\, N(X) + \delta q\, T(X) + w(X) &= 0 \quad , \end{aligned}\right\} \tag{22}$$

where $U = \partial u/\partial E$, $L = \partial u/\partial p$, $R = \partial u/\partial q$, etc., and the corresponding recurrence relations have the starting values
$U_0 = U_1 = V_0 = V_1 = W_0 = W_1 = 0$; $L_0 = L_1 = 0$, $M_0 = 0$, $M_1 = 1$, $N_0 = N_1 = 0$; $R_0 = R_1 = 0$, $S_0 = S_1 = 0$, $T_0 = 0$, $T_1 = 1$.

17. The numerical results are satisfactory, and in all cases convergence to E , and where relevant to p and q , was ultimately quadratic. It is, of course, necessary to take a large enough value of X . For example, the single equation has a root at about $E = -0.17$, and $X = 20$ is a satisfactory representation of infinity. An attempt to find a root in this region for the two equations, starting with $E = -0.17$ and $X = 10$, converged rapidly to $E = -0.105$. The reason for this is that $x = 10$ is a point at which f_0 has almost its maximum value for $E = -0.17$, whereas this point, while equally unsatisfactory as "infinity" for $E = -0.105$, happens to be close to a zero of f_0 for this solution. In both cases f_0 is the dominant function for these roots.

18. <u>Determination of eigenfunctions</u>: This technique cannot conveniently produce accurate eigenfunctions throughout the whole range. For the single equation (16), for example, the general solution is

$$u = A_1u_1 + A_2u_2 \quad , \tag{23}$$

and in the range greater than a particular point x_c , one of the functions is increasing and the other decreasing. The true eigenvalue E effectively suppresses the increasing solution, but the latter will be present if we have only an approximate E, and for large x this term will dominate the solution in the step-by-step process. It may therefore be necessary to obtain E, and in the other cases the starting values p and q, to say twenty figures in order to find an accurate eigenfunction to say four figures.

For example, the three equations have a solution, at interval $h = 0.1$, for which $E = -0.360878$, $p = 0.006436$, $q = 0.000054$, and the maximum values of the three functions are then about 10.3, 3.0 and 1.0 respectively. The technique of integrating ahead, with corrections to E, p and q obtained from (22), and stopping when changes in these quantities do not exceed 0.0001, produced accurate values to this precision, but at $X = 20$ the three functions had respective values 10^4, 3×10^6, and 2×10^8.

19. We can avoid this difficulty by insisting that our functions are zero at X, and by integrating forwards from $x = 0$ to x_c, backwards from $x = X$ to x_c, and choosing parameters so that the solutions are continuous at x_c, we integrate in each case in that direction in which the wanted function is increasing and the unwanted function decreasing, a satisfactory situation.

To illustrate the technique we consider the three equations (15), the most complicated case, and for simplicity rewrite them in the form

$$\left.\begin{aligned} u'' + (2E + g_0)u + g_1 v + g_2 w &= 0 \\ v'' + (2E + g_3)v + g_4 u + g_5 w &= 0 \\ w'' + (2E + g_6)w + g_7 u + g_8 v &= 0 \end{aligned}\right\} \qquad (24)$$

where the g_r as known, and the boundary conditions are $u = v = w = 0$ at $x = 0$ and ∞. For the forward solution, represented by suffix f, we can take $u_f(0) = u_{0,f} = 0$, $u_{1,f} = 1$, $v_{0,f} = 0$, $v_{1,f} = p_f$, $w_{0,f} = 0$, $w_{1,f} = q_f$. The choice $u_{1,f} = 1$ has already fixed the "size" of the solution, and we do not have this arbitrary choice in the backward solution. Representing the backward solution by suffix b we can take $u_b(X) = u_{0,b} = 0$, $u_b(X-h) = u_{1,b} = 1$, $v_{0,b} = 0$, $v_{1,b} = p_b$, $w_{o,b} = 0$, $w_{1,b} = q_b$, and remember that this backward solution must be associated with a factor k, to be determined so that the size of the backward solution is the same as that of the forward solution.

Specifically, we choose the parameters E, p_f, q_f, p_b, q_b and k so that, at $x = x_c$, $u_f = ku_b$, $u'_f = ku'_b$, $v_f = kv_b$, $v'_f = kv'_b$, $w_f = kw_b$, $w'_f = kw'_b$. In practice it seems best to choose k, at each stage, so that one of these is satisfied directly, and to correct the other parameters by use of Newton's rule, for which we would need to solve five linear algebraic equations at each stage.

With the notation of equations (22), we find k from $u_f = ku_b$, and correct the other parameters from simultaneous equations typified by

$$\delta E(V_b - kV_b) + \delta p_f L_f - k\delta p_b L_b + \delta q_f R_f - k\delta q_b R_b + v_f - kv_b = 0, \quad (25)$$

with four other similar equations for the matching of w, u', v' and w', all functions being evaluated at $x = x_c$. The functions U, L, R etc. are obtained as before by differentiating appropriately the original equations (24), and their starting values are the same as those of the previous technique and given in §16.

20. The experiment was largely successful, but it is found that certain precautions are needed to secure rapid convergence, and in some cases we do not get convergence without these precautions.

In general the most important criteria are proper choices of x_c and X. A poor choice of x_c could cause convergence to a different solution. For example, the single equation has a root at about $E=-0.36$ and another at about -0.18, and one attempt to find the solution corresponding to the latter converged quite rapidly to the former. The unsuccessful attempt had as matching point $x_c = 5$, whereas the choice $x_c = 10$ produced the required result. Again, with two equations, the choice $x_c = 5$, with $E = -0.18$, converged rapidly to a solution with $E = +0.23$, a bogus solution for which the functions vanish at a certain X but lack the required asymptotic behavior.

The best choice for x_c is that value of x for which, for the required eigenvalue, the coefficient of the dominating function vanishes in the equation which involves its derivatives. For example, in (24), eigensolutions dominated by u should have the zero of $(2E + g_0)$ as matching point, and if v dominates we want x_c to be close to a zero of $(2E + g_3)$, and so on. If the chosen x_c is somewhere between critical values corresponding to two eigenvalues we may converge to either. Indications are that we would converge to that root closest to our initial guess, but we may lose the desirable speed of quadratic convergence. In certain cases, also, we enter a "closed loop", oscillating about the required solution but never quite reaching it, a phenomenon similar to that encountered in the use of Newton's process for finding roots of polynomials.

A poor choice of X has two effects. The first is obvious, that if X is too small to represent infinity for the eigensolution sought we may converge to a different result or perhaps not at all. The second is more subtle: we find that if X is much larger than necessary we will converge but with linear rather than quadratic convergence. This is probably due to the fact that the best matching point is not the same for all three functions, and if we unnecessarily cover too large a range there is a significant build-up of error which inhibits the Newton process.

21. In the numerical experiments we chose the E and the parameters p_f and q_f for the forward solution which had been obtained from the previous techniques of §§14-16, and it is likely that this is generally valuable in accelerating convergence, the simpler method being very rapid. No attempt was made at analytical investigation to obtain knowledge about the asymptotic behavior of the solutions, which would give better starting values of p_b and q_b . In many cases this information would be available and could materially shorten the iterative process.

22. A non-homogeneous eigenvalue problem: As a final illustration of the method we consider a non-homogeneous eigenvalue problem, of a type encountered in the work of Hartree (1957) on "self-consistent fields". The equation is typified by

$$u'' - (E + f)u = g \quad , \tag{26}$$

in which f and g are known functions, u vanishes at $x = 0$ and as $x \to \infty$, and we want to determine an eigenvalue E so that we satisfy a normalization condition of the form

$$\int_0^\infty u^2 dx = 1 \quad . \tag{27}$$

The more elaborate technique is needed here since we must have, at each stage, solutions u uncontaminated by rounding error even if we seek only the eigenvalue E . Another point is that the equation is non-homogeneous, so that neither u_f nor u_b can have both starting values specified arbitrarily.

We take u_f with starting values $u_{0,f} = 0$, $u_{1,f} = p_f$, and u_b with starting values $u_{0,b} = 0$, $u_{1,b} = p_b$, and integrate forwards and backwards respectively with a guessed E , as far as x_c , an approximate zero of $(E + f)$. The variational equations for $U = \partial u/\partial\lambda$, $L = \partial u/\partial p$ are obtained as before, and the Newton equations are used to match u and u' at x_c and to satisfy condition (27). The equations are given by

$$\left.\begin{aligned}
&\delta E(U_f - U_b) + \delta p_f L_f - \delta p_b L_b + u_f - u_b = 0 \\
&\delta E(U'_f - U'_b) + \delta p_f L'_f - \delta p_b L'_b + u'_f - u'_b = 0 \\
&2\delta E\left(\int_0^{x_c} u_f U_f dx + \int_{x_c}^\infty u_b U_b dx\right) + 2\delta p_f \int_0^{x_c} u_f L_f dx + 2\delta p_b \int_{x_c}^\infty u_b L_b dx \\
&\qquad + \int_0^{x_c} u_f^2 dx + \int_{x_c}^\infty u_b^2 dx - 1 = 0 \quad .
\end{aligned}\right\} \tag{28}$$

In most problems of this kind a good approximation is known in advance for E, and often for p_f and p_b. For experiment we took

$$f = \frac{2}{x}, \quad g = \frac{1}{8} e^{-\frac{1}{2}x} \{1 - (1 + 2x + 2x^2) e^{-2x}\}, \tag{29}$$

and with initial guesses $E = 1$, $p_f = 0.2$, $p_b = 0$, we converged in four iterations, at interval $h = 0.1$, with $X = 6$ and $x_c = 2$, to a solution for which $E = 0.9490$, $p_f = 0.1854$, $p_b = 0.0039$, and the solution was properly matched to four significant figures. Again the matching point x_c and the infinity point X must be chosen with reasonable care to secure good convergence.

23. Conclusion: Within its limitations the methods outlined seem to be particularly useful with high-speed computing machines, minimizing both programming effort and storage space required. Alternative methods, for the homogeneous case, would presumably treat the problem as algebraic, incorporating all the finite-difference equations and boundary conditions in a matrix equation

$$(A - I\lambda)y = 0, \tag{30}$$

in which the elements of y are the pivotal values, at the chosen interval, of all the functions involved. For finding a root near to a given quantity μ we might use the iterative scheme

$$(A - I\mu)y^{(r+1)} = y^{(r)}, \tag{31}$$

for which y would ultimately have the required elements, and the ratio of corresponding values of $y^{(r)}$ to $y^{(r+1)}$ converges to $\lambda - \mu$, giving the required λ.

With best possible choice of order of the elements of y, the matrix in (31) will be of "band" type. Corresponding to three simultaneous differential equations the width of the band is seven, with two zero elements in each row, and with our chosen interval and range the order of the matrix is 600. Any direct method of solving the equations would at least destroy the zero elements within the band, and any method which preserved only this augmented band would have other inconveniences, such as the danger of a very small and even zero term on the diagonal in the elimination process. Moreover, the facility of using only those coefficients which are needed at any stage, and replacing them with the new coefficients for the next pivotal point, is much less convenient in an elimination process. An iterative method for solving the equations would certainly preserve all the zero elements, but convergence cannot be guaranteed.

An alternative method is to evaluate the determinant of $(A - I\lambda)$ in (30), for selected values of λ, followed by inverse interpolation to find a zero. Many of the comments about elimination processes apply to this method also. The techniques of this paper effectively evaluate the determinant and also its derivatives with respect to λ and the other parameters involved, and the Newton process guarantees rapid convergence after a certain stage.

No attempt has been made in the harder examples to make sure that the results obtained are true solutions of the differential equations, in the sense that the truncation errors in the finite-difference equations are negligible, but this would not affect the success or failure of the methods as regards convergence of the iterative processes.

24. The solution of three simultaneous second-order equations appears to be quite practicable with this method, but its convenience might disappear with larger sets of n equations. If only the eigenvalue is required we must integrate $n + 1$ sets of n simultaneous second-order equations, and then obtain the solution of n algebraic equations. For the eigenfunctions, with a match in the middle of the range, we also solve n sets of $(n + 1)$ differential equations, but with both forward and backward integration covering the same total range, followed by $2n$ algebraic equations. The probability of non-convergence may increase quite rapidly with n .

REFERENCES

Fox, L., The numerical solution of two-point boundary problems in ordinary differential equations, Oxford, 1957.

Hartree, D. R., The calculation of atomic structures, Chapman and Hall, 1957.

Garwick, J. V., The solution of boundary-value problems by step-by-step methods, Arch. Math. Natur. 52, pp. 1-67, 1955.

Wittmeyer, H., A new method for developing simple formulae for the eigenvalues of linear self-adjoint differential equations, J. Soc. Ind. and App. Math. 6, pp. 111-143, 1958.

RICHARD BELLMAN

Dynamic Programming, Invariant Imbedding, and Two-Point Boundary Value Problems

CONTENTS

SUMMARY

Ordinary and partial differential equations involving conditions at various points, or at several boundaries, arise naturally from the calculus of variations, the domain of mathematical physics, and from mixtures of both disciplines. As is well-known, problems of this nature are of greater analytic complexity, and present many more obstacles in the way of computational solution, than those whose solutions are determined by initial values.

The object of this paper is to show how certain uniform techniques based upon functional equations can be used to provide new analytic approaches to questions of this type, and to furnish computational algorithms which are far better adapted to modern day computers than those of classical analysis. Our aim is to replace multi-point boundary value problems by initial value problems.

I. DYNAMIC PROGRAMMING

§1. Introduction

Ordinary and partial differential equations involving conditions at various points, or at several boundaries, arise naturally from the calculus of variations, the domain of mathematical physics, and from mixtures of both disciplines. As is well-known, problems of this nature are of greater analytic complexity, and present many more obstacles in the way of computational solution, than those whose solutions are determined by initial values.

The object of this paper is to show how certain uniform techniques based upon functional equations can be used to provide new analytic approaches to questions of this type, and to furnish computational algorithms which are far better adapted to modern day computers than those of classical analysis. Our aim is to replace multi-point boundary value problems by initial boundary value problems.

To treat those problems originating in the calculus of variations, or equivalent to questions with this origin, we employ the theory of dynamic programming, [1]. For various classes of problems emanating from the field of mathematical physics, we invoke the theory of invariant imbedding, [2], [21].

Both theories utilize the fundamental concept of semi-groups of transformations, a subject discussed in great detail and with many applications in [3]. Our applications of this basic idea are, however, quite different from those in the cited reference. We allow as semi-group variables, not only time, but length, radius, area, volume, and so on. In the theory of branching processes, [4], [5], [6], where functional equations play a key role, space and energy semi-group variables are also employed, together with the classic time variable.

§2. Two-point Boundary Value Problems

Although the methods we employ can be, and have been, [7], utilized to some extent for the study of partial differential equations, we shall restrict ourselves in this part of the paper to the case of ordinary differential equations. The second part of the paper will be more closely connected with partial differential equations, of the type stemming from the Boltzmann equation.

Consider an n-th order differential equation of the form

$$(1) \qquad u^{(n)} = g(u, u', \ldots, u^{(n-1)}) \; .$$

If we take initial conditions of the form

$$(2) \qquad u(0) = c_0, \; u'(0) = c_1, \; \ldots \; , \; u^{(n-1)}(0) = c_{n-1} \; ,$$

and impose various reasonable conditions on the function g, as, for example, given in [8], we can assert the existence and uniqueness of a function $u(t)$, satisfying (1) over some interval $[0, t_0]$, and the conditions of (2) at $t = 0$.

With this type of initial information, digital computers, and occasionally analogue computers, can be utilized in a number of very efficient ways to obtain the numerical solution.

For the case of initial value problems of the foregoing kind, both the existence and uniqueness of the solution are plausible, and not particularly difficult to establish. The situation, however, changes radically when we impose not the conditions of (2), but conditions of the form

$$(3) \qquad u(0) = c_0 \; , \; u'(0) = c_1, \; \ldots \; , \; u^{(k)}(0) = c_k \; ,$$

$$u(t_0) = b_0, \; u'(t_0) = b_1, \; \ldots \; , \; u^{(n-2-k)}(t_0) = b_{n-k-2} \; ,$$

or, more generally, n mixed conditions of the form

$$(4) \qquad g_i(u(0), \ldots, u^{(n-1)}(0); \; u(t_0), \ldots, u^{)n-1)}(t_0)) = 0 \; ,$$

$i = 1, 2, \ldots, n$.

Since solutions are constrained at two points, $t = 0$ and $t = t_0$, problems of this type are called <u>two-point boundary value problems.</u> It is no longer clear that solutions satisfying these conditions exist, nor that there is any uniqueness.

Frequently, by means of various analytic artifices, such as successive approximations or fixed-point theorems, existence, and even uniqueness, of solution can be established. However, as is often the case, these tools, so valuable for laying the foundations, are not powerful enough to yield efficient algorithms leading to a numerical solution; cf., however, [29].

The adjective "efficient", as used here, is strongly time-dependent. A quarter of a century ago, the criterion of an algorithm was bound to pencil and paper calculations, carried out perhaps by a team of computers. A few years later, many additional algorithms were admitted as feasible with the appearance of the desk computer. With the entry of the modern digital computer, we can think in terms of algorithms which formerly would have been unthinkable.

The algorithms we present below, derived from dynamic programming and invariant imbedding, are definitely predicated upon the use of a digital computer, although occasionally they do yield results susceptible to hand methods.

One of the pleasures associated with the field of the numerical solutions of differential equations, and indeed of equations of all types, is that we are engaged in a never-ending game. We get to first base when we devise any method, using currently available devices, which will yield an accurate numerical solution. We advance around the bases as we cut down on the time and the memory requirements. Finally, when we have reduced the computational solution to a hand computation, or to the use of simple tables, we have won an inning.

To begin the discussion, let us fasten our attention upon the second order equation

$$u'' = g(u, u') , \quad 0 \leq t \leq T , \tag{5}$$

with two-point boundary conditions of the form

$$u(0) = c_1 , \quad k(u(T), u'(T)) = 0 . \tag{6}$$

To make things interesting, we naturally take the function g to be non-linear.

A straightforward numerical solution via digital computer requires the values of u and u' at $t = 0$ or $t = T$. Given information of the type appearing in (6), the usual approach to these problems involves a search process which zeroes in on the solution. An initial guess of $u'(0)$ is made, and the numerical solution of (5) is obtained, using this hypothesized value and the given value of $u(0)$. Using this solution, the quantity $k(u(T), u'(T))$ is calculated. If this compares favorably with the value zero, we accept this approximate solution; if not, we guess another value, and so on.

This is clearly a rather uninspired and pedestrian approach, with a number of disadvantages. For a large and significant class of problems of the foregoing type, we wish to present another approach which yields an exact solution in terms of initial value problems--although, in different variables.

This approach, an application of the theory of dynamic programming, can be utilized to treat many types of variational processes which resist the classical techniques. In the second part of the paper, we will discuss another class of equations, which can be treated by means of invariant imbedding. Although we shall not enter into any details here, we would like to call attention to still another approach, based upon the technique of "quasilinearization"; see Bellman, [28], Kalaba, [29].

§3. Connection with Calculus of Variations

Our first approach to questions of this type is by means of the connection which exists between the equation in (2.5) and the Euler equation associated with the functional

$$(1) \qquad J(u) = \int_0^T h(u, u')dt \ .$$

In many cases, the variational problem is the original source of the differential equation.

Consider the problem of minimizing the functional $J(u)$ subject only to the initial condition

$$(2) \qquad u(0) = c_1 \ .$$

Under appropriate conditions on $h(u, u')$, the minimizing function u is determined as a solution of the equation

$$(3) \qquad \frac{\partial h}{\partial u} - \frac{d}{dt}\frac{\partial h}{\partial u'} = 0 \ ,$$

the Euler equation. An additional constraint,

$$(4) \qquad \left.\frac{\partial h}{\partial u'}\right|_{t=T} = 0$$

is obtained from the variational procedure.

It is interesting to note that even when the original variational problem does not initially contain a two-point boundary value condition, the variational procedure automatically yields one.

If $h(u, u')$ is quadratic in u and u', the Euler equation is linear, in which case the two-point problem is very much simpler. Otherwise, the equation in (3) is nonlinear.

Let us now assume that (2.5) is precisely the equation that one obtains from (3) after dividing through by $h_{u'u'}$, assumed uniformly nonzero. We shall then resolve the two-point boundary value problem of (2.5) and (2.6) by presenting a direct solution of the variational problem in (1), based upon an initial value equation.

§4. Dynamic Programming

Let us briefly sketch the dynamic programming approach to variational equations of the type described in the foregoing section. What follows will be completely formal. Further details, and some rigorous justification, will be found in [1]; see also Dreyfus, [9], Osborn [10].

We begin with the observation that the minimum of $J(u)$ depends upon the initial value c, and the length of the interval, T. Hence, we write

$$(1) \qquad f(c, T) = \min_u J(u) \ .$$

This function is defined for $T \geq 0$, $-\infty < c < \infty$.

To derive a functional equation for $f(c, T)$, we can use the principle of optimality, [1], or, once we know what we want to obtain, we can proceed directly as follows. Write

$$(2) \qquad f(c,T) = \min_{u[0,T]} \int_0^T h(u,u')dt$$

$$= \min_{u[0,S]} \min_{u[S,T]} \left[\int_0^S h(u,u')dt + \int_S^T h(u,u')dt \right]$$

$$= \min_{u[0,S]} \left[\int_0^S h(u,u')dt + \min_{u[S,T]} \int_S^T h(u,u')dt \right]$$

$$= \min_{u[0,S]} \left[\int_0^S h(u,u')dt + f(u(S), T-S) \right] .$$

In order to obtain a functional equation of conventional type, we regard S as an infinitesimal. Then, to terms in S^2, we have

$$(3) \qquad u(S) = c + vS ,$$

$$\int_0^S h(u,u')dt = h(c,v)S ,$$

where we have set

$$(4) \qquad v \equiv u'(0) \equiv v(c,T) .$$

Furthermore, as $S \to 0$, minimization over all functions defined over $[0,S]$ becomes equivalent to minimization over all initial slopes. Thus, (2) becomes

$$(5) \qquad f(c,T) = \min_v [h(c,v)S + f(c+vS, T-S)] + 0(S^2) .$$

Still proceeding formally, this becomes

$$(6) \qquad f(c,T) = \min_v [h(c,v)S + f(c,T) + Svf_c - Sf_T] + 0(S^2) ,$$

which reduces to

$$(7) \qquad f_T = \min_v [h(c,v) + vf_c] .$$

This equation, together with the <u>initial</u> condition

$$(8) \qquad f(c,0) \equiv 0 \quad \text{for all } c ,$$

determines the function $f(c,T)$.

For the connection between (7) and the Euler variational equation, see Dreyfus, [9], Osborn, [10], or [1].

§5. An Example

As an illustration, consider the problem of minimizing the integral

(1) $$J(u) = \int_0^T (u'^2 + g(u))dt ,$$

over all functions u satisfying the initial condition $u(0) = c$. Writing

(2) $$f(c, T) = \operatorname*{Min}_u J(u) ,$$

we have, from (4.7), the equation

(3) $$f_T = \operatorname*{Min}_v [v^2 + g(c) + vf_c] ,$$

or

(4) $$f_T = g(c) - \frac{f_c^2}{4} .$$

The solution of this equation then leads to the solution of the two-point boundary value problem

(5) $$u'' - \frac{g'(u)}{2} = 0 ,$$

$$u(0) = c , \quad u'(T) = 0 .$$

Similar explicit results can be obtained for variational problems of the form

(6) $$\operatorname*{Min}_{u_i} \int_0^T \left[\sum_{i,j=1}^{M} a_{ij} u'_i u'_j + g(u_1, u_2, \ldots, u_m) \right] dt .$$

A greater variety of nonlinear differential equations may be obtained by starting with the problem of minimizing

(7) $$J(y) = \int_0^T g(x, y)dt$$

over all y where x and y are related by

(8) $$\frac{dx}{dt} = h(x, y) , \quad x(0) = c .$$

§6. Discussion

Let us stop a moment and observe the basic device we have utilized. In place of considering an isolated variational problem for fixed initial value c and fixed interval $[0,T]$, we have treated the whole class of problems arising from any initial value and any $T > 0$.

We have thus imbedded the original variational problem within a family of variational problems. To solve the original variational problem, we derive relations connecting neighboring problems. The equation in (4.7) expresses the way the solution changes as the parameters c and T change.

Precisely the same conceptual trick will be employed in dealing with the transport processes discussed in the second part of the paper.

§7. Computational Aspects

To obtain the numerical solution of (4.7), we can follow the usual approach and replace it by a difference scheme such as

$$(1) \qquad \frac{f(c, T+\Delta) - f(c, T)}{\Delta} = \min_v \left[h(c, v) + v\left(\frac{f(c+\delta, T) - f(c, T)}{\delta}\right)\right] .$$

We found, however, that it was better to use an approximation to (4.5) such as

$$(2) \qquad f(c, T) = \min_v \left[h(c, v)\,\Delta + f(c + \Delta s,\ T - \Delta)\right] ,$$

where $T = 0, \Delta, 2\Delta, \ldots$.

One advantage of this approach is that no ratio of small quantities, Δ/δ, is involved.

Those interested in the computational solutions of particular problems along these lines may refer to Cartaino-Dreyfus, [11], and Bellman-Dreyfus, [12].

The success of this approach suggests that similar techniques may be applicable to other types of partial differential equations. For a treatment of the equation

$$(3) \qquad u_t = uu_x ,$$

and similar equations, see Bellman-Cherry-Wing, [13].

§8. Convergence of Discrete Process to Continuous Process

As soon as we employ a formula such as (7.2), the question arises as to the convergence of the function obtained from (7.2) to the solution of (4.7). This can be approached in several ways, using the connection with the classical calculus of variations, cf. the treatment by Fleming in [14], or directly from (7.2) without any previous foundation of the calculus of variations; see [15].

§9. Dimensionality

Let us now point out what prevents us from applying these methods in a routine fashion to the solution of a large class of current problems of significance. If we apply these methods to the determination of the minimum of the functional

(1) $$J(u_1, \ldots, u_k) = \int_0^T g(u_1, u_2, \ldots, u_k; u'_1, u'_2, \ldots, u'_k)dt ,$$

with constraints $u_i(0) = c_i$, $i = 1, 2, \ldots, k$, we encounter functions of k variables. These can be used for computational purposes with current digital computers if $k = 1, 2$, with the case $k = 3$ soon to be feasible. For general k , the memory requirements become excessive. We must then have recourse to various types of approximations; cf. [16], [17].

§10. Three-point Boundary Value Problems

Precisely the same approach can be used in the study of three-point boundary value problems. Thus, if the fourth order equation

(1) $$u^{(4)} = h(u, u', u^{(2)}, u^{(3)})$$

is derived from a variational problem associated with

(2) $$J(u) = \int_0^T g(u, u', u^{(2)})dt ,$$

we can treat a boundary value problem such as

(3) $$u(0) = c_1 , \quad u'(0) = c_2 , \quad u(t_1) = c_3 , \quad u(T) = c_4 ,$$

$0 < t_1 < T$, by introducing the function

(4) $$f(c_1, c_2, T) = \operatorname{Min} J(u) .$$

§11. Implicit Variational Problems

In many interesting situations, the variational problem may not involve an explicit analytic functional. These are akin to free boundary problems in hydrodynamics in the sense that the solution itself determines some of the points where boundary conditions are applied. For example, one may wish to minimize the time required to restore a physical system to equilibrium; see [18], [19], or one may wish to minimize the terminal velocity when a desired terminal state is attained; see [20].

II. NEUTRON TRANSPORT PROCESSES

§12. Introduction

In this part of the paper, we wish to illustrate the application of the functional equation approach to the study of various types of two-point boundary value problems that arise from mathematical physics. To show how equations of this type arise, we shall formulate some problems in the field of neutron transport theory, first in classical terms and then by means of the theory of invariant imbedding, [21], [22].

Once again, we obtain both a new analytic, and a new computational, approach. First, we shall treat the physical model giving rise to a linear form of the Boltzmann equation, where we have a choice of one approach or the other, and then we shall treat a particular collision process, where the classical approach leads to a nonlinear system of differential equations with two-point boundary values.

§13. A Neutron Process for a One-dimensional Rod

Let us now describe a simple mathematical version of a neutron fission process. By a "rod", we shall mean the interval $[x, 0]$, where to be consistent with notation in other papers we invert the usual direction. By a "neutron", we shall mean a particle which possesses the following property: when entering the sub-interval $[y + \Delta, y]$, from the right, there is a probability $p_1(y)\Delta$ that it divides into two particles of precisely the same nature, one going to the right and one to the left, and a probability $1 - p_1(y)\Delta$ that it traverses the interval with no interaction; when entering from the left, we have a similar situation with $p_1(y)$ replaced by $p_2(y)$. Here Δ is considered to be an infinitesimal, and all expressions are considered exact to terms of order Δ^2.

On the basis of a model of this type, we would like to be able to predict the existence of a critical length. To attain this end, we begin by asking for the reflected and transmitted flux resulting from unit flux per unit time entering the rod at x.

By the terms reflected flux and transmitted flux, we mean the expected number of neutrons per unit time leaving x to the left and the expected number of neutrons leaving 0 to the right per unit time.

§14. Classical Approach

The usual approach to these problems is by way of the determination of the internal fluxes. Let y be a point inside the interval $[x, 0]$, and define

(1) $u(y)$ = the flux to the right at y, per unit time,

$v(y)$ = the flux to the left at y, per unit time.

Once again, the term "flux" is used as a synonym for expected number. For a rigorous formulation of processes of this nature, see the forthcoming monograph by T. E. Harris [6].

An "input-output" analysis yields the following relations, correct to terms in Δ^2,

$$u(y) = u(y + \Delta)(1 - p_1(y)\Delta) + p_1(y)\Delta u(y) + p_2(y)\Delta v(y) . \tag{2}$$

Passing to the limit as $\Delta \to 0$, we obtain the differential equation

(3) $u'(y) = -p_2(y)v(y)$.

A similar analysis leads to the complementary relation

(4) $v'(y) = p_1(y)u(y)$.

The boundary conditions which fix the solution of this system of linear equations are

(5) $u(x) = 1$,

$v(0) = 0$,

which express the known facts that we have unit input from the left at x and none from the right at 0 .

Eliminating $v(y)$, we obtain a single second order differential equation

(6) $(u'(y)/p_2(y))' = -p_1(y)u(y)$,

with the two-point boundary conditions

(7) $u(x) = 1$, $u'(0) = 0$.

What we wish to point out is that the physical setting automatically leads to a two-point boundary condition. A similar situation occurs in the study of transmission lines, where equivalent equations and conditions hold; cf. [23], [24].

§15. Invariant Imbedding Approach

Let us now introduce functional equations. As in the first part of the paper, we imbed the particular process under discussion within a family of processes of the same general nature. In place of regarding x as a fixed constant, we consider it to be a parameter which assumes all positive values.

We then introduce the two functions

(1) $f(x)$ = the reflected flux from $[x, 0]$ due to unit incident flux at x ,

$g(x)$ = the transmitted flux at 0 due to unit incident flux at x .

To derive equations for $f(x)$ and $g(x)$, we proceed in very much the same fashion as before. As the flux proceeds through the subinterval $[x, x-\Delta]$, part of it interacts and part of it proceeds through unaffected. In either case, the flux reflected from the interval $[x-\Delta, 0]$ can be expressed in terms of the function $f(x-\Delta)$. As this reflected flux traverses the interval $[x-\Delta, x]$, part of it interacts and results in a further reflection from $[x-\Delta, 0]$. Since all other processes contribute terms of order Δ^2 , we need merely take account of these to obtain our desired relation.

The analytic result is

(2) $$f(x) = p_1(x)\Delta + p_1(x)f(x)\Delta + (1-p_1(x)\Delta)[f(x-\Delta) + p_2(x)\Delta f^2(x-\Delta)]$$

to terms in Δ^2 .

Taking the limit as $\Delta \to 0$, we obtain the equation

(3) $$f'(x) = p_1(x) + p_2(x)f^2(x) ,$$

with the initial value $f(0) = 0$.

Similarly we can obtain an equation for $g(x)$, which will involve $f(x)$. Further details may be found in [21], [22].

§16. Energy Dependence

A more interesting situation is that where we take the energy of the particle into account. To avoid partial differential equations, the usual practice is to divide the energy range up into a number of different levels or groups. In this way, there arises what is currently called "multi-group theory".

Assume that there are N different energy levels, $i = 1, 2, \ldots, N$, and introduce the following functions:

(1) $f_{ij}(x)$ = the reflected flux in state j (energy level j) due to unit incident flux in state i at x .

In place of the functions $p_1(x)$ and $p_2(x)$, we have functions

(2) $p_{ijk}(x)\Delta$ = the probability that in $[x, x-\Delta]$ a particle in state i will fission into two particles, one in state j and one in state k , where the j-particle goes to the left and the k-particle to the right.

For the sake of simplicity, assume that there is no directional effect.

As in the simple case, the classical approach yields a set of $2N$ linear differential equations with two-point boundary values, for the interval fluxes, while the invariant imbedding approach yields N^2 nonlinear differential equations with initial value constraints.

From the computational point of view, one has to compare the solution of linear differential equations of order $2N$ plus linear algebraic equations of order N versus the solution of an initial value problem for N^2 nonlinear differential equations. For $N = 10$, it would seem preferable to use the systemof 100 nonlinear differential equations. From the standpoint of the determination of critical length, the nonlinear differential equations also seem preferable.

For further discussion, and other geometries, see [21], [22], [25].

§17. Collision Processes

In the preceding cases, we possessed explicit analytic solutions of the two-point boundary value problem. Let us now consider some physical processes which lead to nonlinear transport equations with two-point boundary value problems. These are collision processes where we face the full force of the Boltzmann equation.

In this case, the conventional approach leads to great difficulties, even from the standpoint of existence and uniqueness of solutions; cf. Carleman, [26], while the invariant imbedding approach appears to offer definite advantages.

Let us define the collision process, now assumed purely deterministic, by means of the function

(1) $\phi(u, v, y)\Delta$ = the diminution in intensity of a flux of strength u entering $[y + \Delta, y]$ from the left when a flux of strength v enters from the right.

With $u(y)$ and $v(y)$ defined as before, left- and right-hand fluxes at y, we obtain the equations

$$(2) \qquad u(y) = u(y + \Delta)(1 - p(y)\Delta)(1 - \phi(u, v, y)\Delta/u) + p(y)u(y)\Delta + v(y)p(y)\Delta ,$$

or

$$(3) \qquad u'(y) = p(y)v(y) - \phi(u, v, y) .$$

Similarly,

$$(4) \qquad v'(y) = -p(y)u(y) - \phi(u, v, y) .$$

The boundary conditions, as before, are

$$(5) \qquad u(x) = 1 , \ v(0) = 0 .$$

Due to the nonlinearity, we face a problem of some computational difficulty.

§18. Functional Equation Approach

Let us now apply invariant imbedding techniques. Let

(1) $f(u, x)$ = the reflected flux from x when the incident flux has intensity u .

Then, we have, to terms in $0(\Delta^2)$,

(2) $$f(u,x) = p(x)\Delta + p(x)f(u,x)\Delta + [1-\phi(u,f(u,x),x)\Delta/f(u,x)][f(u + f(u,x)p(x)\Delta - p(x)u\Delta - \phi(u,f(u,x),x)\Delta, x-\Delta)] ,$$

leading to the partial differential equation

(3) $$\frac{\partial f}{\partial x} = p(x) + p(x)f(u,x) - \phi(u,f(u,x),x) + [f(u,x)p(x) - p(x)u - \phi(u,f(u,x),x)]\frac{\partial f}{\partial u} ,$$

with the initial value

(4) $$f(u,0) = 0 , \quad u \geq 0 .$$

This yields a feasible computational approach. Further details may be found in [27].

REFERENCES

1. Bellman, R., Dynamic Programming, Princeton University Press, Princeton, New Jersey, 1957.

2. Bellman, R., and R. Kalaba, "On the principle of invariant imbedding and propagation through inhomogeneous media", Proc. Nat. Acad. Sci. USA, vol. 42, 1956, pp. 629-632.

3. Hille, E., Functional Analysis and Semi-groups, American Math. Soc. Coll. Publ. No. XXXI, 1948.

4. Bellman, R., and T. E. Harris, "On the theory of age-dependent stochastic branching processes," Proc. Nat. Acad. Sci. USA, vol. 34, 1948, pp. 601-604.

5. Harris, T.E., "Some mathematical models for branching processes," Proc. Second Berkeley Symposium on Mathematical Statistics and Probability, University of California Press, Berkeley, California, 1951.

6. Harris, T.E., The Theory of Branching Processes, Ergebnisse der Math., to appear.

7. Bellman, R., and H. Osborn, "Dynamic programming and the variation of Green's functions," J. Math. and Mech., vol. 7, 1958, pp. 81-86.

8. Bellman, R., Stability Theory of Differential Equations, McGraw-Hill Book Company, Inc., New York, 1954.

9. Dreyfus, S., Dynamic Programming and the Calculus of Variations, The RAND Corporation, Paper P-1464, August 19, 1958.

10. Osborn, H., "On the foundations of dynamic programming," J. Math. and Mech., to appear.

11. Cartaino, H., and S. Dreyfus, "Application of dynamic programming to the minimum time-to-climb problem," Aero. Eng. Review, 1957.

12. Bellman, R., and S. Dreyfus, "On the computational solution of dynamic programming processes--I: on a tactical air warfare model of Mengel," J. Oper. Res., vol. 6, 1958, pp. 65-78.

13. Bellman, R., I. Cherry, and G. M. Wing, "A note on the numerical integration of a class of nonlinear hyperbolic equations," Q. Appl. Math., vol. 16, 1958, pp. 181-183.

14. Fleming, W., Dynamic Programming, Chapter IX, Sec. 9, Princeton University Press, Princeton, New Jersey, 1957.

15. Bellman, R., "Functional equations in the theory of dynamic programming--VI: a direct convergence proof," Ann. Math., vol. 65, 1957, pp. 215-223.

16. Bellman, R., and S. Dreyfus, Approximations and Dynamic Programming, The RAND Corporation, Paper P-1176, September 13, 1957.

17. Bellman, R., "Some new techniques in the dynamic programming solution of variational problems," Q. Appl. Math., vol. 16, 1958, pp. 295-305.

18. Bellman, R., I. Glicksberg, and O. Gross, "On the 'bang-bang' control problem," Q. Appl. Math., vol. 14, 1956, pp. 11-18.

19. Gamkreledze, P.B., "On optimal control processes with linear systems," Iszvestia Akad. Nauk. SSSR, Tomo 22, No. 4, 1958, pp. 449-474.

20. Bellman, R., and J. M. Richardson, "On the application of dynamic programming to a class of implicit variational problems," Q. Appl. Math., to appear.

21. Bellman, R., R. Kalaba, and G. M. Wing, "On the principle of invariant imbedding and neutron transport theory--I: one-dimensional case," J. Math. and Mech., vol. 7, 1958, pp. 149-162.

22. Bellman, R., R. Kalaba, and G. M. Wing, "Invariant imbedding and neutron transport theory--II: functional equations," J. Math. and Mech., vol. 7, 1958, pp. 741-756.

23. Pierce, J.R., "Note on the transmission line equations in terms of impedance," Bell Syst. Tech. J., vol. 22, 1943, pp. 263-265.

24. Schelkunoff, S.A., "Remarks concerning wave propagation in stratified media," The Theory of Electromagnetic Waves, A Symposium, Interscience Publishers, Inc., New York, 1951, pp. 181-192.

25. Bellman, R., R. Kalaba, and G. M. Wing, "Invariant imbedding and neutron transport theory--IV: generalized transport theory," J. Math. and Mech., to appear.

26. Carleman, T., Théorie Cínetique des Gaz, Uppsala, 1957.

27. Bellman, R., R. Kalaba, and G. M. Wing, "Invariant imbedding and neutron transport theory--III: neutron-neutron collision processes," J. Math. and Mech., to appear.

28. Bellman, R., "A note on monotone convergence to solutions of first-order differential equations," Proc. Amer. Math. Soc., (to appear).

29. Kalaba, R., On nonlinear differential equations, the maximum operator and monotone convergence, J. Math and Mech., Vol. 8, (1959), pp. 519-574.

RICHARD COURANT

Remarks about the Rayleigh-Ritz Method

The recent trend in numerical analysis has been strongly in favor of finite difference methods. Among the various advantages of these methods for the solution of linear elliptic partial differential equations is the fact that for rectangular nets (not, however, for less regular, say triangular, nets) in the interior of the domain good convergence is assured, even of difference quotients of any order toward the respective derivatives of the solutions of boundary and eigenvalue problems. The effectiveness of such methods, made possible by modern computers, has been impressed on us by some of the preceding papers presented at this symposium.

Yet, it would seem unfortunate if theoretical, as well as experimental, investigation of other methods should be neglected. The simple remarks of the present paper are meant as a plea to give some attention to the highly flexible Rayleigh-Ritz method and generally to the so-called direct variational methods which may have become unfashionable undeservedly. Personally the speaker has a vivid recollection of the impact on the mathematical world of Ritz's publications which turned the difficult theoretical subject of Dirichlet's principle towards practical numerical use for solving classical problems, in particular computing the nodal lines of vibrating plates, a phenomenon which had fascinated and baffled experimenters for a long time. Ritz's tragic death before he could complete his scientific plans enhanced the general interest in his work. Yet, soon it became clear that his genius had led him to a particularly fortunate choice of his problems and that in other cases there might occur serious difficulties for practical achievement. Today I want to describe some of these difficulties briefly and indicate how they can be overcome.

The gist of the method, in modern terminology, is the following: We seek the solution u of a quadratic minimum problem

$$Q(\phi, \phi) - 2(f, \phi) = \min = d \quad , \tag{1}$$

where Q is a positive quadratic form and (f, ϕ) the inner product and where ϕ ranges over a given linear function space. One might also determine a function g such that $(f, \phi) = Q(g, \phi)$, and then consider the minimum problem

(1a) $$Q(\phi - g) = \min = \delta \ .$$

For example, $Q(\phi, \phi)$ may be the Dirichlet integral*

(2) $$D(\phi, \phi) = \iint_G (\phi_x^2 + \phi_y^2)\, dx\, dy \ ,$$

and ϕ may range over the function space of smooth functions vanishing on the boundary Γ of the domain G of integration. Then (1) and (1a) are equivalent if $\Delta g = f$.

Assuming existence, uniqueness, etc., of u the method aims at constructing u as the limit of a sequence of solutions u_n of problems involving only a finite number of parameters. The infinite dimensional space Ω in which we want to locate the solution u is represented as monotone limit of a sequence of linear spaces Ω_n of finite number n of dimensions (Ω_{n+1} containing Ω_n) which are spanned by a finite number of elements $\omega_1, \ldots, \omega_n$ assumed as known. In Ω_n the solution u_n of the minimum problem $Q(\phi - g) = \min. = \delta_n$ is obtained by solving a system of n linear equations; for the minimizing sequences of functions u_n we have $Q(u_n - g) = \delta_n \to \delta$ as n tends to infinity. Finally it is expected that this sequence u_n in one way or another defines the desired solution u and allows us to compute its relevant properties.

This method, which in this generality is merely a plausible prescription for constructing an approximation and which, incidentally, may be broadened, pays for its flexibility by certain drawbacks.

A. In the first place, it does not directly provide the means for estimating accuracy.

B. As easily seen by counter examples, the pointwise convergence of u_n in G is not necessarily true, and even less so the convergence of derivatives of u_n to derivatives of u .

C. For boundary value problems and similar problems with fixed restrictions for u on interior boundaries it may be cumbersome and even prohibitive from a numerical point of view to define acceptable spaces Ω_n or functions $\omega_1, \omega_2, \ldots, \omega_n, \ldots$. In particular this is true if the boundaries are anything but very simple manifolds.

Yet these shortcomings can be overcome, at least in principle.

As to the first objection, I refer to Professor Diaz's illuminating lecture at this symposium. He showed how E. Trefftz's original idea has been developed into a suitable tool for the desired estimates. I shall not dwell on this interesting subject. §

As to the convergence difficulties (B), shortly after Ritz's papers appeared it became clear this this success was partly due to his selection of a differential equation of order four, instead of the second order Laplace equation. The minimizing sequence for the boundary value problem of the clamped plate converges uniformly in the whole domain, as seen easily, and the situation for vibrating plates, etc., is similar. Evaluating this observation one is led to the following procedure# which allows us to enforce convergence of a minimizing sequence to any degree desired:

First we realize that, as long as u is contained in Ω, there is much freedom to choose Ω and the approximating spaces Ω_n; we may introduce a more stringent metric than that given by the original functional Q. For example, Q may be an integral of a quadratic positive definite form in ϕ and the derivatives of ϕ, e.g. $Q = D(\phi)$; the variational problem may be to minimize Q under the condition that $\phi - g = 0$ on Γ for a given g; the Euler differential equation of the problem may be $L(u) = 0$. Then we can replace Q by

$$Q^*(\phi) = Q(\phi) + \iint_G p(x, y)\, L(\phi)^2\, dx\, dy$$

where $p(x, y)$ is an arbitrarily chosen positive function in the region G. Obviously the minimum problem $Q^* = \min$ under the same boundary conditions imposed on the original problem is solved by the same function u which we wanted to construct as the solution of the original variational problem. For, $Q \leq Q^*$ and $Q = Q^*$ only for $L(\phi) = 0$ hence, $\phi = u$.

Now, as in Ritz's example, the minimizing sequence u_n for the functional $Q^*(\phi)$ converges. Similarly, we could add terms of higher order under the integral sign, such as $p(\frac{\partial}{\partial x} L(\phi))^2$ or $p(L\, L(\phi))^2$ to enforce convergence of higher degree, that means of more derivatives of the minimizing sequence.

Variants of this device to produce convergence present themselves quite naturally but may be left aside here.

It should be emphasized that modification of the factor p allows us to adapt locally the degree of sensitizing the functional $Q^*(\phi)$.

To cope with the difficulty (C), that of boundary conditions, two independently significant concepts may be combined. The first of them is that of free or "natural" boundary conditions. This means conditions at the boundary for the solution of a variational problem which merely express the vanishing of the first variation at the boundary if the conditions of admission to competition in the minimum problem allow full or partial freedom for ϕ at the boundary. Obviously, if ϕ is completely free at the boundary, the construction of the spaces Ω_n (that is, the choice of the functions $\omega_1, \omega_2, \ldots$) is not subjected to complications arising from boundary conditions; then we may for example simply choose for Ω_n the space of all polynomials of degree n. At least in principle this choice of Ω_n makes the construction of a minimizing sequence simple.

Thereby all boundary value problems are made easily accessible to the method, if the boundary conditions are natural.

Now the second step extends this class of problems to cover practically all relevant boundary value problems: We realize in advance that natural boundary conditions show a great variety of possibilities if we consider functionals which are e.g. the sum of an integral over the domain G and another integral over the boundary Γ with the arc length s , e.g.

$$Q(\phi) = D(\phi) + \lambda \int_{\Gamma} (\phi - g)^2 \, ds$$

where λ is a positive parameter. Here the natural boundary condition is $\frac{\partial u}{\partial \nu} + \lambda(\phi - g) = 0$, $\frac{\partial}{\partial \nu}$ denoting the outward normal derivative on Γ . Now the principle under consideration is: Non-natural, or "rigid" boundary conditions, such as that of fixed boundary values given by a function g , are limiting cases of free boundary conditions containing a parameter λ which tends to infinity.

In fact, all boundary conditions, as they occur in physics or mechanics, are either natural boundary conditions or limiting cases of natural conditions for free problems containing a parameter which tends to infinity. This principle may again be best illustrated by the example of Dirichlet's problem for Laplace's equation:

$$D(\phi) + \lambda \int_{\Gamma} (\phi - g)^2 ds = \iint_{G} (\phi_x^2 - \phi_y^2) \, dx \, dy + \lambda \int_{\Gamma} (\phi - g)^2 ds = \min = d(\lambda)$$

We consider with a positive parameter λ the minimum problem

$$D(\phi) + \lambda \int_{\Gamma} (\phi - g)^2 ds = \text{minimum} = d(\lambda)$$

where g(s) is given at the boundary Γ . Obviously $d(\lambda)$ is a monotonically increasing function of λ and $d(\lambda) \leq d$, with d the minimum for Dirichlet's problem for fixed boundary values $\phi = g$, since the latter problem originates from the free problem by imposing a new constraint, i.e. $\phi = g$ on Γ . It is not difficult to prove $d(\lambda) \to d$ and $u_\lambda \to u$ for $\lambda \to \infty$.

Thus the rigid boundary condition can be replaced by a natural one with an arbitrary degree of accuracy if λ is taken large enough.

Inasmuch as our variational problems represent the principle of minimal potential energy for states of equilibrium, the procedure described above amounts to replacing rigid constraints by elastic ones for which a small deviation from the ideal rigid constraint produces large potential energies at the boundary. Incidentally, the idea of "freezing" degrees of freedom by additional terms containing a large parameter has been used in various contexts, for example by Rayleigh.

As to this process of freezing, it must be stated that attention must be given to the choice of the parameter λ . For fixed n the respective minimum $d_n(\lambda)$ will tend to infinity with $\lambda \to \infty$. Therefore one has to take in the construction of a minimizing sequence for any n a sufficiently small value of λ , yet nevertheless must choose λ

as large as practicable. General theoretical recipes do not seem within reach. As to the practical utility of the procedures described here, definite claims should not be made without a great deal of numerical experimentation.

A systematic attempt at such numerical experimentation, using the Univac computer, has been started at New York University by Dr. Donald Ludwig. The study has not yet gone beyond its preliminary stages and definite results cannot be reported at this time. However, the indications are that the principle of sensitizing as well as that of freezing provide valuable tools for numerical computation. As to the choice of λ for a given n, it seems from a number of examples that the result remains satisfactory if λ is chosen within a reasonably wide interval, which is encouraging from a practical point of view.

It would be gratifying if the preceding sketchy remarks would stimulate more theoretical and experimental efforts at broadening the front of numerical attack in the wide field of boundary value problems.

NOTES

[*] For the sake of brevity of writing, we consider here two space dimensions.

[§] See Courant-Hilbert, Methods of Math. Physics, vol. I, page 252 ff., and the literature quoted here.

[#] See e.g. Courant, Göttingen Ges. d. Wissensch., 1922, page 144 ff.

B. ANDREAS TROESCH

Free Oscillations of a Fluid in a Container

§1. Introduction

In this paper we shall report two possible techniques for attacking the problem of the free oscillations of an incompressible fluid in an axially symmetrical container. Very few exact solutions for this problem are known, but the cylinder and, under the quite restrictive assumption of shallow fluid, the paraboloid have been treated [1]. Whereas in these two cases all the eigenvalues, i. e, the entire spectrum, can be obtained, there are special cases known for conical containers where just one free oscillation can be expressed in closed form [2], [3].

The first technique, an inverse method, will be described in full detail, while the other technique, namely a variational approach, will be outlined briefly. Finite difference methods were also studied and are reported elsewhere. *

§2. The Inverse Method

An inverse method for the solution of a partial differential equation relaxes some of the boundary conditions but requires the solution to possess certain other properties. Exaggerating slightly, the procedure can be characterized by the statement that, instead of finding a solution to a given problem, a physically reasonable problem is found for a given solution. This idea has been widely used in the mechanics of continua. It seems interesting to observe that L. Euler used the method in hydrodynamics for the same equation that describes our problem, and that he also looked for solutions in the form of polynomials. This was apparently the first time an exact solution for any theory of the dynamics of continua was obtained [7], [8]. In our case, the inverse method reduces a boundary problem with an eigenvalue appearing in the boundary condition to an integration of a system of ordinary differential equations. This integration can be carried out very easily and accurately, and these solutions may be readily used to judge the accuracy of results obtained by the two other techniques mentioned above.

A. Problem Statement-Basic Approach

Let us assume that the motion of the fluid in the container is irrotational and that the amplitude of the motion is so small that the linearized hydrodynamics equations are appropriate. Then the velocity potential $\Phi(x, y, z, t)$ for the free oscillations fulfills the following equation and boundary conditions ([1], §227):

$$\nabla^2 \Phi = 0 \qquad \text{throughout the fluid,} \tag{1}$$

$$\frac{\partial \Phi}{\partial n} = 0 \qquad \text{on the container walls,} \tag{2}$$

$$\frac{\partial^2 \Phi}{\partial t^2} + g \frac{\partial \Phi}{\partial n} = 0 \qquad \text{on the free surface .} \tag{3}$$

To determine the free oscillations we write the velocity potential, Φ , as

$$\Phi = \phi(x, y, z) \cos \omega t \quad ,$$

and Eqs. (1), (2), and (3) become

$$\nabla^2 \phi = 0 \quad , \tag{1'}$$

$$\frac{\partial \phi}{\partial n} = 0 \quad , \tag{2'}$$

$$\frac{\partial \phi}{\partial n} = \lambda \phi \quad , \tag{3'}$$

where $\lambda = \omega^2/g$, and g is the acceleration due to gravity. The free surface elevation is given by $\zeta = -(1/g)\Phi_t = (\omega/g)\phi \sin \omega t$.

In order to find the free oscillations of a fluid in a given container we have to solve the Laplace equation (1') under the condition that the solution possesses a vanishing normal derivative at one part of the boundary, and that equation (3') containing the eigenvalue be fulfilled at the remaining part of the boundary. We note that the eigenvalue does not appear in the differential equation (1') at all. We introduce cylindrical coordinates and can eliminate the θ - dependence by writing

$$\phi = \psi(r, z) \cos m \theta$$

where m is an integer. We then look for solutions in r and z , in the form of polynomials fulfilling equation (1') and the boundary condition (3') exactly. For these polynomials we determine the line in the r-z plane where equation (2') is satisfied. That means, we select a velocity potential and then compute the streamlines, and thus obtain possible container shapes. This reduces the problem to a simple integration of an ordinary differential equation. Although this approach does not lead to all container shapes of practical interest, one obtains very accurate eigenvalues for quite a number of interesting shapes since several coefficients can be chosen arbitrarily. In addition, the conical and hyperbolic shapes mentioned above are obtained in a complete and natural way.

The equations to be satisfied by the function $\psi(r, z)$ are

$$r^2\psi_{rr} + r\psi_r - m^2\psi + r^2\psi_{zz} = 0 , \quad \text{for } z < 0 , \text{ and } r > 0 , \tag{1"}$$

$$\psi_z = \lambda\psi , \quad \text{for } z = 0 . \tag{3"}$$

Let us denote the polynomial of degree n, satisfying equation (1") with a given m, by

$$\psi_n^m(r, z) = \sum_{k=0}^{n} a_k^{(m,n)} r^k z^{n-k} ,$$

which, inserted in equation (1"), yields immediately the two term recursion relations

$$\left.\begin{aligned} & a_k^{(m,n)}(k^2 - m^2) = 0 && \text{for } k = 0 , 1 , \\ & a_k^{(m,n)}(k^2 - m^2) + a_{k-2}^{(m,n)}(n-k+2)(n-k+1) = 0 && \text{for } k = 2, 3, \ldots, n. \end{aligned}\right\} \tag{4}$$

(For $n = 0$ and $n = 1$ the second relation is not used, since $0 \le k \le n$.) A list of some of these polynomials is given in Appendix I.

Any linear combination of the functions $\psi_n^m(r, z)$,

$$\psi = \sum_n a_n \psi_n(r, z)$$

satisfies equation (1"). In order to satisfy equation (3") also, we have to choose the constants a_n properly. The shape of the container belonging to ψ can then be found by integrating the ordinary differential equation

$$\psi_z dr - \psi_r dz = 0 \tag{5}$$

which follows from equation (2') with grad $\psi = (\psi_r, \psi_z)$ and the normal to the surface $\vec{n} = (1 , -\frac{dr}{dz})$.

B. Conical and Hyperboloid Containers

Let us first investigate the solutions to our problem that can be represented in closed form, namely the oscillations in conical and hyperboloid containers.

The simplest case of a conical container is obtained for $m = 1$, i.e., for a motion with one diameter as a nodal line on the free surface. Let us choose

$$\psi = a_1\psi_1^1 + a_2\psi_2^1$$

(there are always groups of two functions ψ_n^m necessary to satisfy the free boundary condition), or

$$\psi = r + a_2\, rz \ ,$$

since there is no loss in generality if $a_1 = 1$. Equation (3") then gives

$$\lambda = a_2 \ .$$

Finally, equation (5) determines the container shape

$$\lambda r\, dr = (1 + \lambda z)dz \ ,$$

which integrated yields

$$r^2 = (z + \frac{1}{\lambda})^2 - C \ .$$

If the integration constant C is chosen to be $C = 0$, then

$$r = \pm(z + \frac{1}{\lambda}) \ ,$$

i.e., the container represents a 45-degree cone with a depth of $h = 1/\lambda$ and a radius at the surface of $R = 1/\lambda$. Since, in this case, there is no nodal circle at the free surface, one can state the following result:

The frequency of the free oscillation with one nodal diameter (i.e., $m = 1$) and with no nodal circle in a cone of 45-degree half angle and depth h is

$$\omega = \sqrt{\lambda g} = \sqrt{g/h} \ .$$

Furthermore, the frequency for the same mode in a container with the shape of a hyperboloid asymptotic to a 45-degree half angle cone is

$$\omega = \sqrt{\frac{2hg}{R^2 + h^2}} \ ,$$

h denoting the depth and R the radius of the container. This result follows easily for $C > 0$ (cf. Figure 3b). In these modes, the fluid surface remains plane throughout the motion.

A slight generalization of these oscillations to containers without axial symmetry is described in Appendix II.

Cones and hyperboloids can also be obtained for $m > 1$ if we choose

$$\psi = \psi_m^m + a_{m+1}\psi_{m+1}^m = r^m + a_{m+1} r^m z \ .$$

From the free surface condition, equation (3'), we find

$$\lambda = a_{m+1} \ ,$$

and the container shape is again obtained from equation (5):

$$\lambda r^m \, dr = (m r^{m-1} + \lambda m r^{m-1} z) dz \ ,$$

which, integrated, leads to

$$r^2 = m(z + \frac{1}{\lambda})^2 - C \ ,$$

(cf. [3]).

Thus, for the mode with m nodal diameters but without nodal circles, the frequency ω of the free oscillations of fluid in a hyperboloid container asymptotic to a cone with a generating angle $\gamma = \tan^{-1}\sqrt{m}$ is

$$\omega = \left(\frac{2ghm}{R^2 + mh^2}\right)^{1/2}$$

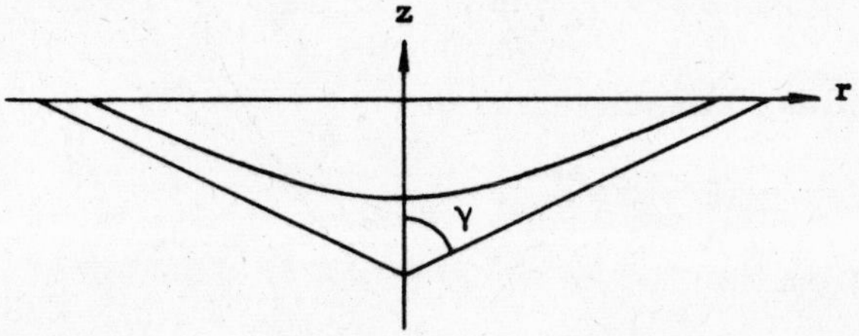

where h denotes the depth and R the surface radius of the container. For the cone the formula simplifies to

$$\omega = \sqrt{\frac{g}{h}}$$

independent of m where $m \geq 1$.

For the oscillations without a nodal diameter, i.e., $m = 0$ the cone with the angle $\gamma = \tan^{-1}\sqrt{m}$ degenerates into an infinitely deep cylinder where the fluid moves up and down like a rigid body. However, besides this physically impossible solution, there still exists a simple solution for a cone or hyperboloid. Four terms are needed for the potential function ψ ,

$$\psi = a_0 + a_1 z + a_2(z^2 - \frac{1}{2}r^2) + a_3(z^3 - \frac{3}{2}r^2 z) \ .$$

The boundary condition (3") leads to

$$a_1 - \frac{3}{2} a_3 r^2 = \lambda(a_0 - \frac{1}{2} a_2 r^2) \ ,$$

and taking $a_0 = 1$, the potential function can be written as

$$\psi = 1 + \lambda z + a_2(z^2 - \frac{1}{2}r^2) + \frac{1}{3}\lambda a_2(z^3 - \frac{3}{2}r^2 z) .$$

The shape of the container belonging to this solution is obtained from equation (5) after multiplying it by the integrating factor r ,

$$(\lambda r + 2a_2 rz + \lambda a_2 rz^2 - \frac{1}{2}\lambda a_2 r^3)dr + (a_2 r^2 + \lambda a_2 r^2 z)dz = 0 ,$$

and integrating

$$\lambda\frac{r^2}{2} + a_2 r^2 z + \lambda a_2 \frac{r^2}{2} z^2 - \frac{1}{8}\lambda a_2 r^4 + C = 0 .$$

(It will be shown below that whenever $m = 0$, the shape can be obtained in closed form with r the appropriate integrating factor.)

Since we are only interested in containers which are closed at the bottom, i.e., $r = 0$ corresponding to a finite z , the integration constant C must vanish. The hyperbolic containers are, therefore,

$$\frac{1}{4}r^2 = (z + \frac{1}{\lambda})^2 + \frac{1}{a_2} - \frac{1}{\lambda^2} , \tag{6}$$

with a surface radius of

$$R = 2/\sqrt{a_2} .$$

From

$$\psi(r, o) = 1 - \frac{a_2}{2}r^2$$

it follows that the surface possesses a nodal circle at

$$r_{nodal} = \frac{R}{2}\sqrt{2} .$$

Note that this circle divides the surface into two equal areas. Furthermore, the frequency of the free oscillation is

$$\omega = \sqrt{\frac{2gh}{h^2 + (R^2/4)}} ,$$

where h again denotes the maximum depth. All these hyperboloid containers have asymptotic cones with $\gamma = \tan^{-1}\sqrt{4}$, and the cone,

$$\frac{1}{4}r^2 = (z + \frac{1}{\lambda})^2 ,$$

is a special case of them, with an eigenfrequency

$$\omega = \sqrt{\frac{g}{h}} \ .$$

We note that for the cone with half-angle $\gamma = \tan^{-1}\sqrt{4} = 63°30'$ and for the corresponding hyperboloids there are two simple exact solutions with the same frequency, namely the oscillation with one nodal circle and the oscillation with four nodal diameters.

C. Oscillations with Cylindrical Symmetry

Up to this point, we have discussed container shapes that can be represented in closed form. In the next two sections we will determine container shapes by numerical integration using a computer. In the first section, the velocity potential is chosen to lead to oscillations with cylindrical symmetry, that is, $m = 0$.

As mentioned above, in the cases with cylindrical symmetry, the factor r always represents an integrating factor for equation (5) which determines the container shape. If this fact is true for all functions ψ^0_n, (cf. Appendix I), it obviously also holds for any linear combination of them. But they all obey equation (1")

$$r\psi_{rr} + \psi_r + r\psi_{zz} = 0 \ ,$$

which exactly represents the condition that

$$(r\psi_z)dr - (r\psi_r)dz = dS$$

be a total differential. The function S describing the container shape is then readily seen to be

$$S(r, z) = \int_0^r \xi\,\psi_z(\xi, z)d\xi \ .$$

Let us now assume that we construct a solution with the first N functions, ψ^0_n, (N must be odd)

$$\psi(r, z) = \sum_{n=0}^{n=N} a_n \psi^0_n (r, z) \ ,$$

where between the values of a the relations

$$\lambda a_{2n} = a_{2n+1}(2n+1) \ , \text{ for } n = 0, 1, \ldots \frac{N-1}{2} \ ,$$

hold. The velocity potential, therefore, turns out to be

$$\psi(r, z) = a_0(\psi^0_0 + \lambda\psi^0_1) + a_2(\psi^0_2 + \frac{1}{3}\lambda\psi^0_3) + a_4(\psi^0_4 + \frac{1}{5}\lambda\psi^0_5) + \ldots \ ,$$

and, hence,

$$S(r, z) = a_0(1 + \frac{1}{2}\lambda r^2) + a_2[r^2 z + \lambda(\frac{1}{2} r^2 z^2 - \frac{1}{8} r^4)]$$

$$+ a_4[2r^2 z^3 - \frac{3}{2} r^4 z + \lambda(\frac{1}{2} r^2 z^4 - \frac{3}{4} r^4 z^2 + \frac{1}{16} r^6)] + \ldots - C = 0 \ .$$

However, the constant C has to equal a_0, since otherwise the container would not be closed. Thus we obtain for the shape of the container

$$S(r, z) = \frac{1}{2} a_0 \lambda + a_2 [z + \lambda(\frac{1}{2} z^2 - \frac{1}{8} r^2)]$$

$$+ a_4 [2z^3 - \frac{3}{2} r^2 z + \lambda(\frac{1}{2} z^4 - \frac{3}{4} r^2 z^2 + \frac{1}{16} r^4)] + \ldots = 0 \ .$$

Evidently, there is no loss in generality by choosing $a_0 = 1$. If only the terms up to a_2 are retained, then the hyperboloid containers of equation (6) result.

For the possibilities which include the higher a's, it is actually simpler to compute the container shape by integrating the ordinary differential equations in parametric form

$$\frac{dr}{dt} = S_z \ , \quad \frac{dz}{dt} = -S_r \ ,$$

e.g.,

$$\left.\begin{aligned} \frac{dr}{dt} &= a_2 (1 + \lambda z) + a_4 [6z^2 - \frac{3}{2} r^2 + \lambda(2z^3 - \frac{3}{2} r^2 z)] \ , \\ \frac{dz}{dt} &= \{a_2 \frac{1}{4}\lambda + a_4 [3z + \lambda(\frac{3}{2} z^2 - \frac{1}{4} r^2)]\} r \ . \end{aligned}\right\} \quad (7)$$

Its solution represents a one parameter family, although there seem to be three parameters involved, namely a_2, a_4, and λ. But, it is easily shown that for similar shapes, the frequency ω of a free oscillation varies like the reciprocal square root of the linear dimensions. We can therefore assume λ to equal unity. Furthermore, setting $a = a_2/a_4$ simply rescales the integration parameter t and equation (7) becomes

$$\left.\begin{aligned} \frac{dr}{dt} &= a(1 + z) + 6z^2 - \frac{3}{2} r^2 + 2z^3 - \frac{3}{2} r^2 z \ , \\ \frac{dz}{dt} &= (\frac{1}{4} a + 3z + \frac{3}{2} z^2 - \frac{1}{4} r^2) r \ . \end{aligned}\right\} \quad (8)$$

Results from this equation for some values of a are shown in Figures 1 and 2.

The corner of the container for $a = 12.6$ is formed by a saddle point of the solution of equation (5). Because of the mean value theorem for potential functions, saddle points are the only singularities possible.

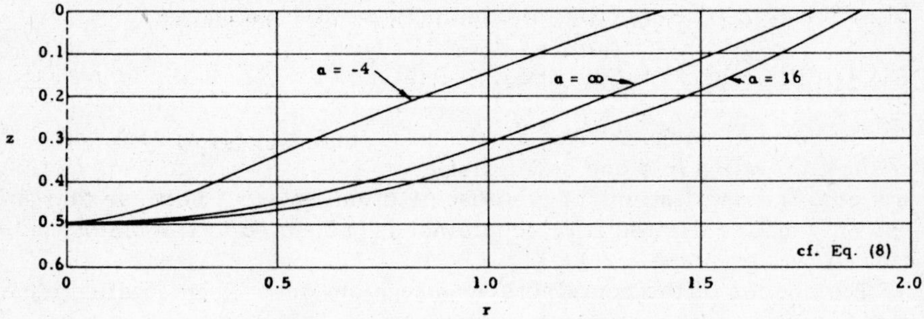

Figure 1. Container Cross Sections for m = 0 , λ = 1 .

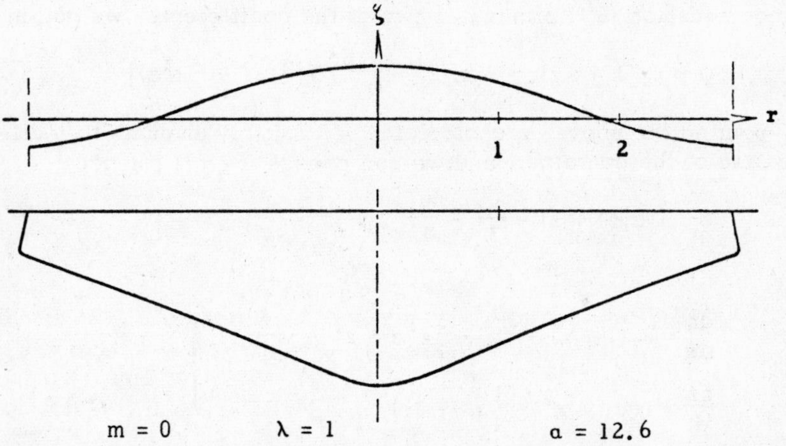

Figure 2. Container Cross Section for m = 0 .

It should be noted that these containers are quite flat, but deep containers may be obtained by introducing more free parameters, a .

D. Oscillations with One Nodal Diameter

The lowest eigenvalue for a cylindrical container is associated with the motion which has one nodal diameter, i.e., $m = 1$. Such motions are also the oscillations of greatest practical interest because they are the only modes excited if the container is restricted to translatory motion in a fixed plane.

The shapes of the containers are again obtained by integrating equation (5), i.e.,

$$\frac{dr}{dt} = \psi_r \ , \quad \frac{dz}{dt} = \psi_z \ ,$$

using a linear combination of the functions ψ_n^1

$$\psi = a_1 \psi_1^1 + a_2 \psi_2^1 + a_3 \psi_3^1 + a_4 \psi_4^1 \ .$$

Since equation (3'') eliminates two of the coefficients, we obtain

$$\psi = a_1(1 + \lambda z)r + a_3 r[(z^2 - \frac{1}{4}r^2) + \frac{\lambda}{3}(z^3 - \frac{3}{4}r^2 z)] \ .$$

As pointed out above, a choice of $\lambda = 1$ simply amounts to a different scaling of the container, and we can choose $a_3 = 1$; hence

$$\psi = r[a_1(1 + z) + \frac{z^3}{3} - \frac{1}{4}r^2 z + z^2 - \frac{r^2}{4}] \ ,$$

and

$$\left.\begin{aligned} \frac{dr}{dt} &= a_1(1 + z) + \frac{z^3}{3} - \frac{3}{4}r^2 z + z^2 - \frac{3r^2}{4} \ , \\ \frac{dz}{dt} &= r(a_1 + z^2 - \frac{1}{4}r^2 + 2z) \ . \end{aligned}\right\} \qquad (9)$$

Some shapes obtained for various choices of a_1 are shown in Figures 3, 4, and 5. In Figure 3a, the container looks like the exact solution of a cone shown in Figure 3b. Nevertheless, the eigenvalue λ differs by 25 percent. This gives an indication that the eigenvalue can be quite sensitive to changes of the container shape. Figure 4 shows, among other solutions, a ring-shaped container.

We have, up to now, considered only the containers obtained from polynomials in r and z . These polynomials represent (cf. Appendix I) the lowest terms in the expansion of

$$J_1(\beta r)e^{\beta z}$$

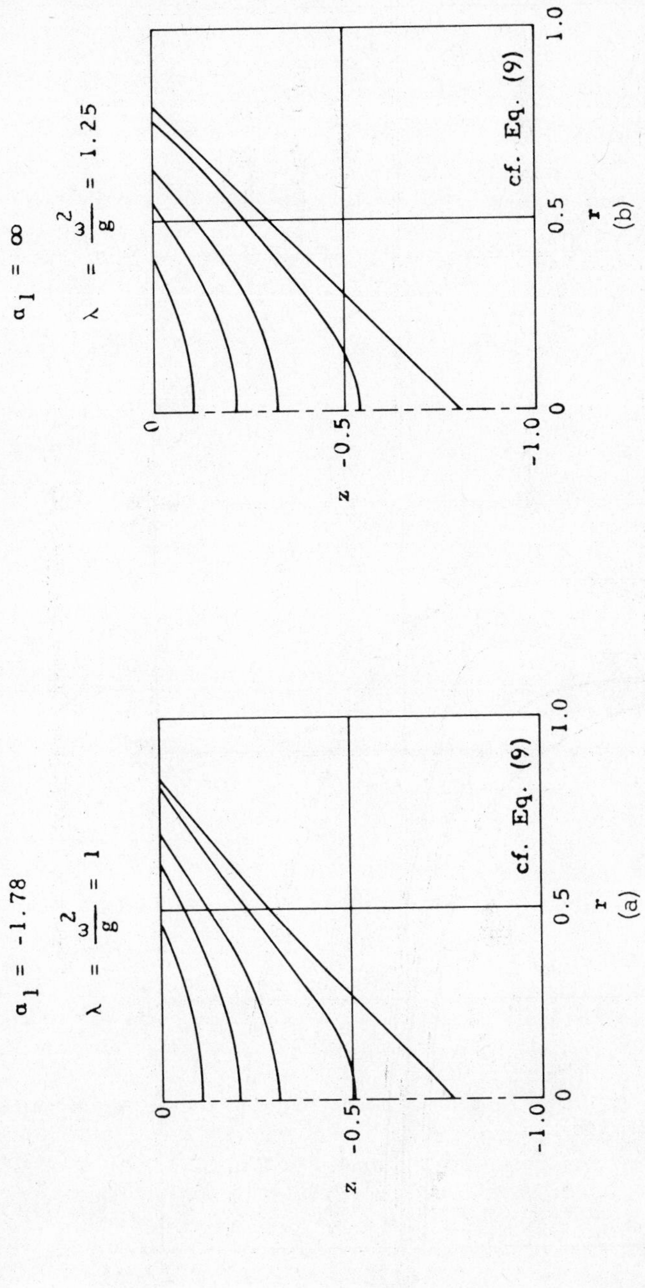

Figure 3. Container Cross Sections for $m = 1$.

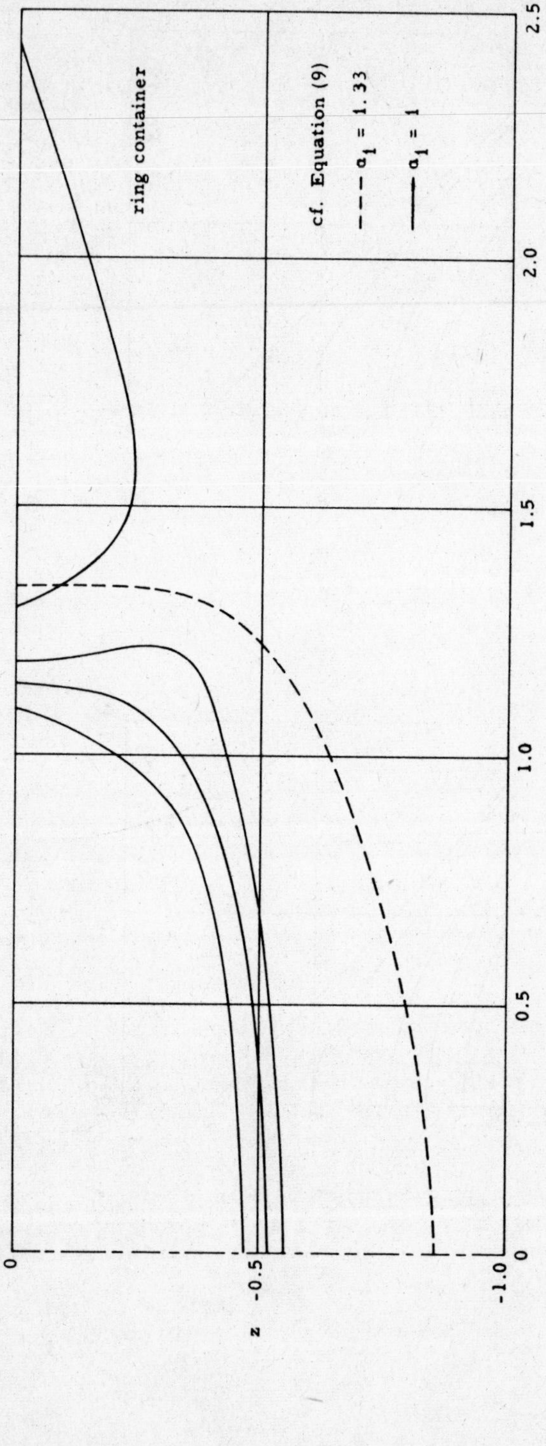

Figure 4. Container Cross Sections for $m = 1$.

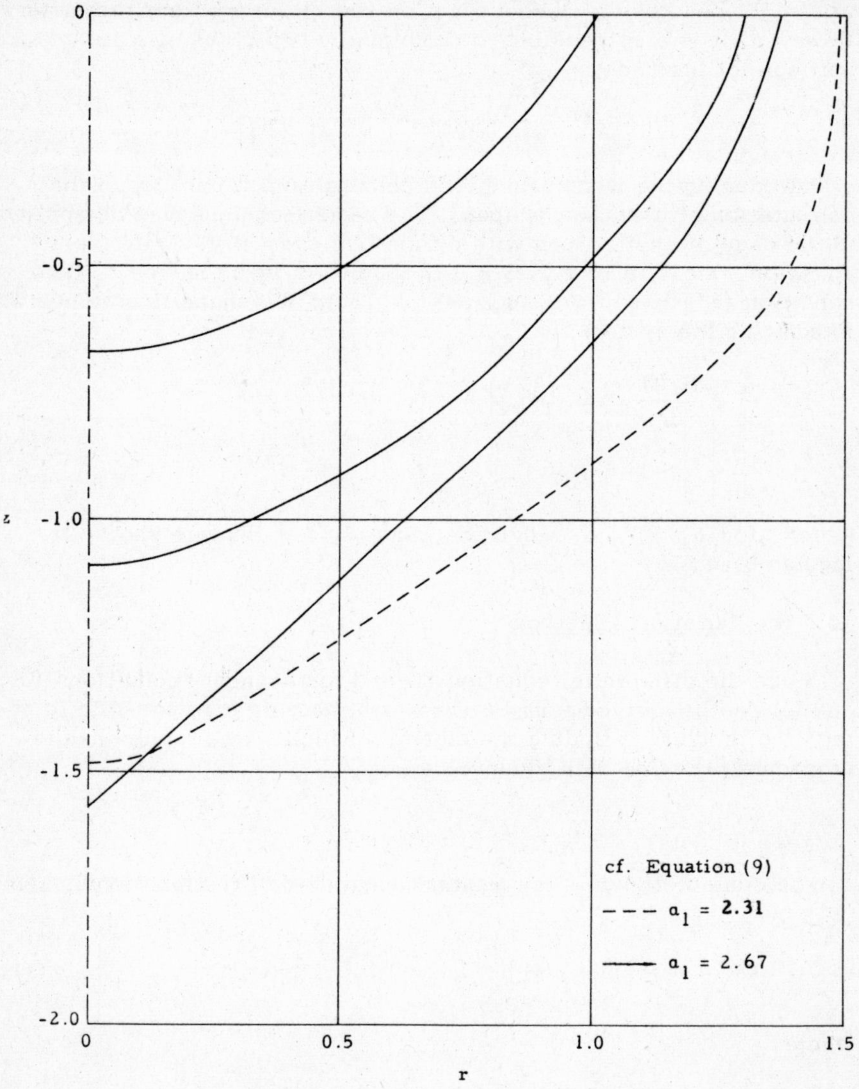

Figure 5. Container Cross Sections for m = 1 .

where J_1 denotes the Bessel function and β an arbitrary parameter. However, it is also possible to combine the two types of solutions by putting, for instance,

$$\psi = a_1 J_1(\beta r)e^{\beta z} + a_2 J_1(\beta r)e^{-\beta z} + \alpha_1 r + \alpha_2 rz + \dots .$$

Introducing the Bessel functions permits more flexibility in the computation of container shapes. The same technique may be applied in the case of oscillations with cylindrical symmetry. With the assumption $\lambda = 1$, $a_1 = 1$, $a_2 = 0$, it follows from the free surface condition (3") that $\beta = 1$, $\alpha_1 = \alpha_2$. Thus, the shape is obtained by integrating the system

$$\left.\begin{aligned} \frac{dr}{dt} &= \frac{dJ_1(r)}{dr} e^z + \alpha_1(1 + z) , \\ \frac{dz}{dt} &= J_1(r)e^z + \alpha_1 r . \end{aligned}\right\} \qquad (10)$$

Results for $\alpha_1 = 0$, $\alpha_1 = 0.0125$, and $\alpha_1 = -0.05$ are shown in Figures 6 and 7.

§3. The Variational Method

Since the differential equation (1) and the boundary conditions (2) and (3) can be derived from Hamilton's principle, it is possible to attack the problem of finding the eigenfrequencies by a Rayleigh-Ritz procedure [4]. The n-th eigenvalue

$$\lambda_n = \frac{\omega_n^2}{g}$$

can be characterized as the maximum-minimum of the functional $L(\phi)$ [11]

$$\lambda_n = \max_{w_i} [\min_{(\phi, w_i)=0} L(\phi)] \qquad i = 1, \dots (n-1), n \qquad (11)$$

where

$$L(\phi) = \frac{\iiint_V (\nabla\phi)^2 dV}{\iint_S \phi^2 dS} . \qquad (12)$$

The triple integral is extended over the volume, V, occupied by the fluid at rest; the double integral is extended over the quiescent free surface, S. The class of admissible functions consists of all continuous functions with piece-wise continuous first derivative for which $L(\phi)$ exists. The arbitrary functions, w_i, in the constraints

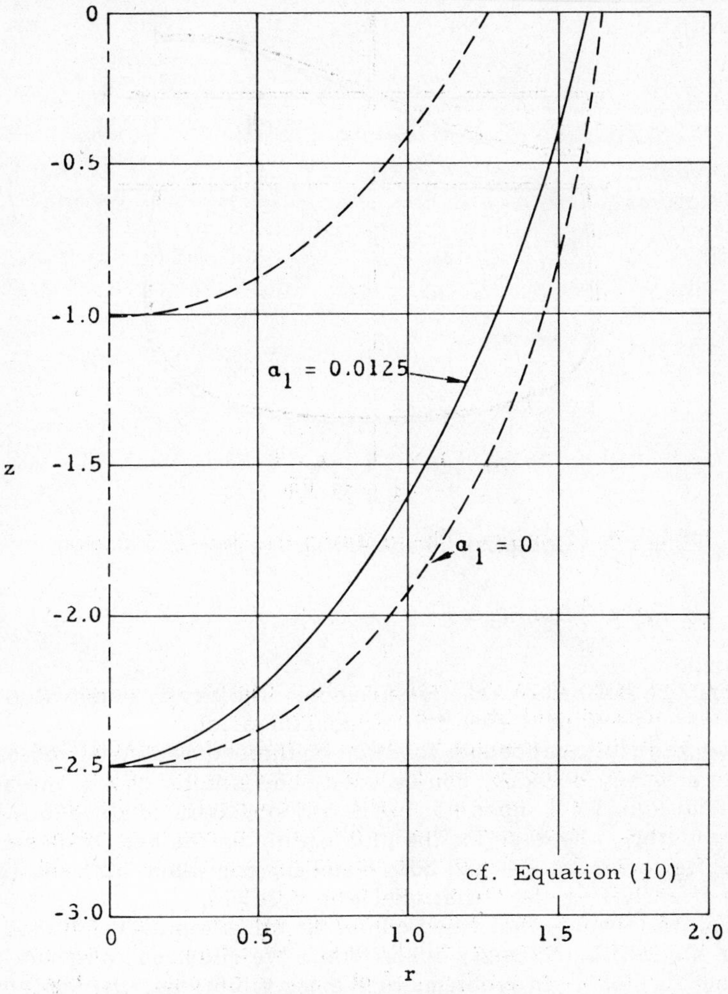

Figure 6. Container Cross Sections for m = 1 .

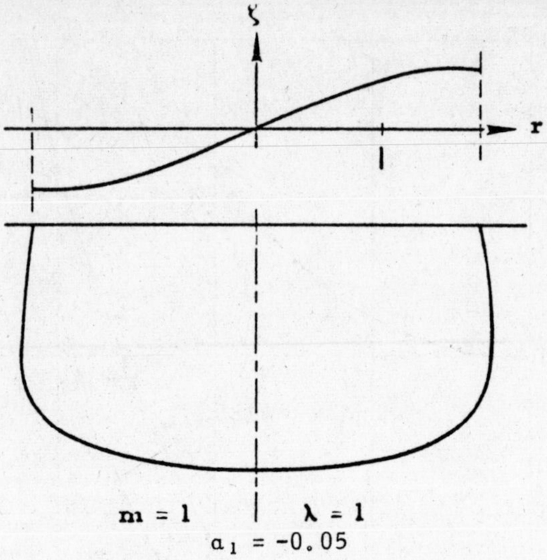

Figure 7. Container Shape Using the Bessel Function

$$(\phi, w_i) = \iint_S \phi w_i dS = 0$$

need only be defined on the free surface. The trivial eigenvalues $\lambda_0 = 0$ can be excluded from further consideration.

A Rayleigh-Ritz procedure for two- or three-dimensional regions with an arbitrary boundary can be used successfully only if the admissible functions, ϕ , need not fulfill any boundary conditions. This is, fortunately, the case for the problem discussed here because the differential equation (1') and both boundary conditions (2') and (3') follow directly from the variational principle (11).

Thus, we observe that fixed container walls represent natural, rather than kinematic, boundary conditions. We might add a remark on the meaning of $L(\phi)$. In problems of elastic vibrations, the Rayleigh quotient is the ratio of the expression for the potential energy and the kinetic energy. Here the situation is reversed, since, as one easily recognizes, the numerator of $L(\phi)$ represents the kinetic energy of the fluid, and the denominator the potential energy.

The fact that the eigenvalue does not appear in the differential equation affects the completeness of the eigenfunctions, ϕ_i . They are not complete over the volume, V , in any class of functions containing non-harmonic functions, since each ϕ_i obeys the Laplace equation. However, the eigenfunctions are orthogonal and complete over the free surface

$$\iint_S \phi_i \phi_k dS = \delta_{ik} \quad ,$$

and, furthermore, the relation

$$\iiint_V (\nabla\phi_i, \nabla\phi_k)dV = \lambda_i \delta_{ik}$$

holds.

Turning back to the maximum-minimum principle, we note that it is very convenient for establishing comparison theorems for the eigenvalues. First, we consider two containers with the same free surface. If one of them is completely contained in the other one, then the smaller container possesses the smaller eigenvalue (cf. Figure 8). This can also be expressed in a different way: that is, if part of the fluid below the free surface is frozen, this condition does not constitute a constraint on the system. It rather represents a special type of baffle which relaxes continuity conditions and decreases the eigenvalue in the same way as cracks in plates do.

On the other hand, if the two containers to be compared differ at the surface, then the smaller container possesses the larger eigenvalue. More precisely, for tanks with circular free surfaces, the relation

$$\lambda_2 < \lambda_1 \frac{r_1}{r_2} < \lambda_1$$

holds (cf. Figure 8) as long as the larger tank 2, with radius r_2 is completely contained in a tank, 3, similar to the smaller tank, 1, with radius r_1 .

These comparison theorems combined with the inverse method described above can be used to obtain lower bounds for the eigenvalues of arbitrarily shaped containers. For upper bounds the same method might be used, but, in fact, a Rayleigh-Ritz procedure represents a more appropriate technique ([4], [9], [10]).** This technique leads to very good results for the eigenvalues when the shallow water approximation and the deep cylindrical tank solution are chosen as the Ritz coordinate functions.

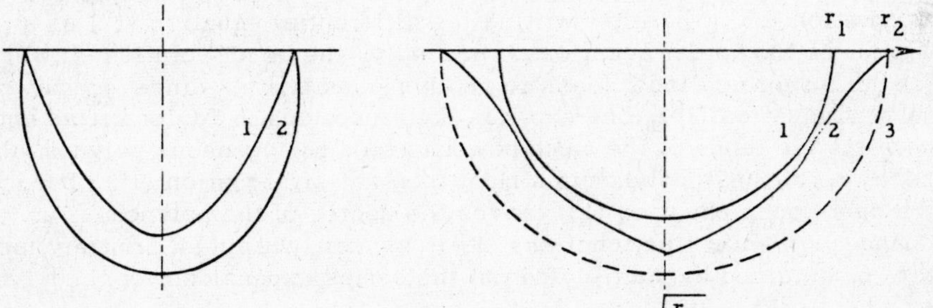

$\omega_1 < \omega_2$ $\qquad\qquad$ $\omega_2 < \omega_1 \sqrt{\frac{r_1}{r_2}} < \omega_1$

Figure 8. Comparison of Eigenfrequencies.

The maximum-minimum principle can also be used to decide whether a classical problem in membrane or plate vibrations has its counterpart in fluid oscillations. We can prescribe the circular free surface area, S, of a container and its volume, V, and look for the shape that makes the lowest non-trivial eigenvalue as small as possible. However, since it can be easily shown that the eigenvalue can be made arbitrarily small, the meaningful problem is to look for the shape which gives the largest possible fundamental eigenvalue for a given S and V.

One last remark in this connection refers to a container with a quite remarkable property. It is not hard to recognize that a container must exist in which the oscillation of the fluid has the same fundamental frequency regardless of the fluid level. The container cross section (shown in Figure 6 for $a_1 = 0$) is given by

$$z(r) = z_0 + \int_0^r \frac{J_1}{(dJ_1/d\zeta)} \, d\zeta \ ,$$

and the velocity potential by

$$\phi = J_1(r)e^z \cos\theta \ .$$

This simply means that the container contour is determined by the streamlines of the fundamental mode in an infinite cylinder.

APPENDIX I

THE POLYNOMIALS $\psi_n^m(r, z)$

By means of the recursion relations, equation (4) on page 281, the polynomials $\psi_n^m(r, z)$ can be readily computed.

However, there are other ways to obtain the coefficients of the ψ_n^m's. One possibility is to build up the coefficients by successive integration (cf. [5]), after writing the differential equation (1") as a system of first order equations. Secondly, the exact solution $J_m(r)e^z$ for the infinite cylinder leads to another possibility. Since $J_m(r)e^z$ fulfills equation (1"), one expands both functions in Taylor series and collects the terms of the same power to form homogeneous polynomials. Each one of these polynomials must then satisfy equation (1"), because the operator in equation (1") leaves the degree of the polynomial unchanged. Hence, the functions $\psi_n^m(r, z)$ can, within an arbitrary factor, be obtained by multiplying out the series expansions for $J_m(r)$ and e^z.

A third method to compute the functions $\psi_n^m(r, z)$ uses the connection between these functions and spherical harmonics. Introducing spherical coordinates by

$$r = \rho \sin\theta \;, \qquad z = \rho\cos\theta \;,$$

we obtain

$$\psi_n^m(r, z) = \rho^n F_n^m(\theta) \;,$$

where the functions F_n^m must, within an arbitrary factor, be the spherical harmonics, namely (cf. [6], p. 11)

$$F_n^m = \frac{2^m m!\,(n-m)!}{(n+m)!} P_n^m(x) \;,$$

with $x = \cos\theta$.

We give here a list of the first few polynomials for $m = 0, 1, 2$,

$$\psi_0^0 = 1 \qquad\qquad \psi_3^0 = z^3 - \frac{3}{2} r^2 z$$

$$\psi_1^0 = z \qquad\qquad \psi_4^0 = z^4 - 3r^2 z^2 + \frac{3}{8} r^4$$

$$\psi_2^0 = z^2 - \frac{1}{2} r^2 \qquad\qquad \psi_5^0 = z^5 - 5r^2 z^3 + \frac{15}{8} r^4 z$$

$$\psi_1^1 = r \qquad\qquad \psi_3^1 = r(z^2 - \frac{1}{4} r^2)$$

$$\psi_2^1 = rz \qquad\qquad \psi_4^1 = r(z^3 - \frac{3}{4} r^2 z)$$

$$\psi_2^2 = r^2 \qquad\qquad \psi_3^2 = r^2 z$$

APPENDIX II

AN EXACT SPECIAL SOLUTION FOR NON-AXIALLY SYMMETRIC BASINS

Among the special solutions found for cones and hyperboloids, there is one which can be extended to non-axially symmetric basins. For $m = 1$ we found (see page 281-282)

$$\psi = r + \lambda r z \;,$$

and, therefore, $\phi = (1 + \lambda z) r \cos\theta = (1 + \lambda z)x$; hence, the velocity vector becomes

$$\vec{V} = \operatorname{grad}\phi = (1 + \lambda z \,,\; 0 \,,\; \lambda x) \;.$$

Since this shows that the velocity vectors are all parallel to the x-z-plane and do not depend on the y coordinate, it is possible to construct new solutions by piecing together the hyperbolic and triangular cross sections of the solution obtained above. A trough of finite or infinite length with a triangular cross section is an obvious example (cf. Figure 3, and [1], p. 443).

We consider a container with the following shape

$$S(x, y, z) = x^2 - f(y) - (z - z_0)^2 + z_0^2 = 0 \quad ,$$

where $z_0 < 0$. Apparently, the curve $x = \pm\sqrt{f(y)}$ represents the contour of the fluid surface at $z = 0$. All the planes perpendicular to the y-axis cut out a hyperbolic cross section. The velocity potential is given by

$$\Phi = (1 + \frac{\omega^2}{g} z)\, x \cos \omega t \quad ,$$

which fulfills equations (1) and (3). But it is easily verified that the solution also satisfies equation (2), if the eigenfrequency ω is $\omega = \sqrt{-g/z_0}$.

Since the wider the basin the deeper it is, the special solutions obtained here apply to basins of quite reasonable shape.

NOTE

*Ehrlich, L., J. Riley, G. Strang, and B. A. Troesch, forthcoming publication.

**For instance, an upper bound for the fundamental eigenvalue λ of a half-sphere of radius $r_0 = 1$ is $\lambda = 1.560$. Using Eqs. (9) which contain only one free parameter a_1 (see curve for $a_1 = 2.31$ in Fig. 5), the inverse method furnishes a lower bound $\lambda = 1.487$. Thus, the upper and lower bounds for the eigenfrequency ω are less than $2\frac{1}{2}$ percent apart.

BIBLIOGRAPHY

1. H. Lamb, Hydrodynamics, 6th Edition, Dover, New York.
2. E. Levin (unpublished memorandum).
3. J. W. Green (unpublished memorandum).
4. H. R. Lawrence, C. J. Wang, R. B. Reddy, Variational Solution of Fuel Sloshing Modes, Jet Propulsion, Vol. 28, No. 11, pp. 729-736, November, 1958.
5. L. Bers and A. Gelbart, On a Class of Differential Equations in Mechanics of Continua, Quarterly of Applied Mathematics 1 , pp. 168-188, 1943.
6. E. Jahnke and F. Emde, Tables of Functions, Dover Publications, 1945.

7. P. F. Nemenyi, Recent Developments in Inverse and Semi-Inverse Methods in the Mechanics of Continua, Advances in Applied Mechanics, Vol. II, Academic Press, Inc., New York, 1951.

8. L. Euler, Principia motus fluidorum, Novi Commentarii Academiae Scientiarum Imperialis Petropolitanae, Tom. VI, pp. 271-311, 1761.

9. N. Trembath (unpublished memorandum).

10. J. Riley (unpublished memorandum).

11. R. Courant and D. Hilbert, Methods of Mathematical Physics, Vol. I, Ch. VI, Interscience, New York, 1953.

CALVIN H. WILCOX

A Variational Method for Computing the Echo Area of a Lamina

Introduction

This work is concerned with the diffraction of a time-harmonic acoustic wave by a rigid lamina. Its purpose is to derive a method for computing the amounts of energy scattered in various directions by the lamina. As a first step, the scattered field is characterized in terms of the solution of an integro-differential equation for a function defined on the lamina. Second, this equation is used to establish a variational principle for the quantities of interest. Finally, the Rayleigh-Ritz method is applied to derive a procedure for computing these quantities.*

The diffraction problem for plane laminas has a large literature [1].** By contrast, very little work has appeared for the case of curved laminas. Sommerfeld discussed the diffraction of plane waves by a spherical mirror [14, pp. 29-31 and 159-164]. His method involves expanding the field outside and inside the sphere in spherical harmonics, and matching the expansions by applying the boundary condition on the part of the sphere occupied by the mirror and continuity conditions on the remainder. The result is a system of infinitely many equations in an infinite number of unknowns for the coefficients in the expansions of the field. Sommerfeld developed a method for solving these approximately when the opening of the mirror is small (i.e., when the mirror is a sphere with a small hole in it). The method leads to no results for the hemisphere.

The diffraction of plane electromagnetic waves by a conducting hemisphere has been discussed by E. M. Kennaugh [8]. He expands the fields inside and outside the sphere in spherical harmonics and obtains a system of infinitely many equations for the coefficients. However, he has given no solution, either exact or approximate to this system.

A. W. Maue [10] has derived the integro-differential equation used here, but has not discussed its solution.

§1. Formulation of the Boundary Value Problem

A lamina is a thin plate or shell; i.e., one whose thickness is a small fraction of the wavelength λ of the incident radiation. Our mathematical model for a lamina is a surface L. We shall assume that

$$L = S \cup \Gamma$$

where

(1) S is a smooth, open, orientable, bounded surface, and

(2) Γ is the boundary of S and consists of a finite number of smoothed closed curves.

A hemispherical shell is an example of such a lamina. If (x, y, z) are rectangular coordinates, then S is the set of points whose coordinates satisfy

$$x^2 + y^2 + z^2 = a^2 , \qquad z > 0 ,$$

while Γ consists of the points for which

$$x^2 + y^2 + z^2 = a^2 , \qquad z = 0 .$$

We imagine L to be situated in an incident acoustic field described by a potential u_0 . The function u_0 is assumed to be defined near L and to satisfy the Helmholtz equation

$$\Delta u_0 + k^2 u_0 = 0$$

there. The time dependence is assumed to be given by a factor $e^{-i\omega t}$ where $k = \omega/c = 2\pi/\lambda$, c is the wave velocity, and λ is the wavelength. Let us write the total field u_T that results from the interaction of u_0 and L as a sum

$$u_T = u_0 + u .$$

Then the potential u of the scattered wave must have the following properties [1, 16] .

(1.1) $\Delta u + k^2 u = 0$ in V = the complement of L .

(1.2) $$\lim_{p \to q} \left\{ \frac{\partial u(p)}{\partial n} + \frac{\partial u_0(p)}{\partial n} \right\} = 0 , \quad q \in S .$$

Here $\frac{\partial u}{\partial n} = \nabla u \cdot \mathbf{n}$, $\mathbf{n}$ is a normal to S at q , and p approaches q along $\mathbf{n}$, from either side of S .

(1.3) $$\lim_{r \to \infty} \int_{S(0,r)} \left| \frac{\partial u}{\partial r} - iku \right|^2 dS = 0 .$$

Here $S(0, r)$ is the surface of a sphere with radius r and center at a fixed origin 0 . This is one of a number of equivalent forms of Sommerfeld's radiation condition [16].

(1.4) u satisfies the edge condition [5],

$$\int_T \{ |\nabla u|^2 + k^2 |u|^2 \} dV < \infty$$

for every cube T (including those that contain a portion of the edge Γ).

We remark that (1.4) does not imply that u is continuous across S ; u(p) may approach different limits as p approaches S from opposite sides. The physical significance of the edge condition is that it implies that the energy contained in any cube is finite.

It can be shown that there is at most one function u with the above properties [5, 13]. The question of the existence of such a function has not been answered. Our object is to use the properties to derive a functional equation characterizing u . We begin by using Green's theorem to express u(q) , $q \in V$, as an integral over S .

§2. Application of Green's Theorem

We shall distinguish between the two sides of S , denoting one as the "positive" side and the other as the "negative" side. If **n** is a unit normal to S , pointing into V on the positive side of S , we shall denote by $u_+(q)$ and $u_-(q)$ the limits of u(p) as p approaches $q \in S$ along **n** on the positive and negative sides, respectively. Let us isolate the edge Γ by enclosing it in a "tube" T_ϵ , i.e., the surface whose points are a fixed distance ϵ from Γ . Next, let us apply Green's theorem to u(p) and

$$G(p, q) = \frac{e^{ikR}}{4\pi R}, \quad R = d(p, q) ,$$

in the part of V lying outside T_ϵ and inside a large sphere S(q, r) (of radius r and center q), but excluding a small sphere $S(q, \alpha)$. Since both u(p) and G(p, q) satisfy the Helmholtz equation (1.1) in this region, Green's theorem gives

$$(2.1) \qquad \int_{S(q,\alpha) + S(q,r) + T_\epsilon + S_\epsilon^+ + S_\epsilon^-} \{ u \frac{\partial G}{\partial \nu} - G \frac{\partial u}{\partial \nu} \} dS = 0 .$$

Here S^+ and S^- denote the positive and negative sides of S , respectively, and S_ϵ^+ and S_ϵ^- denote the parts of S^+ and S^- lying outside of T_ϵ , while ν denotes a unit normal to the boundary of the region, pointing into the region. The integral over $S(q, \alpha)$ equals $-u(q)$. For, (2.1) shows that it is independent of α and it is easily shown to tend to $-u(q)$ when $\alpha \to 0$. Moreover, the integral over S(q, r) is zero, by the radiation condition [16]. The integral over T_ϵ tends to zero with ϵ , by the edge condition [5]. Notice that $\nu = \mathbf{n}$ on S^+ and $\nu = -\mathbf{n}$ on S^- . Thus

$$u_+(p)\frac{\partial G(p,q)}{\partial \nu_+} + u_-(p)\frac{\partial G(p,q)}{\partial \nu_-} = \{u_+(p)-u_-(p)\}\frac{\partial G(p,q)}{\partial n},$$

since ∇G is continuous across S, while

$$G_+(p,q)\frac{\partial u(p)}{\partial \nu_+} + G_-(p,q)\frac{\partial u(p)}{\partial \nu_-} = G(p,q)\{\frac{\partial u(p)}{\partial n_+} - \frac{\partial u(p)}{\partial n_-}\} = 0,$$

since $\frac{\partial u}{\partial n}$ has the same value on both sides of S, by (1.2). Combining these facts, we see that (2.1) implies

$$(2.2) \quad u(q) = \int_S \psi(p)\frac{\partial G(p,q)}{\partial n}\,dS, \qquad q \in V,$$

where

$$(2.3) \quad \psi(p) = u_+(p) - u_-(p), \qquad p \in S.$$

This equation enables us to compute u at any point, once ψ is known.

§3. The Far Field Amplitude and Scattering Cross Sections

We shall use (2.2) to estimate $u(q)$ for points q that are a large distance from S. To do this we introduce an origin O and identify points q, p by their position vectors $\mathbf{r} = \vec{Oq}$, $\mathbf{r}' = \vec{Op}$. On writing

$$\mathbf{r} = x\hat{\mathbf{x}} + y\hat{\mathbf{y}} + z\hat{\mathbf{z}}, \qquad \mathbf{r}' = x'\hat{\mathbf{x}} + y'\hat{\mathbf{y}} + z'\hat{\mathbf{z}},$$

where $\hat{\mathbf{x}}, \hat{\mathbf{y}}, \hat{\mathbf{z}}$ are unit vectors along rectangular coordinate axes, we have

$$R = |\mathbf{r} - \mathbf{r}'| = \sqrt{(x-x')^2 + (y-y')^2 + (z-z')^2}$$

whence, if ∇' is the gradient operator for the point p,

$$\nabla' R = \frac{\mathbf{r}'-\mathbf{r}}{R}.$$

Thus

$$\nabla' G = (ik - \frac{1}{R})\frac{e^{ikR}}{4\pi R}\nabla' R = (ik - \frac{1}{R})\frac{e^{ikR}}{4\pi R}\frac{\mathbf{r}'-\mathbf{r}}{R}$$

whence

$$\frac{\partial G(p,q)}{\partial n} = (ik - \frac{1}{R})\frac{e^{ikR}}{4\pi R}\frac{(\mathbf{r}'-\mathbf{r})\cdot\mathbf{n}}{R}.$$

Notice that if we write $\mathbf{r} = r\,\hat{\mathbf{r}}$, $\mathbf{r}' = r\,\hat{\mathbf{r}}'$ where $|\hat{\mathbf{r}}| = |\hat{\mathbf{r}}'| = 1$ and put $w = 1/r$ then

$$R = \sqrt{r^2 + (r')^2 - 2rr'(\hat{\mathbf{r}}\cdot\hat{\mathbf{r}}')} = \frac{1}{w}\sqrt{1 + (r'w)^2 - 2r'w(\hat{\mathbf{r}}\cdot\hat{\mathbf{r}}')} .$$

Thus

$$\frac{r}{e^{ikr}}\,\frac{\partial G(p,q)}{\partial n}$$

(3. 1)

$$= \left(ik - \frac{w}{\sqrt{1+(r'w)^2-2r'w(\hat{\mathbf{r}}\cdot\hat{\mathbf{r}}')}}\right)\frac{e^{ik\left\{\frac{\sqrt{1+(r'w)^2-2'w(\hat{\mathbf{r}}\cdot\hat{\mathbf{r}}')}-1}{w}\right\}}}{4\pi\sqrt{1+(r'w)^2-2r'w(\hat{\mathbf{r}}\cdot\hat{\mathbf{r}}')}}\;\frac{(w\mathbf{r}'-\hat{\mathbf{r}})\cdot\mathbf{n}}{\sqrt{1+(r'w)^2-2r'w(\hat{\mathbf{r}}\cdot\hat{\mathbf{r}}')}}$$

The last expression defines a function of w that is analytic near $w = 0$. It follows easily that the function obtained by multiplying this by $\psi(p)$ and integrating over S is also analytic near $w = 0$. Thus

(3. 2) $$\frac{r}{e^{ikr}}\,u(q) = \int_S \frac{r}{e^{ikr}}\,\frac{\partial G(p,q)}{\partial n}\,\psi(p)\,dS = \sum_{n=0}^{\infty} a_n w^n ,$$

where the series converges near $w = 0$, or

$$u(q) = \frac{e^{ikr}}{r}\sum_{n=0}^{\infty}\frac{a_n(\hat{\mathbf{r}})}{r^n} , \quad r > r_0 .$$

In particular, we have proved that

$$u(q) = \frac{e^{ikr}}{4\pi r}A(\hat{\mathbf{r}}) + O\left(\frac{1}{r^2}\right) , \quad r\to\infty ,$$

where $A(\hat{\mathbf{r}}) = 4\pi\, a_0(\hat{\mathbf{r}})$. Moreover, by (3. 1) and (3. 2),

$$A(\hat{\mathbf{r}}) = -ik\int_S (\hat{\mathbf{r}}\cdot\mathbf{n})e^{-ik(\hat{\mathbf{r}}\cdot\mathbf{r}')}\psi(p)\,dS .$$

The function $A(\hat{\mathbf{r}})$ is called the far field amplitude for $u(q)$. It determines the amount of energy scattered from u_0 by L in any direction $\hat{\mathbf{r}}$.

Let us suppose that the incident field is a plane wave coming from the direction $\hat{a}$;

$$u_0(q) \equiv u_{\hat{a}}(q) = e^{-ik\,\hat{a}\cdot\mathbf{r}} ,$$

$$A(\hat{a}, \hat{\beta}) = \begin{cases} \text{Far field amplitude \underline{in the direction } } \hat{a} \text{ due to} \\ \text{a plane wave incident from the direction } \hat{\beta} . \end{cases}$$

Then

$$A(a, \hat{\beta}) = -ik \int_S (\hat{a} \cdot \mathbf{n}) e^{-ik\hat{a}\cdot\mathbf{r}'} \psi_{\hat{\beta}}(p) dS .$$

where $\psi_{\hat{\beta}}$ denotes the function (2. 3) produced by the incident field $u_{\hat{\beta}}$. Since

$$\frac{\partial u_{\hat{a}}(p)}{\partial n} = -ik(\hat{a}\cdot\mathbf{n})e^{-ik\hat{a}\cdot\mathbf{r}'}$$

this can be also written

(3. 3) $$A(\hat{a}, \hat{\beta}) = \int_S \frac{\partial u_{\hat{a}}}{\partial n} \psi_{\hat{\beta}} dS .$$

The scattering cross sections of the lamina L can be expressed in terms of $A(\hat{a}, \hat{\beta})$. Thus the total scattering cross section $\sigma_T(\hat{a})$, which measures the total amount of energy scattered from $u_{\hat{a}}$ by L , is given by [6, 9]

$$\sigma_T(\hat{a}) = \frac{1}{(4\pi)^2} \int_\Omega |A(\hat{\mathbf{r}}, \hat{a})|^2 d\Omega = \frac{1}{k} \operatorname{Im}\{A(-\hat{a}, \hat{a})\}$$

where Ω is the unit sphere and $d\Omega$ the element of area on it. The differential scattering cross section $\sigma(\hat{\beta}, \hat{a})$, giving the fraction of the energy $\sigma_T(\hat{a})$ scattered in the direction $\hat{\beta}$, is given by

$$\sigma(\hat{\beta}, \hat{a}) = \frac{1}{4\pi} |A(\hat{\beta}, \hat{a})|^2 .$$

In particular, the back scattering cross section or <u>echo area</u> $\sigma(\hat{a})$, giving the fraction of $\sigma_T(\hat{a})$ scattered back towards the source of $u_{\hat{a}}$, is given by

$$\sigma(\hat{a}) = \frac{1}{4\pi} |A(\hat{a}, \hat{a})|^2 .$$

§4. Derivation of the Functional Equation

In this section we use the integral representation (2. 2) and the boundary condition (1. 2) to derive a functional equation for ψ . To begin, let q be a point of S and p a point in V on the normal line to S at q . Then (2. 2) implies

(4. 1) $$\frac{\partial u(p)}{\partial n} = \int_S \frac{\partial^2 G(q', p)}{\partial n \, \partial n'} \psi(q') dS'$$

where q' is the integration point, $\mathbf{n} = \mathbf{n}(q)$, and $\mathbf{n}' = \mathbf{n}(q')$. The functional equation for ψ will be obtained from this equation by finding the limit of the right hand member, for $p \to q$, and setting it equal to $-\frac{\partial u_0(q)}{\partial n}$ as required by (1.2). Notice that the limit is not given by the integral with $p = q$; this integral diverges.

To find the limit in (4.1) we first integrate by parts to reduce the order of the singularity of the integrand. Notice that if ∇ and ∇' denote the gradient operators for the points p and q' , respectively, then $(\nabla + \nabla')G(q', p) = 0$. Hence we can write, using the dyadic notation of Gibbs [3],

$$\frac{\partial^2 G(q', p)}{\partial n\, \partial n'} = \mathbf{n} \cdot \nabla'(\nabla G \cdot \mathbf{n}) \equiv \mathbf{n} \cdot (\nabla'\nabla G) \cdot \mathbf{n} = -\mathbf{n}' \cdot (\nabla'\nabla' G) \cdot \mathbf{n} \quad .$$

Upon using the dyadic identity

$$\mathbf{a} \cdot (\nabla\nabla\phi) \cdot \mathbf{b} = (\mathbf{a} \cdot \mathbf{b}) \Delta\phi - \mathbf{a} \cdot \nabla \times (\mathbf{b} \times \nabla\phi) \quad , \quad \mathbf{b} \text{ constant} \quad ,$$

and the equation $\Delta G + k^2 G = 0$, this becomes

$$(4.2) \qquad \frac{\partial^2 G(q', p)}{\partial n\, \partial n'} = \mathbf{n}' \cdot \nabla' \times (\mathbf{n} \times \nabla' G) + k^2 (\mathbf{n} \cdot \mathbf{n}') G \quad .$$

The last expression is related to the divergence operator for the surface S . To explain this we consider a field α of tangent vectors to S . Let $q \in S$, let C be a curve on S enclosing q , and let ν be a unit vector tangent to S , normal to C , and pointing out of the domain D bounded by S and containing p . Moreover, let A(C) and δ be the area and diameter of D , respectively. Then the divergence of α at q is defined to be

$$(4.3) \qquad \nabla_t \cdot \alpha = \lim_{\delta \to 0} \frac{\int_C \alpha \cdot \nu\, ds}{A(C)}$$

when the limit exists. It is known [11, pp. 156-157] that if α is continuously differentiable, then $\nabla_t \cdot \alpha$ exists and is continuous and the divergence theorem,

$$(4.4) \qquad \int_S (\nabla_t \cdot \alpha)\, dS = \int_\Gamma (\alpha \cdot \nu)\, ds \quad ,$$

holds for S . If ψ is a scalar function on S , let $\nabla_t \psi$ be the surface gradient of ψ , i.e., the tangent vector to S with covariant components $\frac{\partial \psi}{\partial u_1}$, $\frac{\partial \psi}{\partial u_2}$ relative to surface coordinates (u_1, u_2) . It follows that

$$\nabla_t \cdot (\psi \alpha) = \nabla_t \psi \cdot \alpha + \psi \nabla_t \cdot \alpha \quad ,$$

whence, by (4.4),

(4.5) $$\int_S (\nabla_t\psi \cdot \alpha)\,dS + \int_S \psi(\nabla_t \cdot \alpha)\,dS = \int_\Gamma \psi(\nu \cdot \alpha)\,ds \ .$$

To see the relation of the surface divergence to the identity (4.2) let $\mathbf{A}$ be a vector field defined in a region containing S. Let $\mathbf{n}$ be a unit normal to S and $\mathbf{t}$ a unit tangent on C, oriented so that

$$\mathbf{t} = \mathbf{n} \times \nu \ .$$

Then, by Stokes' theorem,

$$(\nabla\times \mathbf{A})\cdot\mathbf{n} = \lim_{\delta\to 0} \frac{\int_D (\nabla\times\mathbf{A})\cdot\mathbf{n}\,dS}{A(C)} = \lim_{\delta\to 0} \frac{\int_C (\mathbf{A}\cdot\mathbf{t})\,ds}{A(C)} = \lim_{\delta\to 0} \frac{\int_C (\mathbf{A}\times\mathbf{n})\cdot\nu\,dS}{A(C)}$$

whence

(4.6) $$\mathbf{n}\cdot(\nabla\times \mathbf{A}) = -\nabla_t\cdot(\mathbf{n}\times\mathbf{A}) \ .$$

Using this relation (4.2) can be rewritten

(4.7) $$\frac{\partial^2 G(q',p)}{\partial n\,\partial n'} = -\nabla'_t\cdot(\mathbf{n}'\times(\mathbf{n}\times\nabla' G)) + k^2(\mathbf{n}\cdot\mathbf{n}')G \ .$$

We can now integrate by parts in (4.1), by using (4.7) and Green's theorem (4.5) for S. It is known that the edge condition (1.4) implies that $\psi = 0$ on Γ [5]. Thus (4.5) with $\alpha = \mathbf{n}'\times(\mathbf{n}\times\nabla' G)$ implies

$$-\int_S \psi\,\nabla'_t\cdot(\mathbf{n}'\times(\mathbf{n}\times\nabla' G))\,dS' = \int_S \nabla'_t\psi\cdot(\mathbf{n}'\times(\mathbf{n}\times\nabla' G))\,dS'$$

whence

(4.8) $$\frac{\partial u(p)}{\partial n} = -\int_S \{(\mathbf{n}\times\nabla' G)\cdot(\mathbf{n}'\times\nabla'_t\psi) - k^2(\mathbf{n}\cdot\mathbf{n}')G\psi\}\,dS' \ .$$

We can find the limit approached by the right side of (4.8) when p tends to q. For, the first term in the integral involves only the tangential derivatives of G at q. It follows, from potential theory, that it tends to limits as p tends to q along $\mathbf{n}$ from either side, that these limits are equal, and that they are equal to the Cauchy principle value of the integral for $p = q$ [12, p. 117 and 7, pp. 160-162]. The second term converges for $p = q$ and defines a continuous function across S [7, p. 160]. Thus on making $p\to q$ in (4.8) and using the boundary condition (1.2) we get the functional equation

$$\frac{\partial u_0(q)}{\partial n} = \int_S \{(\mathbf{n}\times\nabla' G)\cdot(\mathbf{n}'\times\nabla'_t\psi) - k^2(\mathbf{n}\cdot\mathbf{n}')G\psi\}\,dS' \ , \quad q \in S \ .$$

This equation was first stated by A. W. Maue [10], and we shall refer to it as Maue's equation. We now use it to derive a variational principle for the far field amplitude.

§5. The Variational Principle

Let us define the operator K by

$$(K\psi)(q) = \int_S \{(\mathbf{n} \times \nabla' G)\cdot(\mathbf{n}' \times \nabla'_t \psi) - k^2(\mathbf{n}\cdot\mathbf{n}')G\psi\} dS'$$

so that Maue's equation, corresponding to the incident field $u_{\hat{a}}$ takes the concise form

$$\frac{\partial u_{\hat{a}}}{\partial n} = K\psi_{\hat{a}} \ .$$

Moreover, let us introduce the notation

$$(\phi, \psi) = \int_S \phi\psi\, dS$$

and consider the quantity $(\psi, K\phi)$. We have

$$I \equiv \int_S \psi\, dS \int_S (\mathbf{n} \times \nabla' G)\cdot(\mathbf{n}' \times \nabla'_t \phi) dS' = -\int_S dS' \int_S \psi \mathbf{n}\cdot \nabla G \times (\mathbf{n}' \times \nabla'_t \phi) dS$$

$$= -\int_S dS' \int_S \psi \mathbf{n}\cdot \nabla \times \{G(\mathbf{n}' \times \nabla'_t \phi)\} dS = \int_S dS' \int_S \psi \nabla_t \cdot \{G\, \mathbf{n} \times (\mathbf{n}' \times \nabla'_t \phi)\} dS \ ,$$

where the primed and unprimed operators refer to the integration points q' and q , respectively. The relation (4.6) was used in the last step of the calculation. If we use Green's theorem (4.5) in the last integral and assume that $\psi = 0$ on Γ we get

$$I = -\int_S dS' \int_S \nabla_t \psi \cdot (G\, \mathbf{n}) \times (\mathbf{n}' \times \nabla'_t \phi) dS$$

$$= \int_S \int_S (\mathbf{n} \times \nabla_t \psi) \cdot (\mathbf{n}' \times \nabla'_t \phi)\, G(q, q') dS\, dS' \ .$$

Thus, from the definition of K we have

$$(5.1) \quad (\psi, K\phi) = \int_S \int_S \{(\mathbf{n} \times \nabla_t \psi)\cdot(\mathbf{n}' \times \nabla'_t \phi) - k^2(\mathbf{n}\cdot\mathbf{n}')\psi\phi'\} G(q, q') dS\, dS' \ .$$

In particular, it proves that

$$(5.2) \quad (\psi, K\phi) = (K\psi , \phi)$$

for function ψ and ϕ that vanish on Γ .

The far field amplitude $A(\hat{a}\ \hat{\beta})$ satisfies

$$A(\hat{a},\hat{\beta}) = (\frac{\partial u_{\hat{a}}}{\partial n}, \psi_{\hat{\beta}}) = (K\psi_{\hat{a}}, \psi_{\hat{\beta}}) ,$$

by (3. 3) and Maue's equation, and these relations, with (5.2), imply the reciprocity theorem

$$A(\hat{\beta},\hat{a}) = A(\hat{a};\hat{\beta})$$

for the diffraction of plane waves by laminas. It follows that

$$A(\hat{a},\hat{\beta}) = (\frac{\partial u_{\hat{a}}}{\partial n}, \psi_{\hat{\beta}}) = (\frac{\partial u_{\hat{\beta}}}{\partial n}, \psi_{\hat{a}}) = (K\psi_{\hat{a}}, \psi_{\hat{\beta}}) . \tag{5.3}$$

These representations of the far field amplitude can be used to construct a variational principle of the type introduced by Levine and Schwinger [9]. Indeed, the functional

$$J[\psi,\phi] = \frac{1}{4\pi} \left| \frac{\left(\frac{\partial u_{\hat{\beta}}}{\partial n}, \psi\right)\left(\frac{\partial u_{\hat{a}}}{\partial n}, \phi\right)}{(K\psi, \phi)} \right|^2 \tag{5.4}$$

has the following properties:

(a) $J[\psi_{\hat{a}}, \psi_{\hat{\beta}}] = \frac{1}{4\pi} |A(\hat{a},\hat{\beta})|^2 = \sigma(\hat{a},\hat{\beta})$, by (5. 3) ,

(b) $J[\psi,\phi] \geq 0$,

(c) $\delta J[\psi,\phi] = 0 \iff \frac{\partial u_{\hat{a}}}{\partial n} = K\psi , \quad \frac{\partial u_{\hat{\beta}}}{\partial n} = K\phi$.

Thus the cross section $\sigma(\hat{a},\hat{\beta})$ can be computed by the Rayleigh-Ritz method [4].

§6. Application of the Rayleigh-Ritz Method

For the sake of simplicity we shall discuss only the echo area

$$\sigma(\hat{a}) = \frac{1}{4\pi} |A(\hat{a},\hat{a})|^2 .$$

It is related to the functional

$$I[\psi] = \frac{1}{4\pi} \left| \frac{\left(\frac{\partial u_{\hat{a}}}{\partial n}, \psi\right)^2}{(K\psi, \psi)} \right|^2$$

which satisfies

$$\text{(a)}\quad I[\psi_{\hat{a}}] = \sigma(\hat{a}) \;,$$

$$\text{(b)}\quad I[\psi] \geq 0 \;,$$

$$\text{(c)}\quad \delta I[\psi] = 0 \leftrightarrow \frac{\partial u_{\hat{a}}}{\partial n} = K\psi \;.$$

To compute $\sigma(\hat{a})$ we construct a sequence $\{\psi_N\}$ of the form

$$\psi_N(q) = \sum_{n=0}^{N} c_n \, \phi_n(q) \;,$$

where we require that $\{\phi_n\}$ be a complete sequence and that

$$(6.1)\quad \left(\frac{\partial u_{\hat{a}}}{\partial n}, \psi_N\right) = c_0 \;, \quad N = 0, 1, 2, \ldots \;.$$

The utility of (6.1) is explained below. Our Nth approximation to $\sigma(\hat{a})$ is

$$\sigma_N(\hat{a}) = I[\psi_N] = \frac{1}{4\pi} \left| \frac{c_0^2}{\sum_{m=0}^{N} \sum_{n=0}^{N} K_{mn} \, c_m \, c_n} \right|^2$$

where

$$K_{mn} = (K\phi_m, \phi_m) = K_{nm}$$

and the coefficients $c_0, c_1, \ldots, c_N$ are fixed by the Rayleigh-Ritz condition

$$(6.2)\quad \frac{\partial I[\psi_N]}{\partial c_m} = 0 \;, \quad m = 0, 1, \ldots, N \;.$$

If we define

$$A_N = \frac{c_0^2}{\sum_{m=0}^{N} \sum_{n=0}^{N} K_{mn} \, c_m \, c_n}$$

then a sufficient condition for (6.2) is clearly

$$\frac{\partial A_N}{\partial c_m} = 0 \;, \quad m = 0, 1, \ldots, N \;.$$

Notice that

$$\frac{\partial}{\partial c_\ell}(c_m c_n) = c_m \delta_{\ell,n} + c_n \delta_{\ell,m}$$

where $\delta_{m,n}$ is the Kronecker delta. Hence

$$(6.3)\quad \frac{\partial}{\partial c_\ell}\left(\sum_{m=0}^{N}\sum_{n=0}^{N} K_{mn} c_m c_n\right) = \sum_{m=0}^{N} K_{m\ell} c_m + \sum_{n=0}^{N} K_{\ell n} c_n = 2\sum_{n=0}^{N} K_{\ell n} c_n .$$

Thus $\frac{\partial A_N}{\partial c_0} = 0$ implies

$$(6.4)\quad 2\left(\sum_{m=0}^{N}\sum_{n=0}^{N} K_{mn} c_m c_n\right) c_0 - 2c_0^2 \sum_{n=0}^{N} K_{on} c_n = 0 .$$

Now $c_0 \neq 0$, by (6.1), since $\frac{\partial u_{\hat{a}}}{\partial n} \neq 0$ and $\{\phi_n\}$ is complete. Hence (6.4) implies

$$\sum_{m=0}^{N}\sum_{n=0}^{N} K_{mn} c_m c_n = c_0 \sum_{n=0}^{N} K_{on} c_n .$$

This can be written, using the definition of A_N ,

$$\sum_{n=0}^{N} K_{on} c_n = \frac{c_0}{A_N} .$$

The conditions $\frac{\partial A_N}{\partial c_m} = 0$, $m > 0$, imply by (6.3)

$$\sum_{n=0}^{N} K_{mn} c_n = 0 , \quad m = 1, 2, \ldots , N .$$

These equations are equivalent to the system

$$\sum_{n=0}^{N} K_{mn} c_n = \frac{c_0}{A_N} \delta_{mo} , \quad m = 0, 1, \ldots , N .$$

If we divide this system by c_0/A_N and put

$$x_n = A_N \frac{c_n}{c_0}$$

we obtain the linear system

$$(6.5)\quad \sum_{n=0}^{N} K_{mn} x_n = \delta_{mo} , \quad m = 0, 1, \ldots , N ,$$

for the unknowns $x_0 , x_1, \ldots , x_N$ and the first unknown

$$x_0 = A_N$$

determines our Nth approximation to $\sigma(\hat{\alpha})$. The simplicity of this procedure for applying the Rayleigh-Ritz method to the Levine-Schwinger functional is a consequence of the condition (6. 1). The procedure is due to C. J. Bouwkamp [2].

The computation of a given approximation $\sigma_N(\hat{\alpha})$ falls into two parts,

(1) Computation of the matrix $((K_{mn}))m, n = 0, 1, \ldots , N$, where

$$K_{mn} = (K\phi_m, \phi_n) = \iint_{SS} \{(\mathbf{n} \times \nabla_t \phi_m)\cdot(\mathbf{n}' \times \nabla'_t \phi_n) - k^2 (\mathbf{n}\cdot\mathbf{n}')\phi_m \phi'_n\} G(q, q')dSdS' ,$$

e. g., by numerical integration, and

(2) Solution of the linear system (6. 5) for the first unknown $x_0 = x_0(N)$.

The rapidity with which the method converges depends, of course, on the particular sequence $\{\phi_n\}$. In applying the method, all available knowledge concerning the functional behavior of $\psi_{\hat{a}}$ should be used to construct a sequence $\{\phi_n\}$ that approximates $\psi_{\hat{a}}$ as rapidly as possible.

Acknowledgment: The author would like to thank Professor Harold Levine for suggesting the approach employed in this work, and for helpful discussions of it.

NOTES

*An analogous method for studying the diffraction of electromagnetic waves by a perfectly conducting lamina is derived in the author's Lockheed report (reference [15], p. 314).

**Numbers in square brackets denote references in the list on pp. 314.

The work reported here was performed for the Electromagnetic Research Department of the Lockheed Aircraft Corporation's Missile Systems Division, Sunnyvale, California.

REFERENCES

1. Bouwkamp, C. J., Diffraction Theory, Reports on Progress in Physics, V. XVII (1954), pp. 35-100.

2. Bouwkamp, C. J., Diffraction Theory--A Critique of Some Recent Developments, Technical Report EM-50, New York University Institute of Mathematical Sciences, Contract No. AF 19 (122)-42 (1953).

3. Brand, L., Vector and Tensor Analysis, J. Wiley and Sons, New York (1947).

4. Courant, R., and D. Hilbert, Methods of Mathematical Physics, V. I, Interscience, New York (1953).

5. Heins, A. E., and S. Silver, The Edge Condition and Field Representation Theorems in the Theory of Electromagnetic Diffraction, Proc. Cambridge Phil. Soc., V. 51 (1955) 149-161.

6. Jones, D. S., On the Scattering Cross Section of an Obstacle, The Philosophical Magazine, Sec. 7, V. 46 (1955) pp. 957-962.

7. Kellogg, O. D., Foundations of Potential Theory, F. Ungar, New York (1929).

8. Kennaugh, E. M., The Scattering of Plane Electromagnetic Waves by a Perfectly Conducting Hemisphere or Hemispherical Shell, Ohio State University Research Foundation, Project Report 302-35, Contract W 36-039 SC 33634 (1950).

9. Levine, H., and J. Schwinger, On the Theory of Electromagnetic Wave Diffraction by an Aperture in an Infinite Plane Conducting Screen, Comm. Pure Appl. Math. V. III (1950), pp. 355-391.

10. Maue, A. W., Zur Formulierung eines allgemeinen Beugungsproblems durch eine Integralgleichung, Zeit. für Physik. V. 126 (1949), pp. 601-618.

11. Müller, C., Grundprobleme der mathematischen Theorie elektromagnetischer Schwingungen, Springer-Verlag, Berlin (1957).

12. Poincaré, H., Theorie du potential Newtonien, Paris (1899).

13. Rellich, F., Über das asymptotische Verhalten der Lösungen von $\Delta u + ku = 0$ in unendlichen Gebieten, Jahr. der Deutschen Math. Verein., V. 53 (1943) pp. 57-64.

14. Sommerfeld, A., Partial Differential Equations in Physics, Academic Press, New York (1949).

15. Wilcox, C. H., The Diffraction of Radiation by Laminas, Lockheed Aircraft Corp., Missile Systems Division, Technical Report LM SD-2202 (1957).

16. Wilcox, C. H., Spherical Means and Radiation Conditions, Archive of Rational Mechanics and Analysis, V. 3, No. 2, (1959), pp. 133-148.

Index

Index